W9-APR-012

Building Success in Math

Building Success in Math

Carol R. Langbort

San Francisco State University

Virginia H. Thompson

Lawrence Hall of Science
University of California, Berkeley

DALE SEYMOUR PUBLICATIONS

Sponsoring Editor: Carol Butterfield

Production: Stacey C. Sawyer, San Francisco

Manuscript Editor: Stephan Bodian

Interior Design: Albert Burkhardt

Cover Design: Bruce Kortebein

Illustrations: Mary Burkhardt

Order number DS01024
ISBN 0-86651-500-3
(Previously published as ISBN 0-534-03394-6)

4 5 6 7 8 9 10 11 12 13-MA-95 94 93 92 91

Special thanks to Professor Diane Resek, who founded the Center for Math Literacy at San Francisco State University in 1977. Many of her ideas about teaching mathematics to adults are reflected in this book. In particular, she introduced us to the technique of using guessing to solve algebra problems. We thank her also for her ongoing support and encouragement.

Contents

Foreword

Before I began teaching mathematics, I had always assumed that I was more successful in math classes because my mind worked differently from other students'. I thought that math would always be slow going for them. However, when I started teaching math, I started having doubts about my theory of learning, which was based on the existence of "special" minds. I began to think that any of my students could do well in mathematics if. . . . I wasn't sure what came after the "if," but I was sure that nothing was wrong with my students' minds.

It was not until I sat next to a professor of German on an airplane that I began to realize what should come after the "if." He told me his profession, and I told him I was a professor of mathematics. "Oh," said he, "I've always hated math." Well, that didn't seem to be a very strange thing for him to say; I knew that 95% of the people say exactly that on meeting a mathematician. But this time I had a comeback. I told him that I hated German and that I had gotten Ds in German in college no matter how hard I had tried to memorize. "But you don't need to memorize in German," he said. "It's logical." I was shocked. I had chosen to major in math because it seemed to be the one field where I didn't have to memorize. It occurred to both of us that he knew a secret about learning German and I knew one about learning mathematics.

Since that time I have needed to learn several new languages. Unfortunately no one ever showed up who could teach me the secret of learning languages without painful memorization. However, since meeting the professor of German I have viewed my own teaching differently. My goal now is to teach my students the secrets of learning mathematics without that painful memorization.

If you are someone who has always viewed learning mathematics as a troublesome exercise in memorization, then you have come to the right place—this book. Carol Langbort and Virginia Thompson are about to let you in on some closely guarded secrets.

The first secret, and one you may not believe until you've read some of this book, is that math *can* be fun. You've probably thought it could be fun for people whose minds worked in strange ways, but you are about to find out that it can be fun even for *you*. This secret will be the most important one you will learn from this book. The feeling that learning math can be enjoyable will be what motivates you to learn more and more.

You will learn other valuable secrets from this book that will help you as you learn more about math. These secrets include using guessing, visualization, and finding patterns to solve problems. They may not sound like helpful processes to use to solve math problems, but many previous students of the authors will assure you that these methods really work.

Both authors are experienced teachers of adults who thought they didn't like math. A common remark I have heard from their students is: "That course really taught me how to think." This book is really going to teach you how to think—about mathematics.

Diane Resek
Professor of Mathematics
San Francisco State University

Preface

Do you avoid math? People of all ages find themselves intimidated by the mathematical aspects of today's technical society. Many feel insecure when faced with a math problem to do on the spot. Others feel threatened when they realize that, to get a promotion at work, they will need to acquire more math skills. As adults conclude that their math backgrounds are insufficient for their needs, many look for a way to change this situation.

The purpose of this book is to help people who feel uncomfortable with math. The approach is deliberately nontraditional. Ideas are developed with an emphasis on understanding concepts rather than memorizing formulas. The goal is not to cover specific content in depth but to present a variety of approaches to problems to help dispel the myth that there is only one "right way" to solve a problem. Working in pairs or small groups is encouraged to develop the skill of talking about math. We hope that instructors using this book will employ the nontraditional techniques of encouraging group interaction, using hands-on materials to aid the development of concepts, and providing a supportive classroom atmosphere.

The book evolved from materials presented in a University of California continuing education course, "Building Confidence in Mathematics." Although the students varied greatly in age, mathematics background, and occupation, the content met their needs. Their success in solving problems in a variety of mathematical areas served to build their confidence to take the next step in their mathematics education. The enthusiasm generated by these students toward the approach and materials developed for the course encouraged us to write this book.

This book can be used by individuals working at their own pace, in an informal two-day workshop, or in a longer course. If you are reading the book on your own, you may want to find a friend to work with you.

The chapters present an introduction to basic mathematical concepts and include topics from coordinate graphing and functions, use of calculators, geometry and measurement, word problems, probability and statistics, and logic and spatial reasoning. The format allows you to write directly in the text as well as on the special worksheet pages.

Ultimately, the aim of this book is to hook you on problem solving—so that you can enjoy doing mathematics successfully—and to help provide the encouragement for you to take your next math course.

In closing, we would like to thank the following reviewers for their help and suggestions: Jan Davis, University of Southern Mississippi; Joel Fingerman, Roosevelt University; Herbert Hooper, Chattanooga State Technical Community College; Tralee Johnson, Shaklee Corporation; Beatrice Mikulecky, Boston University; and Susan Nerton, Cabrillo College.

Carol R. Langbort
Virginia H. Thompson

CHAPTER One
Introduction

This book is an expansion of the materials used in a short continuing education course for adults. The course was held on two consecutive Saturdays. The students were able, even in this brief time, to gain confidence in their ability to tackle math problems.

The age of the students varied considerably. In the same class were two high school juniors, a woman over 65, and adults of all ages in between. More fascinating was the variety of backgrounds and occupations of the participants. Among the 25 students in one class were a secretary, a landscape architect, a vocational counselor, a music director, and a computer programmer.

People were taking the course for very different reasons. Some were feeling insecure in their present jobs when they needed to do anything math-related. Some were planning to take entrance exams for business or law school. One student was already enrolled in a Ph.D. program but still felt the course would help her. Students who have been simultaneously enrolled in calculus courses have also benefited. Most of the students had not studied any math for many years but had decided that they now needed to take some basic math courses. This course was to serve as a warm-up.

The fact that the material worked effectively for this diverse group of people was reflected by their comments about the course.

> Even though I didn't get every single problem, I realized that figuring out the answer is a process. A person doesn't arrive at the answer by magic, it's step by step.

> It all makes math less mystical. I liked the group participation. I don't think I've ever been so outspoken about math. It made me think.

The course has been beneficial in that it has made it quite obvious that I am not alone in math avoidance/anxiety. This course is serving to reinforce what I have recently begun to suspect—that I am not "poor" in math but just have never developed my math skills.

The class has provided me with tools to be able to visualize what had been so intangible before now. The logic activities provided me with new ways to reason or think about problems. Also, this class helped to make some of the terminology less scary.

Interactions with people really help—it's good to have another student help you to an insight.

These comments led us to believe that the process, as much as the particular math content of the course, contributes to the students' success. Part of the process includes creating a nonthreatening atmosphere in the classroom. We have attempted to create this atmosphere for you, the reader, throughout the book. Working in groups is one way of relaxing the students in a class. If you are not enrolled in a class, we suggest that you work with another person, if possible. Although not essential, working with another person will help you capture some of the flavor of the course.

This chapter gives you an opportunity to experience the same introductory activities that we use in the classroom. These serve to break the ice and make you aware that you are not alone in your feelings about yourself and mathematics. We believe that you can gain confidence as you become more successful at solving math problems. For this reason, most of the work in the book is math work. But there are also psychological reasons why people avoid math. To address this side of the issue, we spend some time giving class members a chance to discuss their past experiences learning math.

Jot down your answers to the following questions: Do you remember when you stopped learning math? What grade were you in? What math topics were you studying? Who was your teacher?

Many people remember their math teachers at that time in vivid detail. They also remember the particular topic they were studying that they 'just couldn't get.' It was downhill from then on. The dropout point was usually reached when their methods of learning math no longer worked. Memorizing formulas was no longer sufficient; it became necessary also to *understand* the material in order to progress. Different people reached this point at different times. For some, it happened in elementary school, when they had the measles and missed multiplication or long division and never seemed to be able to catch up. High school algebra and geometry are also common points at which people just don't catch on and memorizing doesn't suffice. Some people even reach calculus before the problem arises. No matter when it occurs, the process is the same. People report that they could not understand the concepts and so stopped learning or even trying to learn. Here are some sample student comments.

I vividly remember my seventh-grade math teacher, who doted on the brainy kids and sort of accepted us average or below-average

> ones. Class time was frightening—especially when she'd call on me, giving me little time to respond, then turn to the "brainy row" for the correct answer.
>
> My turn-off point was in fourth grade when I moved from one school to another and completely missed remainders. For months I struggled until my teacher sent a note home saying I had severe problems with math. By that time I had lost all confidence.
>
> In high school and eighth grade, when algebra was introduced, I didn't understand after reading it once. Therefore, I thought I wasn't capable of ever understanding it.
>
> In the second grade, a math resource teacher told my mother that it took me a while to learn something, but, once I understood it, I would be able to do the problems. My mother told me what the teacher had said, and I interpreted it as my being stupid because it took me longer to learn how to do a problem than other people.

In our "Building Confidence in Math" class, we spend time giving students an opportunity to discuss these memories with others in small groups. Some people are amazed at the clarity and at the intensity of feeling with which, many years later, they remember their school math experiences. For all, the discussion clears the air. No one is alone here. We hope that, after reading this section and the comments presented, you will not feel alone, either.

We begin our mathematics with a group cooperative logic problem. To do this problem, you will need a group of three to six people sitting around a table. Each group needs an envelope of clue cards. Cut out the clue cards from the "Who Won the Race?" problem on Worksheet 1.1. Distribute all the clue cards to the group members. Some people may receive more than one card. You may read the information on your clue card(s) out loud to the group, but you may not show your card(s) to anyone. The extra small slips of paper are to be used to help the group organize the information in the problem. Everyone in the group must agree on the solution. If you would like to do another, similar problem, try the "Baby Quilt" problem on p. 247 in Chapter 7.

Did you find that everyone in your group was involved in solving the problem? We deliberately chose this type of problem to get you started doing math. At the very least, each person in the group needs to share his or her clue(s) with the others. Group participants usually find that it's hard to resist getting involved in solving the problem—even if they dislike math or think they can't do it.

Besides involving you in actually solving a logic problem, this activity also gets you to talk to others about a mathematics problem. This skill of "talking mathematics" is rarely taught or even mentioned in high school mathematics classes. In fact, students usually come away thinking that it is cheating to discuss math problems with their friends. They feel that, unless they are able to figure out all the answers on their own, they are dumb.

This is a clear contrast to what mathematicians do. Although they spend time thinking and writing ideas on their own, they also discuss their ideas and proofs with one another. They need to check if their thinking is clear or to brainstorm and talk when they are stuck.

As you work through this text, find someone to discuss the problems with so you can clarify each other's thinking. When you work with others, you are forced to develop the skills of asking appropriate questions and explaining your own reasoning. These interactions will improve your understanding of mathematics.

Worksheet 1.1

Who Won The Race?

The *Sunbeam*

The *MarySue*

The *Lightning*

The *Infinity*

CLUE CARD

These clues will help solve your problem. You may read them out loud, but don't show your card to anyone.

Problem: Find the order in which the sailboats placed in the race. Which boat will race in the finals?

*The *Sunbeam*, the *MarySue*, the *Lightning*, and the *Infinity* placed first, second, third, and fourth in a qualifying race, but not necessarily in that order.

CLUE CARD

These clues will help solve your problem. You may read them out loud, but don't show your card to anyone.

Problem: Find the order in which the sailboats placed in the race. Which boat will race in the finals?

*The *Sunbeam* came in just behind the *MarySue*.
*Only one of the boats will race in the finals.

CLUE CARD

These clues will help solve your problem. You may read them out loud, but don't show your card to anyone.

Problem: Find the order in which the sailboats placed in the race. Which boat will race in the finals?

*The *Sunbeam* beat the *Infinity* by 20 seconds.
*The *MarySue* came in ahead of the *Lightning*.

CLUE CARD

These clues will help solve your problem. You may read them out loud, but don't show your card to anyone.

Problem: Find the order in which the sailboats placed in the race. Which boat will race in the finals?

*The *Lightning* came in 50 seconds behind the second-place boat.
*The *Sunbeam* and the *Infinity* have all-women crews.

CLUE CARD

These clues will help solve your problem. You may read them out loud, but don't show your card to anyone.

Problem: Find the order in which the sailboats placed in the race. Which boat will race in the finals?

*The *Infinity* did better than the *Lightning*.
*All four sailboats are from the same yacht club.

CLUE CARD

These clues will help solve your problem. You may read them out loud, but don't show your card to anyone.

Problem: Find the order in which the sailboats placed in the race. Which boat will race in the finals?

*The *MarySue* beat the *Infinity*.
*The crew of the *Lightning* wishes they had done better.

CHAPTER Two

Coordinate Graphing and Functions

Coordinate graphing is an important tool in mathematics. Many algebraic problems can be solved using this geometric approach. The work of René Descartes, a 17th-century French philosopher and mathematician, greatly influenced the development of the field of mathematics called *analytic geometry*. This field unites algebra and geometry. The concept of using coordinates to graph equations and functions is the underlying basis for analytic geometry. A two-dimensional plane that is a coordinate system is often referred to as a *Cartesian plane*, after Descartes.

In the first section of this chapter, a variety of methods are introduced that develop the skill of locating points on a plane. In the next section, patterns are recorded in table form, and coordinates are used to make a geometric graph or record of these patterns. The concept of function is presented in the third section. Again, coordinates are used to make a graphical representation of these functions. The final section presents a variety of applications where coordinate graphing is used to solve problems.

NAMING COORDINATES

In this section we will break a code to read some messages. Here are some clues. First find the letter on the chart in Figure 2.1, then look at the matching code. The code for C is (1,3); the code for H is (4,1); the code for M is (0,3); the code for F is (2,0). Do you have any ideas about how the code works? Describe them. ______________________________

____

____

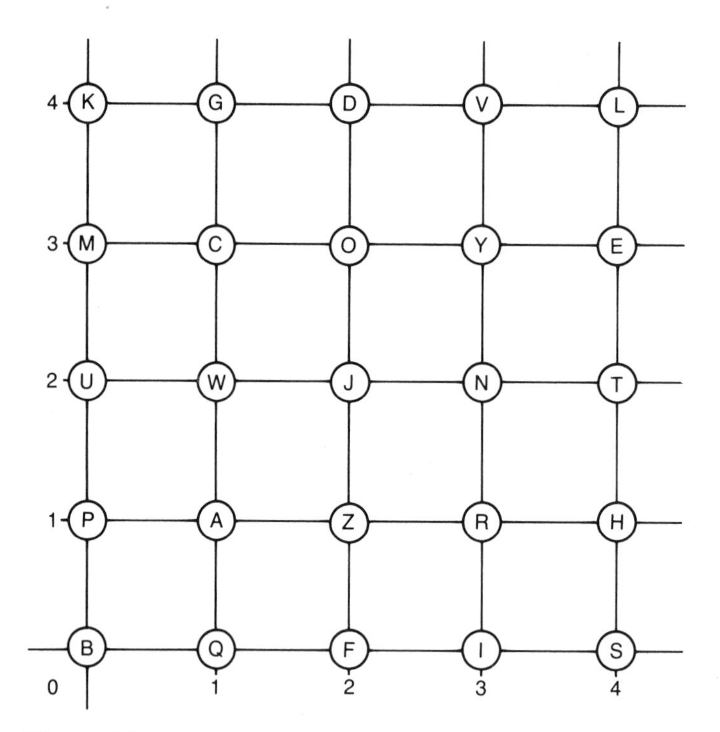

Figure 2.1

Check your description. Does it work for these number pairs? The code for *R* is (3,1); the code for *G* is (1,4); the code for *T* is (4,2). Note that the order of the numbers is important: (3,1) is the code for *R*, but (1,3) is the code for *C*. The two numbers needed to locate a point on this grid are called an *ordered number pair*.

By now you might have figured out that the code works something like this: start at the zero and first move horizontally until you reach the vertical line on which your letter is located. Then move vertically to your letter. For example, for the letter *E*, you first move horizontally from 0 to 4. Then move vertically up to the 3. So the code for *E* is (4,3)—over to 4, up to 3. Moving horizontally first, then vertically, is a convention that has been agreed on for people to communicate mathematically.

Next, instead of the letters of the alphabet, ordered number pairs will be used to name the intersection points on a coordinate grid. Playing the game of Coordinate Tic-Tac-Toe provides practice in locating these points.

This is a two-player game with rules similar to other tic-tac-toe games. In this version, however, each player has an individual blank grid for the playing board. One player uses *X*s and the other uses *O*s to mark intersection points. The first player to mark four in a row, either horizontally, vertically, or diagonally, wins the game.

Taking turns, the players name the coordinates for the point they wish to mark. Both players keep track on their own grids of all the points called. Recording the number pairs called, in addition to marking the points, makes it easier to check the points at the end of the game.

In the classroom, first play Coordinate Tic-Tac-Toe as a whole class activity with the class split into two teams. As the team members call

Worksheet 2.1

1. Decode this message.

____ ____ ____ ____ /
(1,4) (2,3) (2,3) (2,4)

____ ____ ____ ____
(4,4) (0,2) (1,3) (0,4)

2. Write the code for your name. First write the letters on the blanks, then fill in the number pairs.

____ ____ ____ ____ ____ ____ ____ ____
( ) ( ) ( ) ( ) ( ) ( ) ( ) ( )

Decode the following questions, then write the answers.

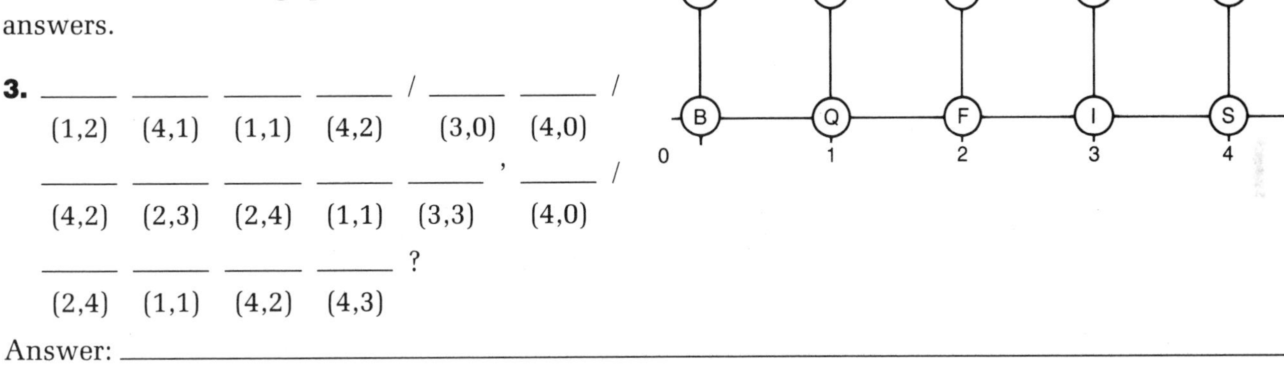

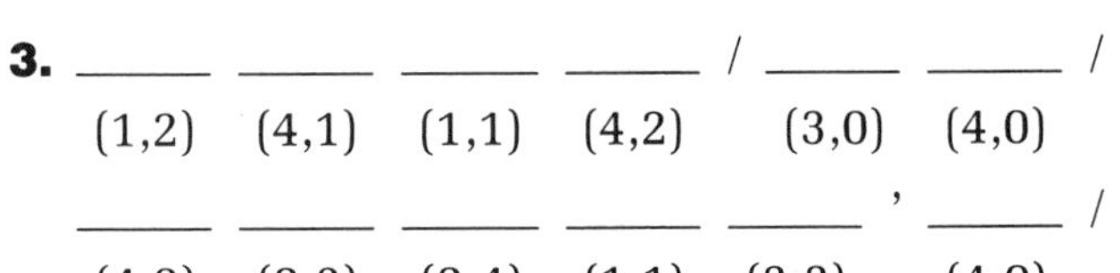

3. ____ ____ ____ ____ / ____ ____ /
(1,2) (4,1) (1,1) (4,2) (3,0) (4,0)

____ ____ ____ ____ ____ , ____ /
(4,2) (2,3) (2,4) (1,1) (3,3) (4,0)

____ ____ ____ ____ ?
(2,4) (1,1) (4,2) (4,3)

Answer: ____________________

4. ____ ____ ____ ____ / ____ ____ ____ / ____ ____ ____ /
(1,2) (4,1) (4,3) (3,2) (2,4) (3,0) (2,4) (3,3) (2,3) (0,2)

____ ____ ____ ____ / ____ ____ ____ ____ / ____ /
(4,4) (1,1) (4,0) (4,2) (4,2) (1,1) (0,4) (4,3) (1,1)

____ ____ ____ ____ / ____ ____ ____ ____ ____ ____ ?
(0,3) (1,1) (4,2) (4,1) (1,3) (2,3) (0,2) (3,1) (4,0) (4,3)

Answer: ____________________

5. ____ ____ ____ ____ ____ / ____ ____ ____ ____ ____ /
(0,2) (3,2) (2,4) (4,3) (3,1) (1,2) (4,1) (3,0) (1,3) (4,1)

____ ____ ____ ____ / ____ ____ ____ ____ / ____ ____ ____ /
(4,0) (3,0) (1,4) (3,2) (1,2) (4,3) (3,1) (4,3) (3,3) (2,3) (0,2)

____ ____ ____ ____ ?
(0,0) (2,3) (3,1) (3,2)

Answer: ____________________

out the coordinates, record them on a chalkboard grid. In the second game, each student records the points on individual grids while the instructor records only the number pairs. After the game is over, the list of coordinates can be checked to settle any questions.

Play Coordinate Tic-Tac-Toe with a partner. Keep a record of the number pairs that have been used. (See Appendix pages 277 and 278 for a record sheet and a master that can be used to make an overhead transparency.)

The grids that we have been using are really only one section of a larger grid like the one in Figure 2.2. Up to now we have been working in only one section (called a *quadrant*). The upper-right section of the grid in Figure 2.2 is called the *first quadrant*. This more complete grid, which includes four quadrants, is made by extending the horizontal and vertical number lines to include negative numbers. The quadrants are numbered counterclockwise: the second quadrant is the upper-left section; the third quadrant is the lower-left section; the fourth quadrant is the lower-right section. The code doesn't change; we still move horizontally first, then vertically. But now, starting at zero, we can move horizontally either to the right (positive) or to the left (negative). And we can move vertically either up (positive) or down (negative).

When naming coordinates for points in this four-quadrant grid, remember to start at zero, move first horizontally, right or left, then move vertically, up or down. What are the coordinates for point *M*? (____,____) They are ($^{-}2$,1)—which is read as "negative 2, positive 1." We moved horizontally to the left and vertically upward. Positive 1 may be written as $^{+}1$ or just 1.

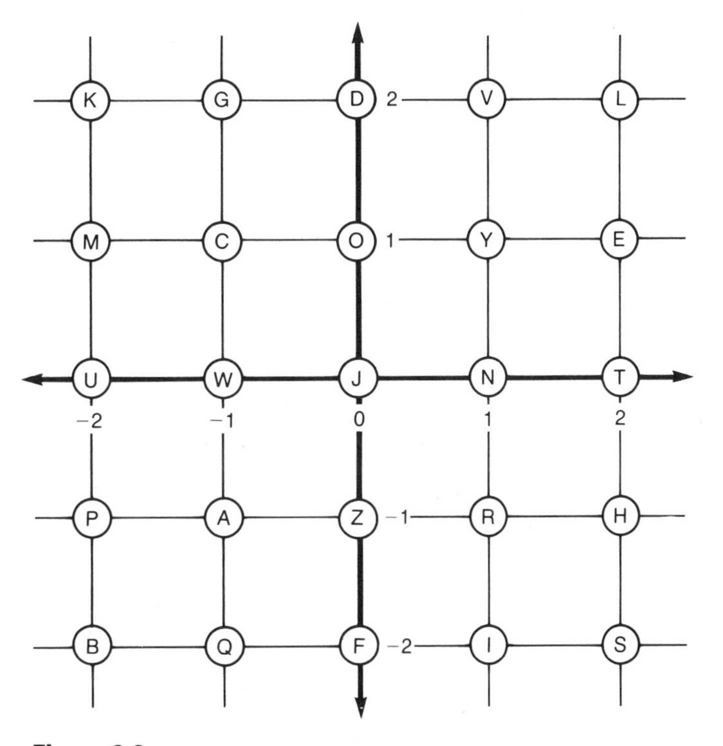

Figure 2.2

What are the coordinates for point P? (____,____) Move horizontally to the left, then down to P, named $(^-2,^-1)$.

What are coordinates for point H? (____,____) Move horizontally to the right, then down. The answer is $(2,^-1)$.

What are the coordinates for point E? (____,____) Move horizontally to the right, then up. The coordinates for point E are (2,1).

Play Coordinate Tic-Tac-Toe (four in a row) using both positive and negative numbers to name the points. By limiting the size of the grids, you will find it necessary to name points in all four quadrants. (See Appendix pages 279 and 280 for a record sheet for this game and also a master to make an overhead transparency).

Making coordinate pictures gives yet another opportunity to practice the skill of locating and plotting points on a coordinate grid. The coordinates (ordered number pairs) for each picture in Figure 2.3 and Worksheet 2.3 are listed. Use a pencil to mark the first point, then mark the second and immediately connect it to the first. Proceed in this manner, marking the point, then connecting it to the preceding point. Cross out the following number pairs as you use them in Figure 2.3 (the picture of a seagull has been started).

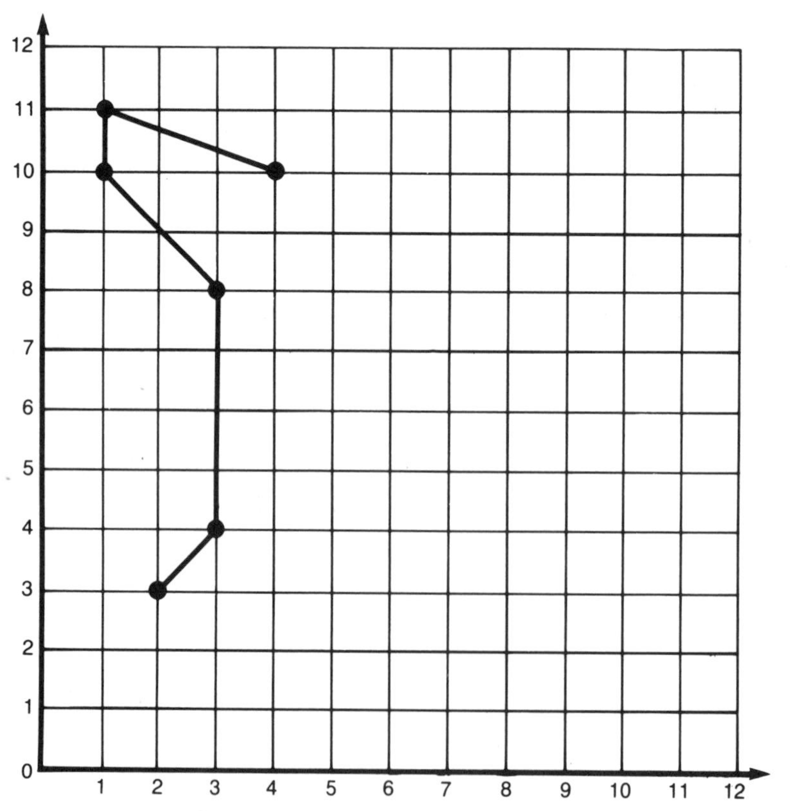

Figure 2.3

(2,3) (3,4) (3,8) (1,10) (1,11) (4,10) (5,6)
(7,7) (6,5) (10,4) (11,1) (10,1) (8,3) (4,3)
(3,2) (2,3)

Worksheet 2.2

Decode the following messages using both positive and negative coordinates.

1. ___ ___ / ___ ___ ___ ___ ___ /
(1,−2) (1,0) (−1,0) (2,−1) (1,−2) (−1,1) (2,−1)

___ ___ ___ ___ / ___ ___ ___ ___ /
(−1,1) (1,−2) (2,0) (1,1) (−1,0) (2,1) (1,−1) (2,1)

___ ___ ___ / ___ ___ ___ ___ ?
(1,1) (0,1) (−2,0) (−2,−2) (0,1) (1,−1) (1,0)

Answer: ______________________________

____

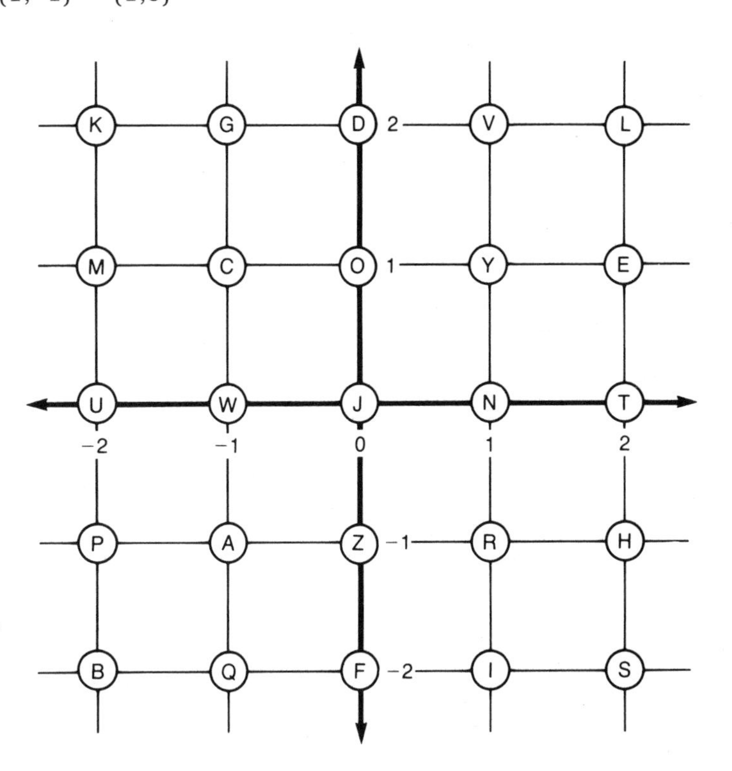

2. ___ ___ ___ ___ /
(−1,0) (2,−1) (−1,−1) (2,0)

___ ___ ___ ___ /
(−2,2) (1,−2) (1,0) (0,2)

___ ___ /
(0,1) (0,−2)

___ ___ ___ ___ /
(−1,0) (0,1) (1,−1) (−2,2)

___ ___ /
(0,2) (0,1)

___ ___ ___ / ___ ___ ?
(1,1) (0,1) (−2,0) (0,2) (0,1)

Answer: ______________________________

____

3. ___ ___ ___ ___ /
(1,0) (−1,−1) (−2,1) (2,1)

___ ___ ___ / ___ ___ ___ ___ /
(2,0) (2,−1) (2,1) (2,2) (−1,−1) (2,−2) (2,0)

___ ___ ___ ___ ___ / ___ ___ ___ , ___ ___ /
(−2,1) (0,1) (1,2) (1,−2) (2,1) (1,1) (0,1) (−2,0) (1,2) (2,1)

___ ___ ___ ___ .
(2,−2) (2,1) (2,1) (1,0)

Answer: ______________________________

(continued)

4. ______ ______ ______ ______ / ______ ______ / ______ ______ ______ /

$(^-1,0)$ $(2,^-1)$ $(^-1,^-1)$ $(2,0)$ $(1,^-2)$ $(2,^-2)$ $(2,0)$ $(2,^-1)$ $(2,1)$

______ ______ ______ ______ ______ / ______ ______ / ______ ______ ______ /

$(2,0)$ $(1,^-2)$ $(2,0)$ $(2,2)$ $(2,1)$ $(0,1)$ $(0,^-2)$ $(2,0)$ $(2,^-1)$ $(2,1)$

______ ______ ______ ______ / ______ ______ ______ ______ /

$(2,2)$ $(^-1,^-1)$ $(2,^-2)$ $(2,0)$ $(^-2,^-2)$ $(0,1)$ $(0,1)$ $(^-2,2)$

______ ______ ______ ' ______ ______ / ______ ______ ______ ______ ?

$(1,1)$ $(0,1)$ $(^-2,0)$ $(1,2)$ $(2,1)$ $(1,^-1)$ $(2,1)$ $(^-1,^-1)$ $(0,2)$

Answer: ____

Worksheet 2.3

Connect the points to form pictures on the grids.

1.

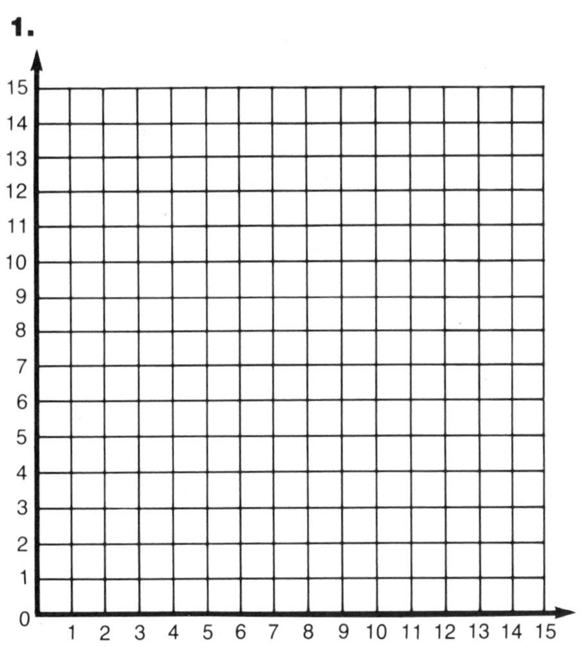

(5,8) (6,9) (8,8) (9,8) (8,7) (10,8) (12,9) (10,10) (8,11) (9,10) (8,10) (6,9) (5,10) (5,8)

2.

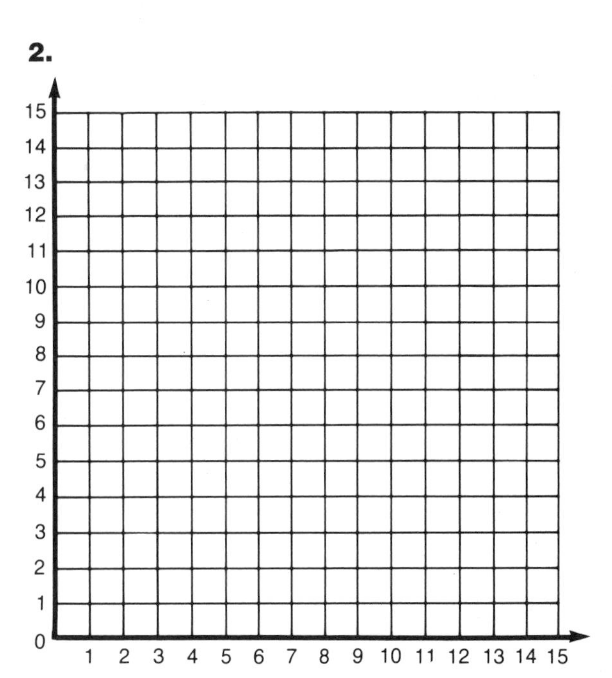

(1,1) (2,2) (3,3) (4,4) (5,5) (6,6) (7,7) (9,11) (7,12) (5,11) (7,7)

3.

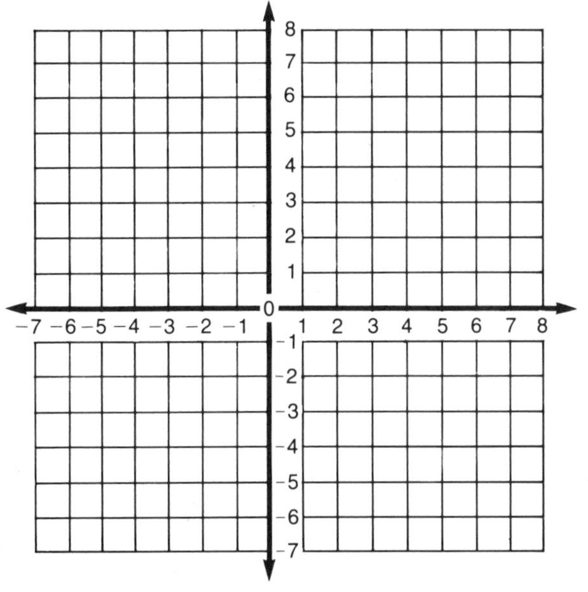

(2,0) (6,2) (2,4) (0,8) ($^-2$,4) ($^-6$,2) ($^-2$,0) (0,$^-4$) (2,0)

4.

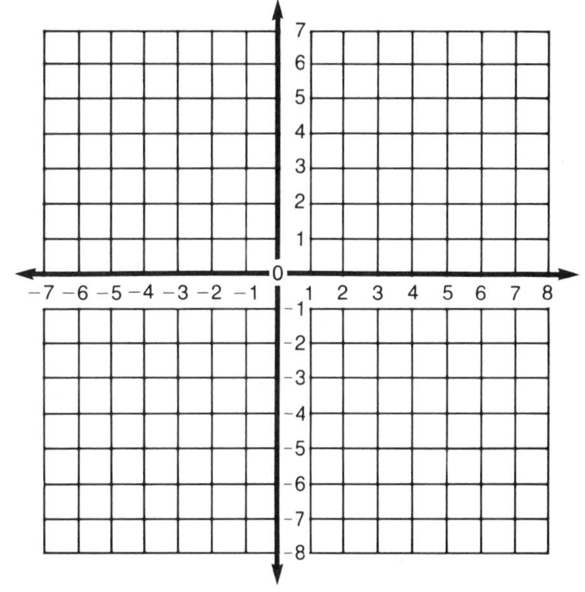

(4,$^-1$) (6,1) (0,1) (5,3) (0,6) ($^-2$,6) (0,7) (0,1) ($^-4$,1) ($^-2$,$^-1$) (4,$^-1$)

GRAPHING PATTERNS

In this section we use what we have learned about coordinates to record information about patterns. You will need some toothpicks or small sticks. Build a shape that looks like the one in Figure 2.4.

Figure 2.4

How many squares do you have? ______
How many toothpicks did you use? ______

Hook on another square to make a total of two squares, as in Figure 2.5. How many sticks have you used altogether? ______ Keep a record of the patterns in Table 2.1.

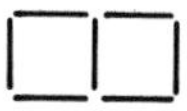

Figure 2.5

Use toothpicks to figure out what will happen for 3, 4, and 5 squares. Can you see a pattern? How many toothpicks would you need for 6 squares? For 7? Fill in the numbers on the table. Can you find a pattern that will help you predict how many sticks you will need for 10 squares? For 20?

Sketch	No. of Squares	No. of Toothpicks
	1	4
	2	7
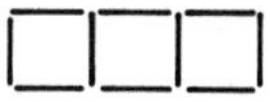	3	
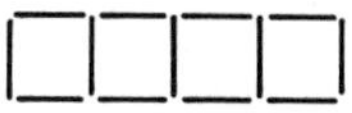	4	
	5	
	6	
	7	

Table 2.1

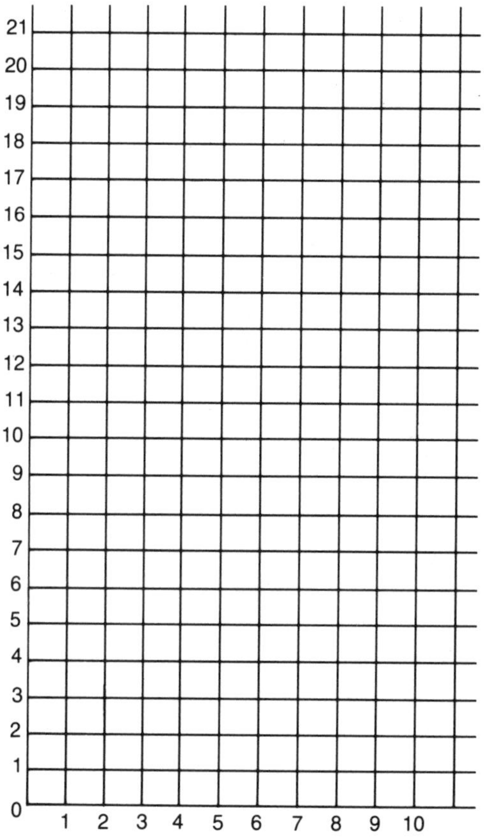

Figure 2.6

Another way to record this pattern is to consider the numbers in each row of the table as an ordered number pair and plot them on a coordinate graph. From Table 2.1 we have (1,4), (2,7), (3,10), (4,13), and (5,16). Plot these points on the graph in Figure 2.6.

What seems to be happening?

____

____

A straight line should be formed when you connect the points you have plotted.

Do Worksheet 2.4 before reading page 18.

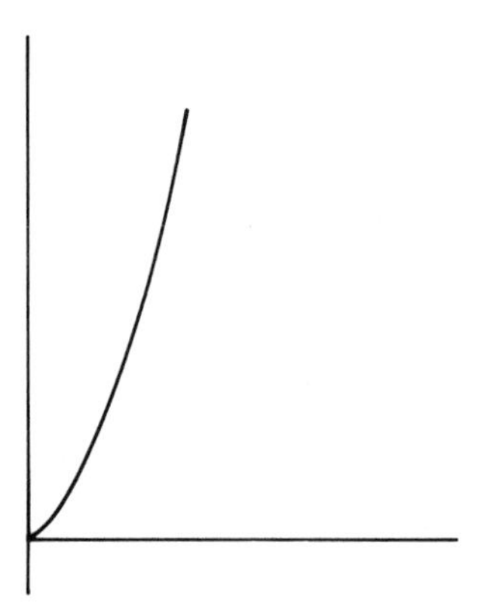

Figure 2.7

The first five patterns on Worksheet 2.4 form straight lines when the points are connected. But the last one does not. It should make a shape like the one in Figure 2.7. Later we will discuss how you can predict what kind of graph a pattern will make.

Make up some different patterns with a partner, and draw their graphs. Use any materials (toothpicks, pins, matchsticks, and so on) that are easily available. You can base your patterns on squares, triangles, rectangles, or other shapes or designs. Record your patterns. Include a sketch, table, and graph for each pattern. Do you have any ideas about which patterns generate straight lines and which generate curved lines? (There is a master for graph paper on page 281 in the Appendix.)

Worksheet 2.4

Try these patterns with a partner. First use toothpicks to add several more numbers to each table. Then plot the ordered number pairs on the graph.

1.

	No. of Triangles	No. of Toothpicks
△	1	3
△▽	2	5
△▽△	3	______
	______	______
	______	______
	______	______

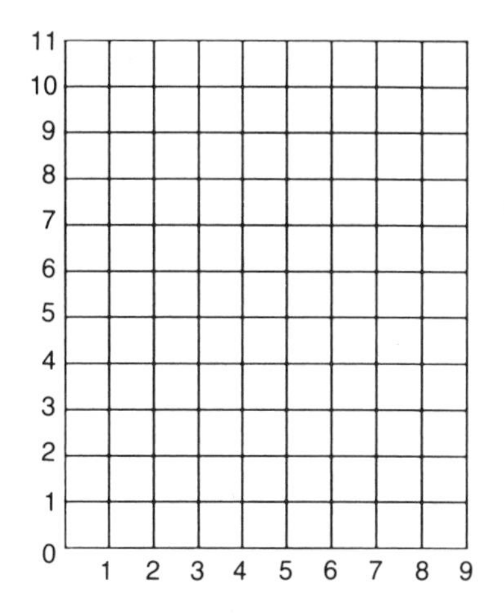

2.

	No. of Triangles	No. of Toothpicks
△	1	3
△▽	2	4
△▽△	3	5
△▽△▽	4	______
	______	______
	______	______

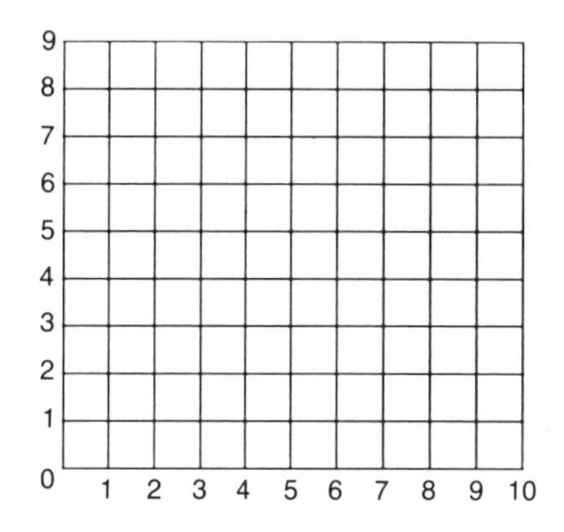

3.

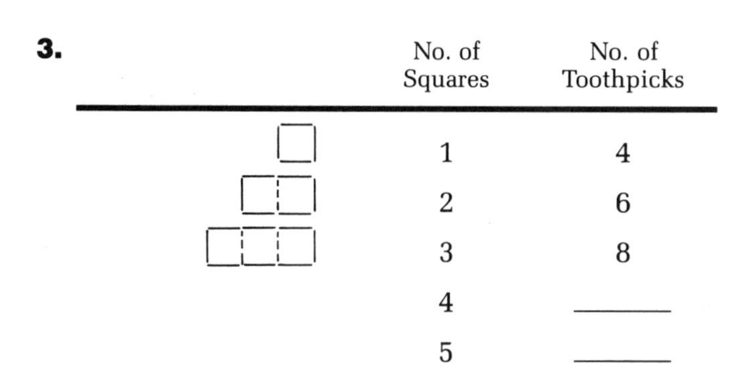

	No. of Squares	No. of Toothpicks
□	1	4
□□	2	6
□□□	3	8
	4	______
	5	______

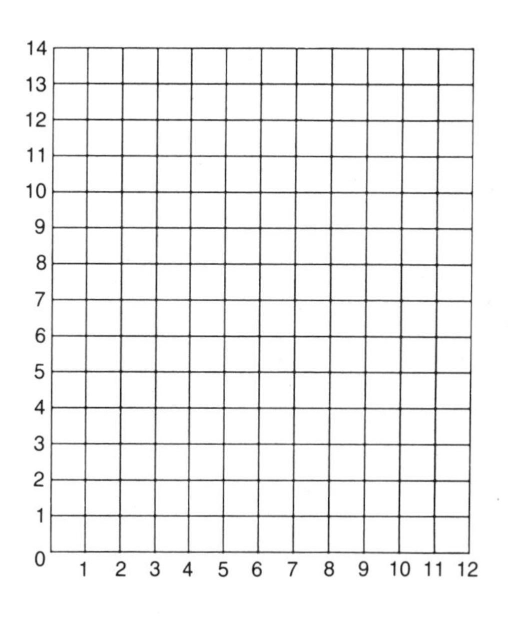

(continued)

4.

	No. of Squares	No. of Toothpicks
	2	6
	4	8
	6	10
	_____	_____
	_____	_____
	_____	_____

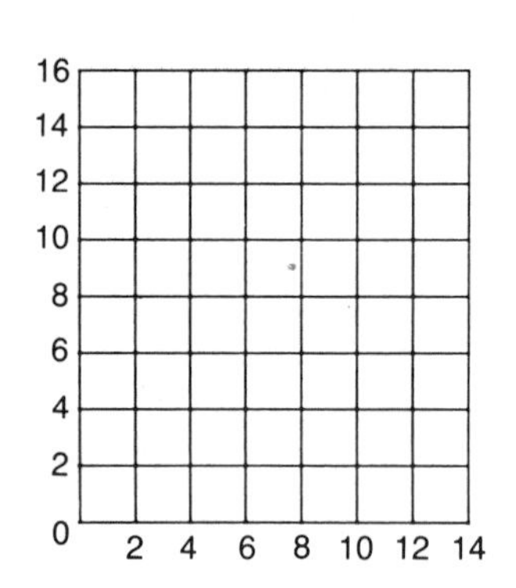

Note that the axes in this problem and the next are labeled by multiples of two in order to save space.

5.

	No. of Squares	No. of Toothpicks
	2	7
	4	12
	6	17
	8	_____
	_____	_____
	_____	_____

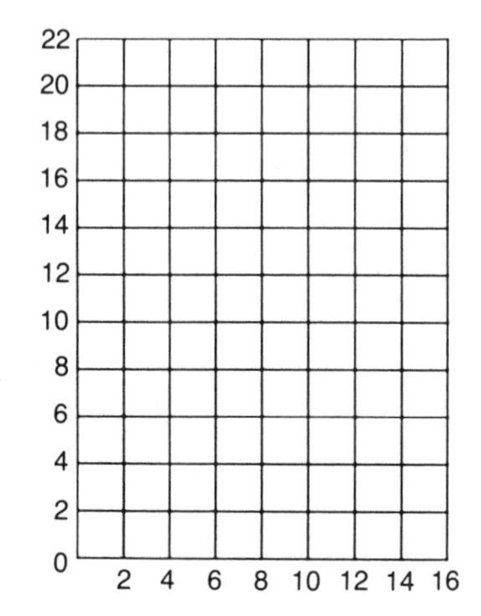

6.

	No. of Rows	No. of Points
•	1	1
	2	3
	3	6
	4	_____
	5	_____
	6	_____

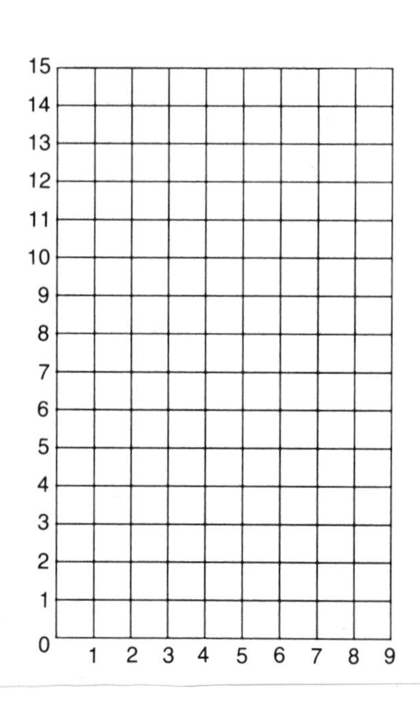

FUNCTIONS AND THEIR GRAPHS

In this section, we use tables to help us figure out patterns without using toothpicks or other materials. Each of the patterns in the preceding section, as well as each of the patterns in the following tables, can be described by a rule.

We will use the concept of a machine that has the following characteristic: when you put something into it, something comes out. For example, you put money into a coffee machine, and some coffee comes out. Jot down a list of other examples. Be sure to name the machine and say what goes in and what comes out.

Machine	*In*	*Out*
____________	____________	____________
____________	____________	____________
____________	____________	____________
____________	____________	____________

This section introduces a different kind of machine—a *function machine*. In our first function machine, words go in and letters come out. The task is to guess the rule according to which this machine operates. Note that the rule or function is always consistent, and, for any one word that goes in, only one letter comes out. Table 2.2 contains a record of some of the inputs and outputs for this machine.

Input Word	Output Letter
computer	d
receptionist	s
calligraphy	d
executive	f

Table 2.2

Can you guess the rule? ________________________________

Does it help to look at the words that have the same output letter? If the word *paper* goes in, what letter comes out? Some people might say, "The machine looks at the first letter in the word and puts out the next letter in the alphabet." Thus, if we have *paper* as input, we would have *q* as output. Does this rule seem to fit all of the entries in the table?

Table 2.3 records the results from another machine. It, too, has a consistent rule that does not change. The * indicates that the machine has rejected the word *zero*; this machine's rule does not know what to do with the word *zero*.

Can you describe this machine's rule?

____

____

____

Input Word	Output Letter
computer	d
receptionist	s
handout	i
executive	y
zero	*
equal	r
conference	d

Table 2.3

Compare your idea with another person's. You might say, "For every word that goes in, the next letter after the first consonant comes out."

Did this table look suspiciously like the first one? Where did it start to behave differently? *Executive* had an output of *f* for the first machine and an output of *y* this time. Did that output help to refine or clarify your guess for the rule? Often it takes several inputs before you can be completely sure of the rule.

What about the input for *zero*? Why do you think the machine rejected it? Can you think of a reasonable output for *zero* that would prevent it from being rejected? Now do Worksheets 2.5 and 2.6.

As you may have noticed, not all function machines that take in words can handle every word we want to put in. We will find that this happens in number-based function machines as well. Just what is acceptable input for particular functions is an important topic in mathematics.

Now we will consider a function machine that takes numbers as input and gives numbers for output. Let's say that the machine changes a 6 into a 12. What is a possible rule that would fit these results? Can you think of a different rule that would also fit?

A more complete record of results is shown in Table 2.4. What rule will fit all of these outcomes? ______________________

____

____

Input	Output
6	12
4	10
8	14
3	9

Table 2.4

Did we need to see Table 2.4 to find the appropriate rule? Most often, people guess that (6,12) represents an outcome from the rule that doubles the input. However, when we look at (4,10) we see that the doubling rule won't work. The additional information of (8,14) and (3,9) helps us to decide that the rule is "Take the input number and add 6." Another way to describe the function or rule is to let A stand for any input number and write the rule as $A + 6$.

Notes to Instructor: The introduction to function machines is best presented as a whole class discovery lesson. You can ask the students to suggest input numbers as well as to guess output numbers. When some of the students begin to discover the function, ask them to keep it to themselves until the others have had a chance to find it. Their challenge is to think of input numbers that will help the others figure out the rule. Try to give every student an opportunity to discover the function before asking someone to state it in words.

Another activity is to look at the first input/output pair—for example, (6,12)—and ask the students to generate as many functions as possible that would work for that number pair. For example: $2A$, $A + 6$, $3A - 6$, $2(A - 1) + 2$, and so on.

Finding the inverses for function machines is also a valuable activity. When some students have guessed a rule, give an output and ask them for the input. Then talk about what they did to find the input when given an output. Ask them to express this procedure in words and then mathematically, using Y for output. Your students may like to know that this reversing process often stumps college algebra and calculus students.

Worksheet 2.5

Describe the rule for each of the function machines below. A * in the output column indicates that the input will not work in that machine.

1.

Input	Output
river	r
subtract	t
happy	y
blue	e
saucer	r
pancake	______
salad	______

Rule: ______________________

2.

Input	Output
stones	f
abacus	b
hour	v
action	j
dog	*
edge	f
return	v

Rule: ______________________

3.

Input	Output
lost	p
that	b
loud	v
falling	j
street	f
neighborhood	______
ritual	______

Rule: ______________________

4.

Input	Output
river	q
blue	d
stones	r
action	m
falling	______
______	m
______	c

Rule: ______________________

5.

Input	Output
list	t
random	o
words	s
try	z
be	*
often	______
cute	______

Rule: ______________________

6.

Input	Output
pumpkin	o
broccoli	g
banana	y
tomato	r
cauliflower	______
______	r
______	g

Rule: ______________________

Worksheet 2.6

Describe the rule for each function machine. Notice that word function machines can also have numbers as outputs.

1.

Input	Output
river	5
subtract	8
happy	5
blue	4
______	3
______	2
vacation	______

Rule: ______________________________

____

2.

Input	Output
are	1
arrive	2
rose	1
burr	2
ring	______
bat	______
______	0

Rule: ______________________________

____

3.

Input	Output
starch	19
work	23
about	1
nowhere	14
hello	______
______	3
zebra	26

Rule: ______________________________

____

4.

Input	Output
car	1
sweet	2
neighborhood	5
weasel	3
go	1
wagon	______
______	2

Rule: ______________________________

____

5.

Input	Output
lace	1
clown	0
eviction	1
breeze	3
money	1
enter	______
______	2

Rule: ______________________________

____

6.

Input	Output
mynah	3
cod	1
mouse	2
canary	3
trout	______
cat	______
______	2

Rule: ______________________________

____

Worksheet 2.7

Complete the table and describe the rule in words for each of the function machines. A * in the output column indicates that the input will not work for that machine.

1.

Input	Output
15	6
12	3
20	11
9	0
34	______
10	______
87	______
______	4
A	______

Rule: ______________________

2.

Input	Output
6	2
15	5
11	*
42	14
30	______
117	______
______	19
36	______
A	______

Rule: ______________________

3.

Input	Output
4	10
2	8
7	13
13	______
5	______
______	28
100	______
20	______
A	______

Rule: ______________________

4.

Input	Output
3	12
14	56
7	28
12	48
5	______
9	______
16	______
______	32
______	4
A	______

Rule: ______________________

5.

Input	Output
2	98
7	93
60	40
75	25
10	______
43	______
100	______
______	81
______	20
A	______

Rule: ______________________

6.

Input	Output
5	25
1	1
7	49
10	100
4	______
12	______
20	______
______	64
______	36
A	______

Rule: ______________________

Worksheet 2.8

Complete the tables and graphs, and connect the ordered number pairs. The first problem is done for you. If you are not sure of the outputs for the negative inputs, you can check your output as follows. Plot and connect the other points. Extend the line across the whole graph. Find the negative input on the horizontal axis, and move up or down to the line you have drawn. Then move across the graph paper to see what output number you have on the vertical axis. Study Point *P* in Problem 1, as an example.

1.

Input	Output
2	5
4	7
7	10
$^{-}4$	$^{-}1$
0	3
$^{-}3$	0
A	*A* + 3

Rule: Input plus 3 equals output.

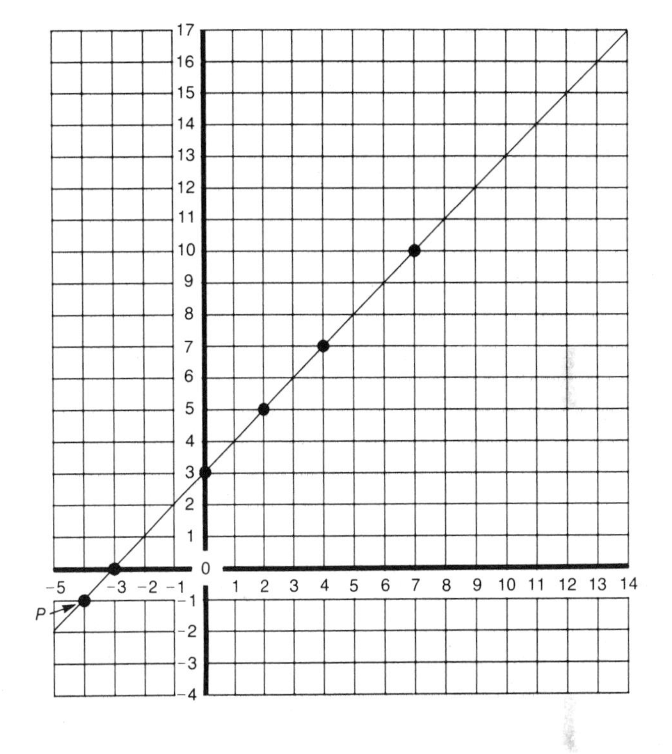

2.

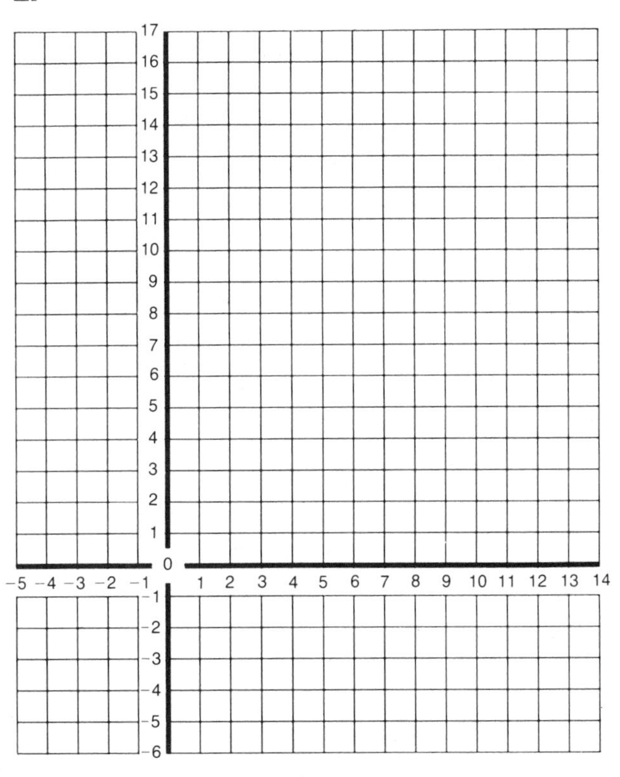

Input	Output
5	4
1	0
12	11
9	______
4	______
$^{-}2$	$^{-}3$
$^{-}1$	______
______	1
A	______

Rule: ____________________

____

(continued)

3.

Input	Output
3	9
5	15
2	6
1	______
4	______
$^{-}1$	$^{-}3$
$^{-}2$	______
A	______

Rule: ____________________

____

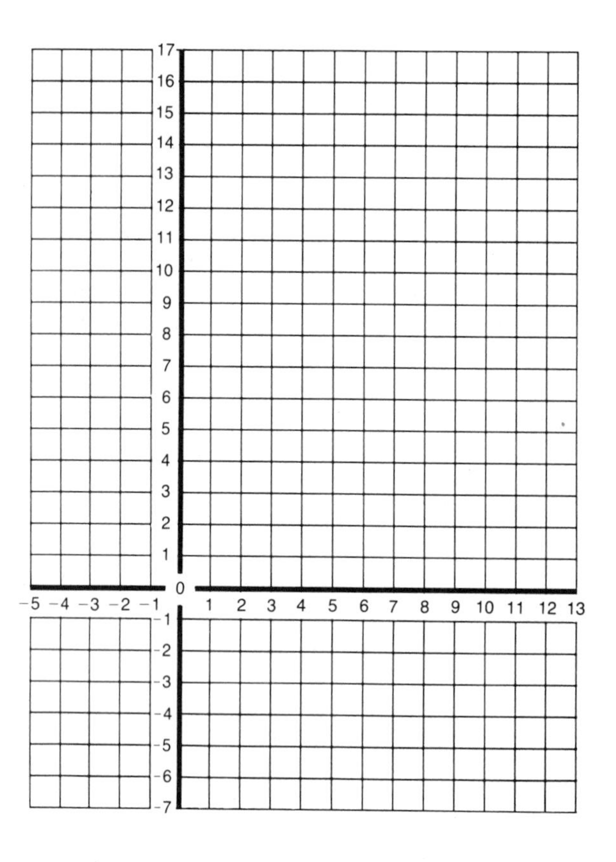

4.

Input	Output
1	7
0	8
4	4
2	6
$^{-}1$	9
3	______
A	______

Rule: ____________________

____

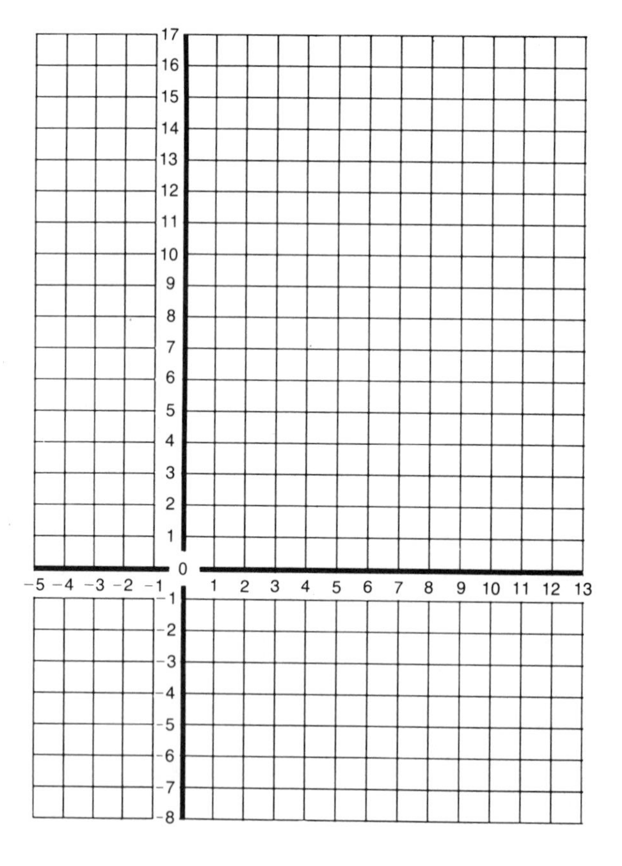

Table 2.5 contains inputs and outputs for another function machine. Can you guess the rule? ____________________

____

____

Input	Output
2	7
4	13
8	25
5	16
⁻3	⁻8
1	4
10	31

Table 2.5

Some useful hints:

(1) Rearrange the table so the inputs are in numerical order;
(2) Look at pairs that have 1,10, and 100 in the input column and use them to help you guess.

First try rearranging the inputs. Can you make a guess at the rule? Now look at what happens to 10 as an input. It becomes a 31. What can you do to a 10 to get close to 31? ____________ What about multiplying by 3? Then what else do you have to do to hit 31 exactly? ____________ Since $3 \times 10 = 30$, if we add 1, we get 31. The function for this machine might be: "Multiply the input number by 3 and add 1." Check this rule to see if it works for other inputs.

The following is a shorter way to express the rule: "If we put in any number, again abbreviated by an A, then the output will be 3 times A plus 1, or $3A + 1$."

Worksheet 2.9

Study the tables below. Describe the function for each table in words. Be sure to express it in an abbreviated form, using *A* to represent any input number. Check that your rule works for all of the input numbers in the table. Fill in any missing information.

1.

Input	Output
2	1
5	7
4	5
10	17
100	197
$^-1$	$^-5$
7	____
A	____

Rule: ____________________

____

2.

Input	Output
5	12
12	26
3	8
8	18
$^-4$	$^-6$
0	____
A	____
____	____

Rule: ____________________

____

3.

Input	Output
4	8
6	14
10	26
3	5
$^-2$	$^-10$
____	20
$^-1$	____
A	____

Rule: ____________________

____

4.

Input	Output
7	37
4	22
12	62
8	42
1	____
____	52
3	____
20	____
0	____
____	27
A	____

Rule: ____________________

____

5.

Input	Output
50	22
120	57
24	9
6	0
80	____
10	2
____	7
____	65
62	28
88	41
A	____

Rule: ____________________

____

6.

Input	Output
2	19
5	49
14	139
20	199
____	99
0	____
8	____
1	____
6	____
____	69
A	____

Rule: ____________________

____

Worksheet 2.10

Complete the tables below, and graph your results.

1.

Input	Output
5	11
2	5
6	13
$^{-}2$	$^{-}3$
4	______
$^{-}1$	______
______	7
A	______

Rule: ____________

____

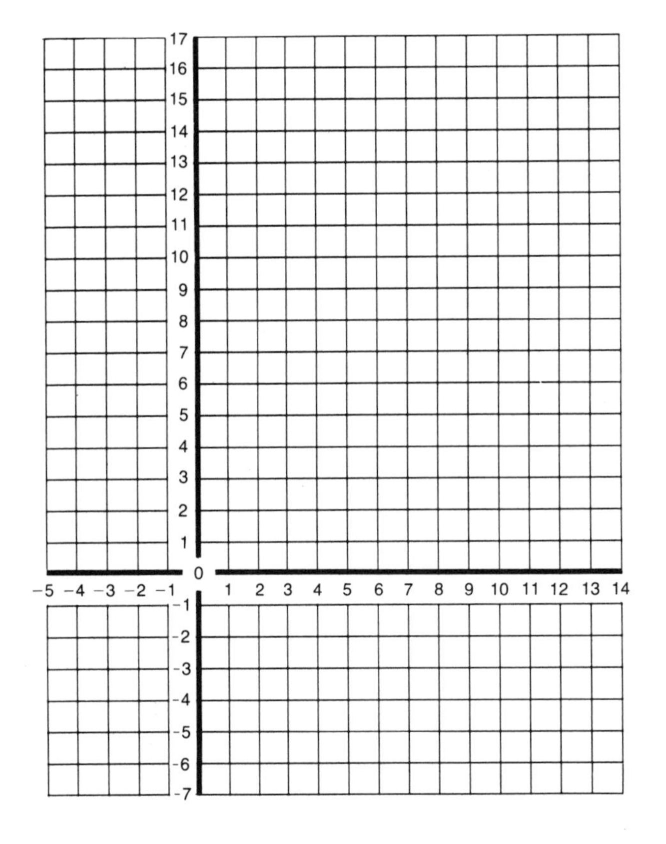

2.

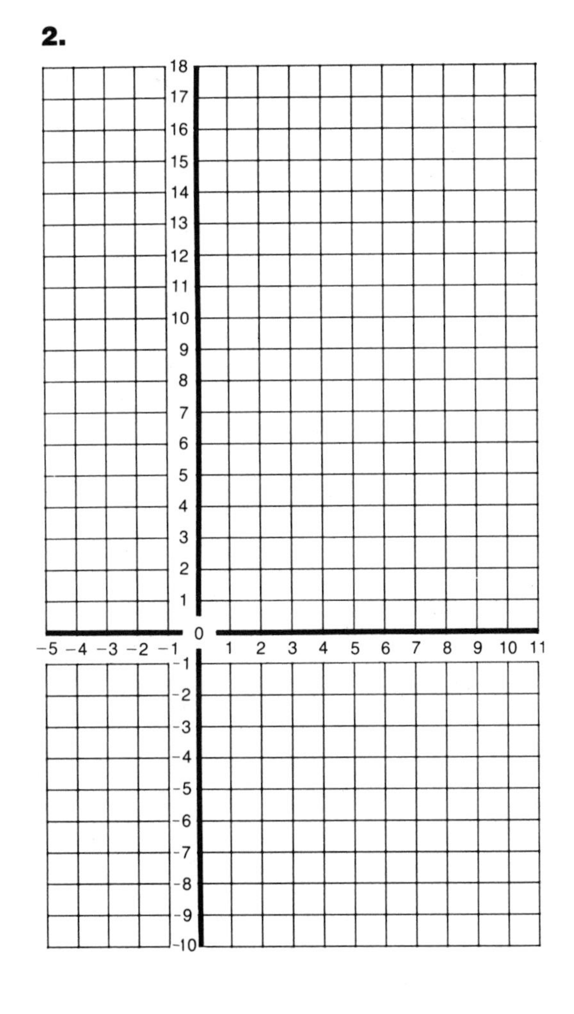

Input	Output
6	10
10	18
5	8
8	14
1	______
0	______
A	______
______	______

Rule: ____________

____

(continued)

3.

Input	Output
$^{-}1$	$^{-}2$
2	7
3	10
1	______
______	16
10	______
______	______
A	______

Rule: ____________________

____

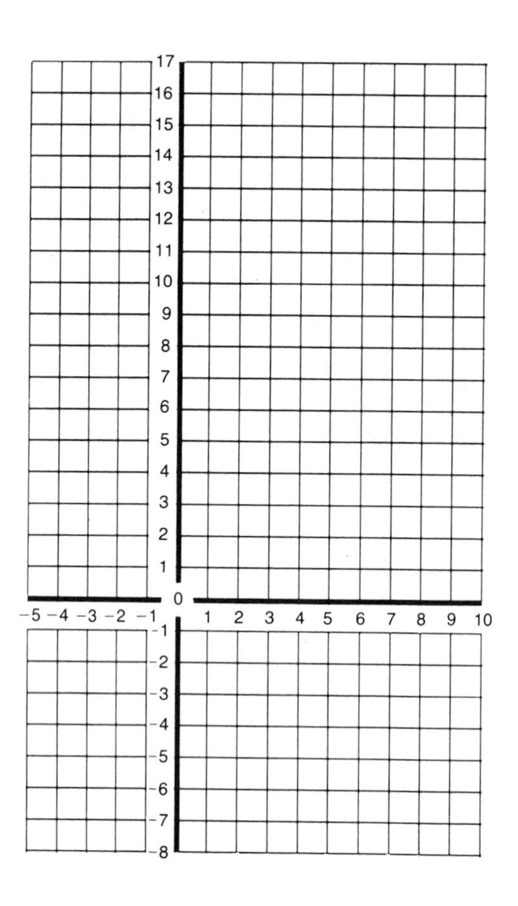

4.

Input	Output
0	10
1	8
2	6
5	0
$^{-}1$	12
4	2
3	______
6	$^{-}2$
A	______

Rule: ____________________

____

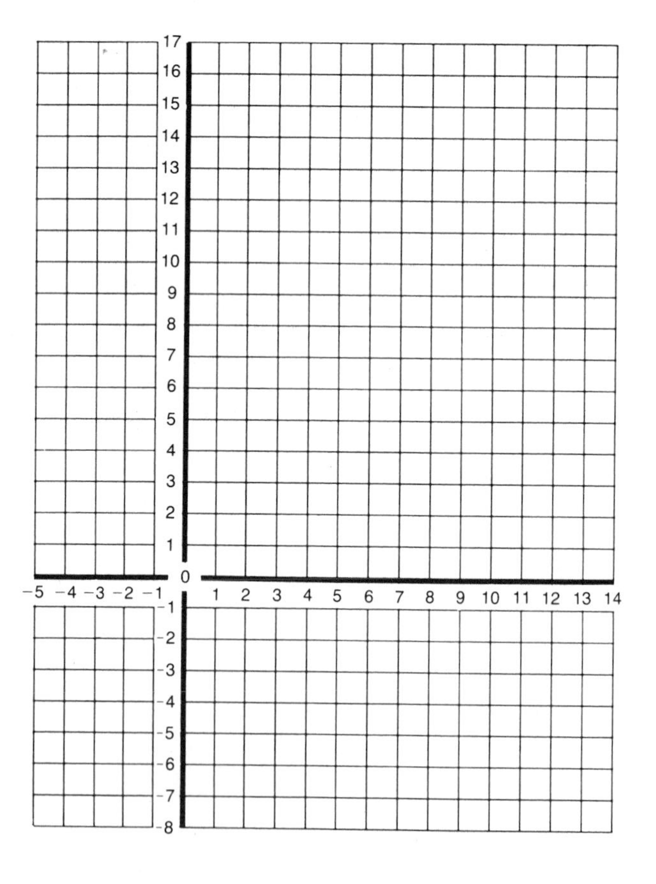

Worksheet 2.11

You are given a rule or function for each problem. Complete an input/output table, and graph your results. Some of these graphs will be curves. Can you see any pattern that tells when curves will occur?

1.

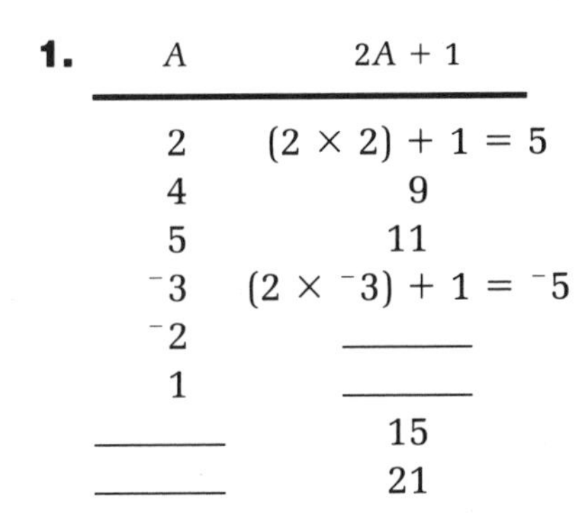

A	$2A + 1$
2	$(2 \times 2) + 1 = 5$
4	9
5	11
$^{-}3$	$(2 \times {}^{-}3) + 1 = {}^{-}5$
$^{-}2$	______
1	______
______	15
______	21

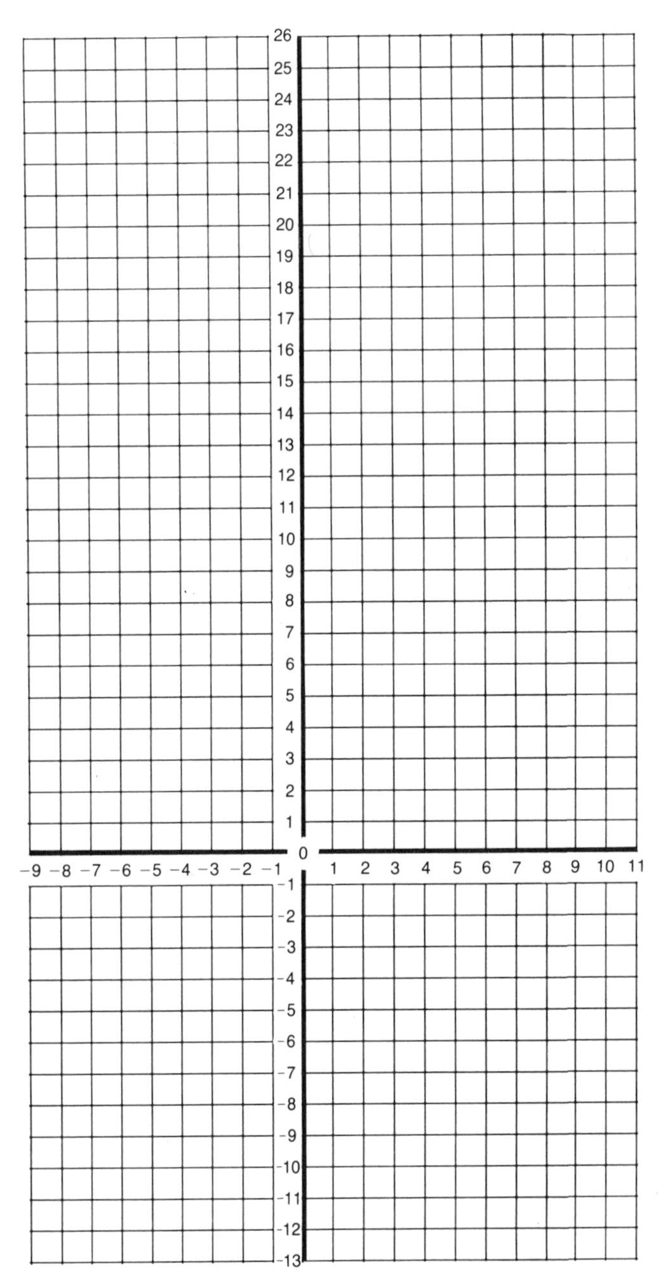

(continued)

2.

A	$A \times A$
2	4
1	1
0	0
$^{-}1$	1
$^{-}2$	4
3	
$^{-}3$	
	25

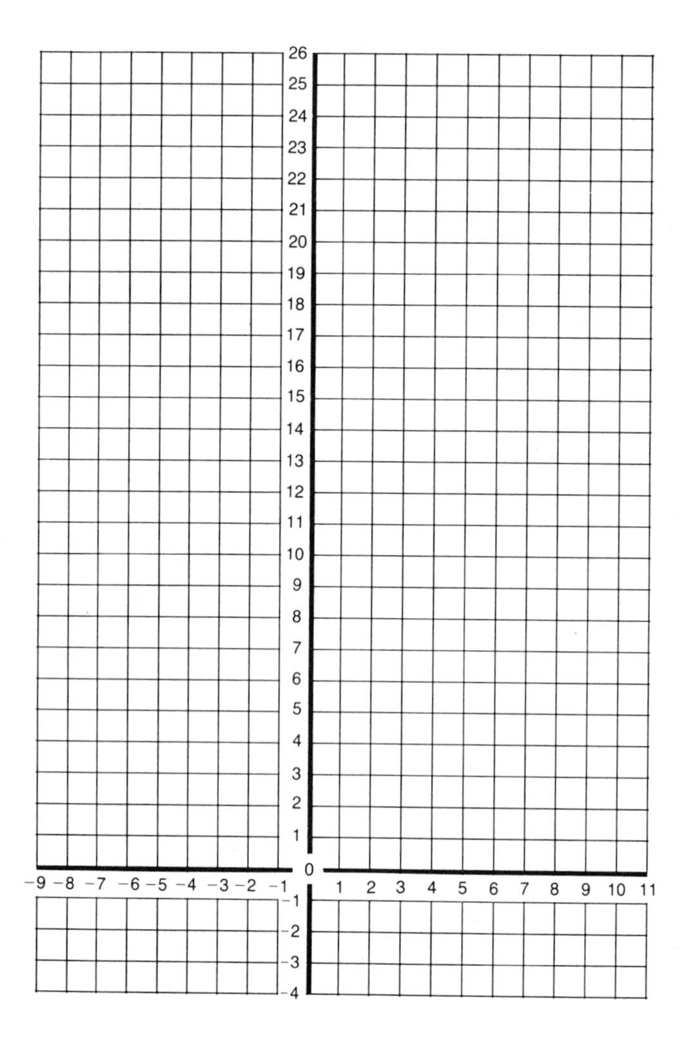

3.

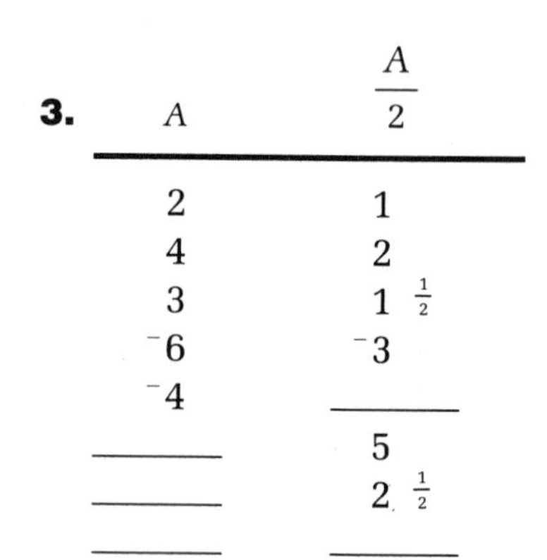

A	$\frac{A}{2}$
2	1
4	2
3	$1\frac{1}{2}$
$^{-}6$	$^{-}3$
$^{-}4$	
	5
	$2\frac{1}{2}$

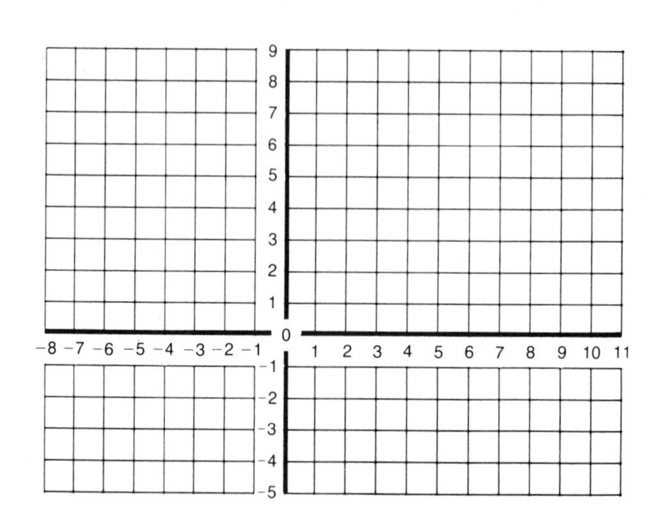

(continued)

4.

A	$A \times (A - 1)$
1	$1 \times 0 = 0$
2	$2 \times 1 = 2$
3	6
0	0
$^-1$	2
5	______
$\frac{1}{2}$	$\frac{^-1}{4}$

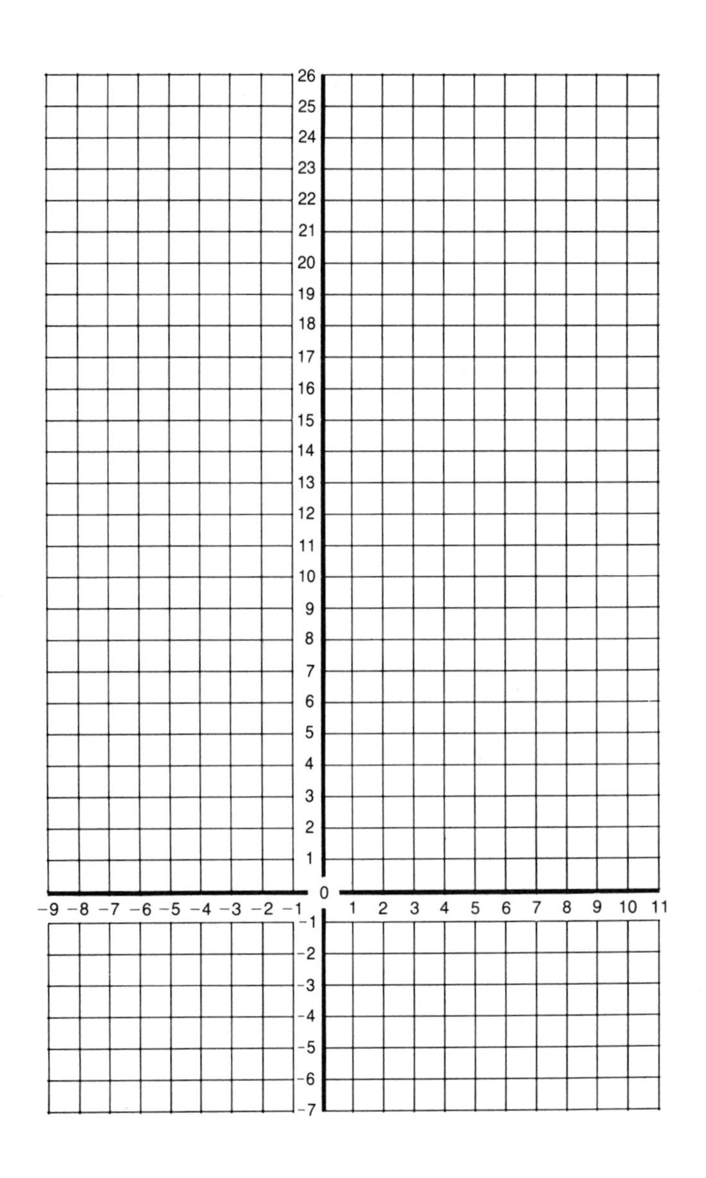

Worksheet 2.12

Complete the input/output tables, and determine the functions. The input is the *horizontal* distance from the graphed line to the vertical axis, and the output is the *vertical* distance from the line to the horizontal axis. Point X is recorded for you in Problem 1.

1.

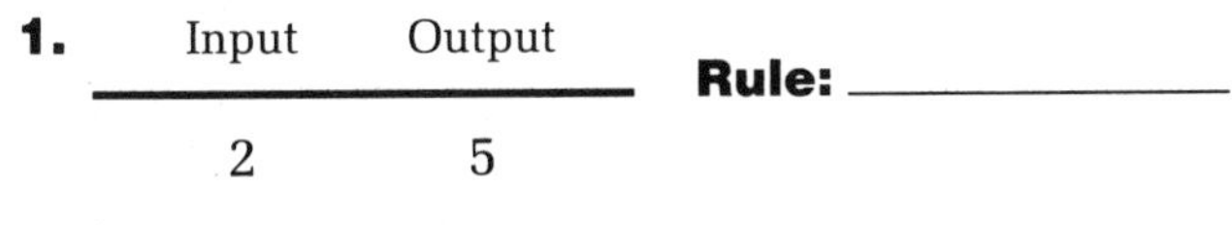

Input	Output
2	5
____	____
____	____
____	____
____	____

Rule: ____________

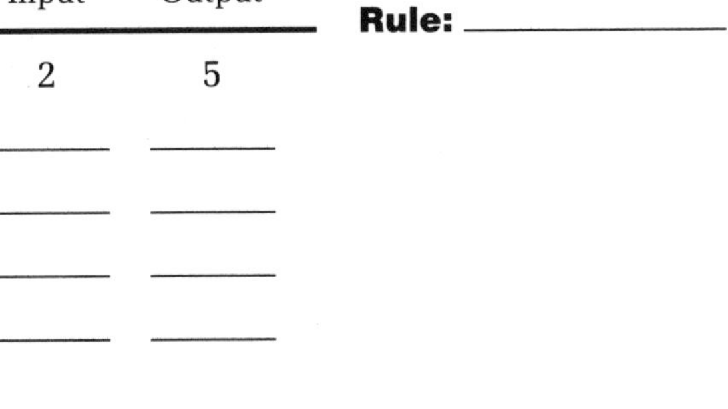

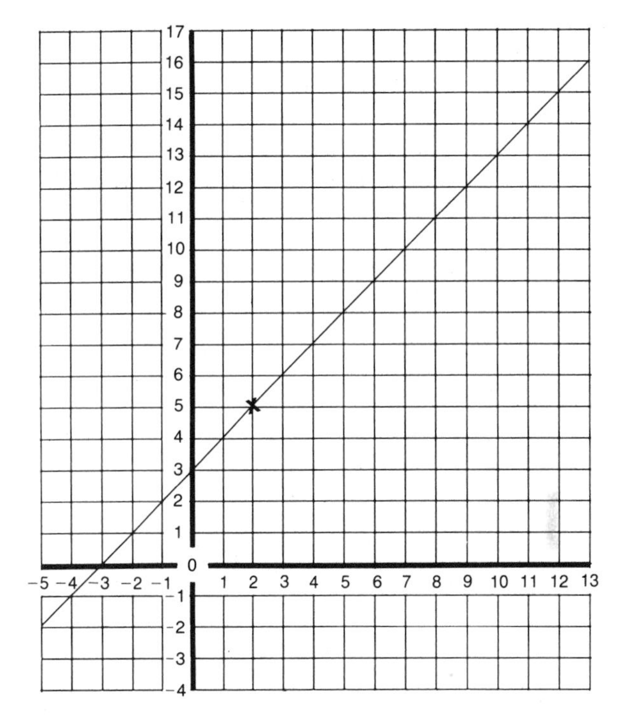

2.

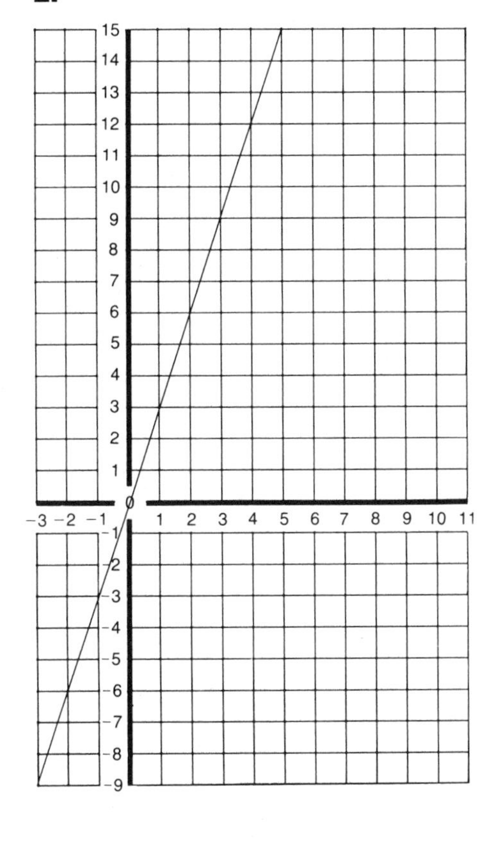

Input	Output
____	____
____	____
____	____
____	____
____	____
____	____

Rule: ____________

(continued)

3. Input Output **Rule:** ________

Input	Output

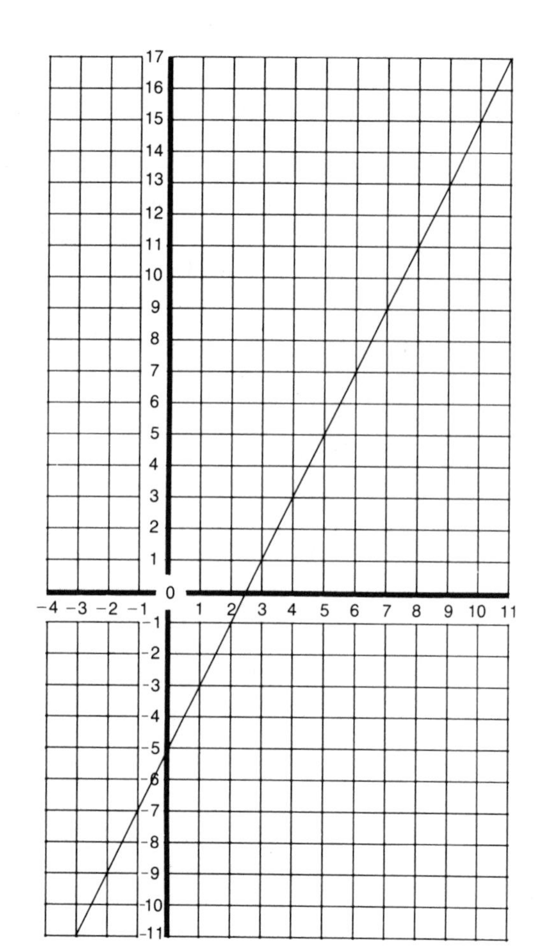

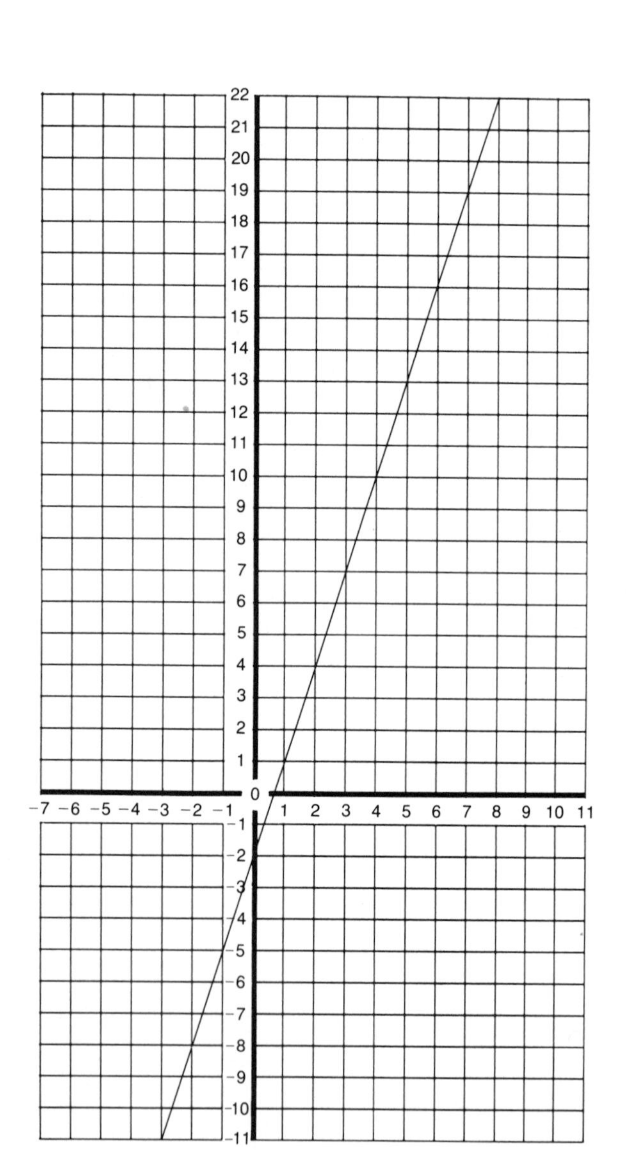

4. Input Output **Rule:** ________

Input	Output

Worksheet 2.13

Complete the tables, and graph the functions in different colors.

1.

A	$2A$
5	10
7	14
9	______
10	______
⁻1	⁻2

2.

A	$2A - 1$
5	9
7	13
9	______
10	______
⁻1	⁻3

3.

A	$2A + 2$
5	12
7	16
9	______
10	______
⁻1	0

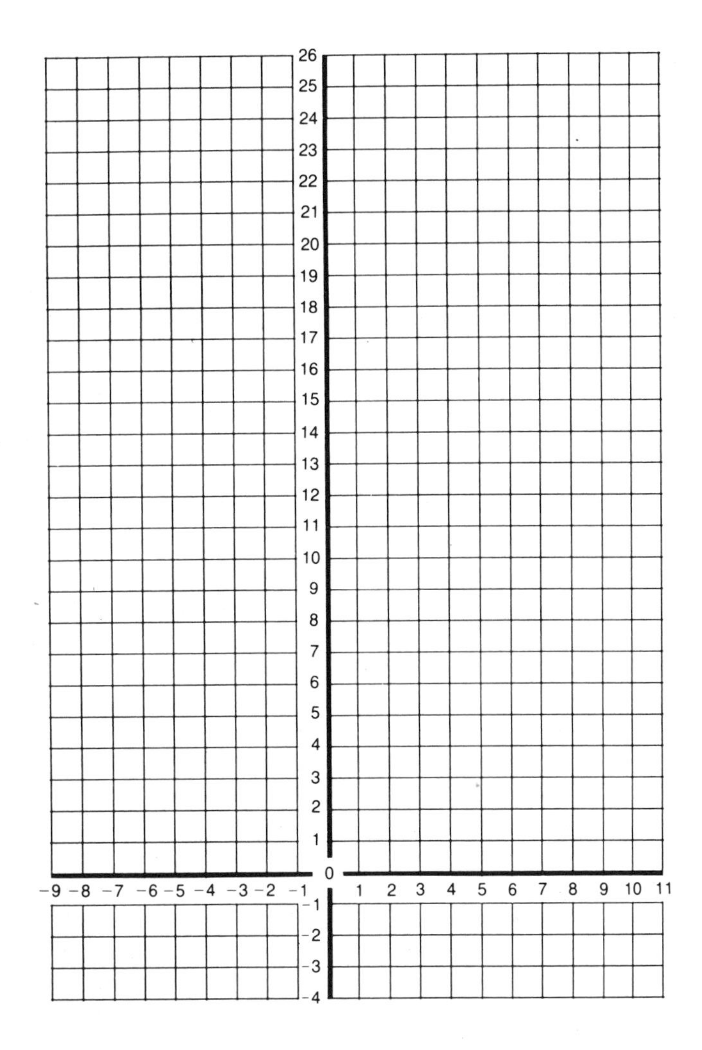

Note that the graphs of all of these functions are parallel straight lines. The number that multiplies the input of each function is 2. This is called the *slope* of the line. Straight lines that have the same slope are parallel.

Worksheet 2.14

Complete the tables, and graph the functions in different colors.

1.

A	$A + 3$
4	7
2	5
0	______
3	______
$^{-}1$	2

2.

A	$2A + 1$
4	9
2	5
0	______
3	______
$^{-}1$	$^{-}1$

3.

A	$5A - 2$
4	18
2	8
0	______
3	______
$^{-}1$	$^{-}7$

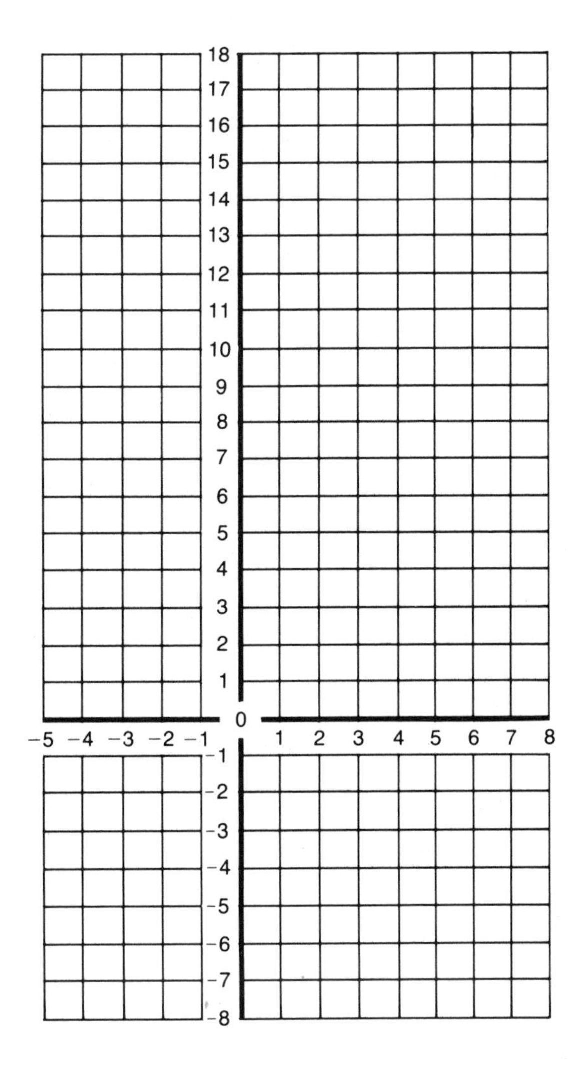

These graphs are straight lines that intersect. The number that multiplies the input is different for each rule.

Look over the worksheets you have completed. Have you formulated an idea of which functions have curved graphs and which ones have straight lines? Work through the examples below to see if you can determine the pattern. Graph the results from Tables 2.6 and 2.7 on the same graph in Figure 2.8. Connect the points of each graph in a different color.

Input	Output
$^-1$	$^-3$
1	$^-1$
2	0
3	1
4	2
6	4
A	______
______	______

Table 2.6

Input	Output
$^-1$	1
1	3
2	4
3	5
4	6
______	8
A	______
______	______

Table 2.7

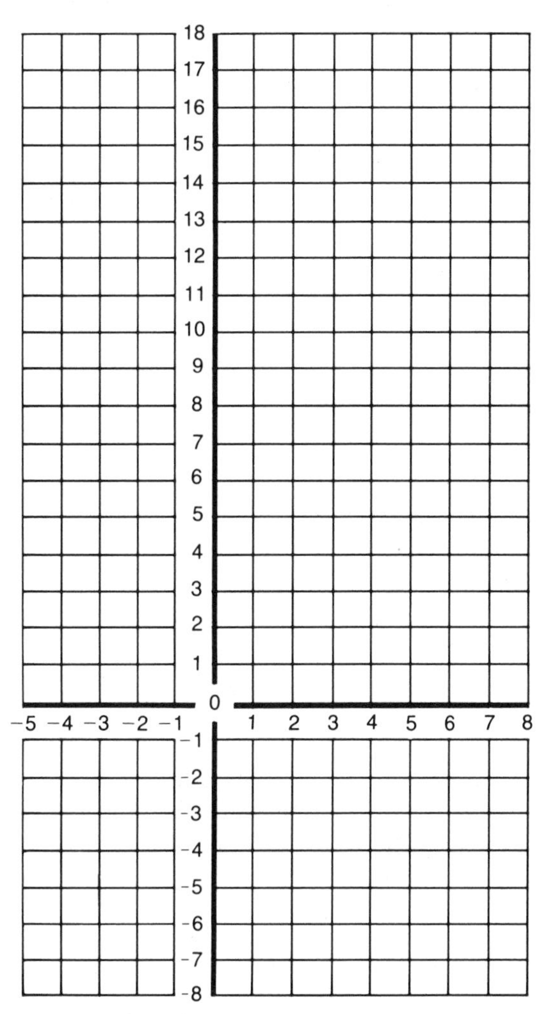

Figure 2.8

Graph the results from Tables 2.8 and 2.9 on the same graph in Figure 2.9. Connect the points of each graph in a different color.

Input	Output
0	0
1	1
2	4
3	9
$^{-}1$	______
4	______
A	______

Table 2.8

Input	Output
$^{-}1$	3
0	2
1	3
$^{-}2$	6
2	6
$^{-}3$	______
3	11
4	______
A	______

Table 2.9

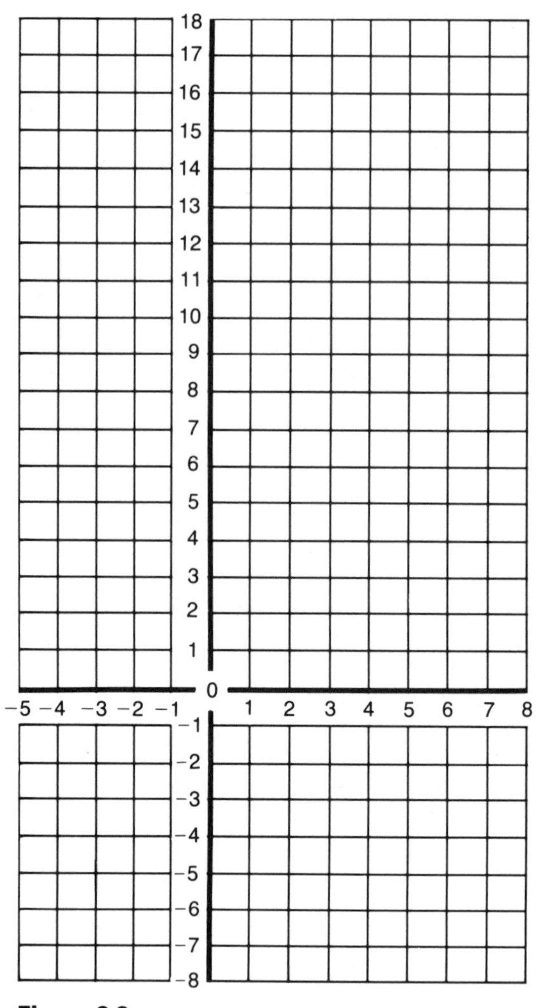

Figure 2.9

What happened to the graphs with functions of the form: *A* plus or minus a number? What happened for rules of the form: $A \times A$?

APPLICATIONS

This section contains a variety of problems that use the skills we have developed in this chapter. The first problem consists of reading information from a metric conversion graph that converts liters to gallons and gallons to liters. The second problem involves making a temperature conversion graph to read Celsius and Fahrenheit temperatures. The third set of problems are word problems. Their solutions can be found by graphing the given information. The final set of problems requires you to use graphing techniques to solve algebraic equations.

Worksheet 2.15

The graph below represents a conversion chart that can be used to convert gallons to liters or liters to gallons. We know that 1 gallon = 3.8 liters, and 10 gallons = 38 liters. The line was made by connecting the two points (1,3.8) and (10,38).

Notice that on the vertical scale for liters each line represents 1 liter, whereas on the horizontal scale for gallons each line represents ⅕, or 0.2, gallon. These scales were used to make the graph easier to read.

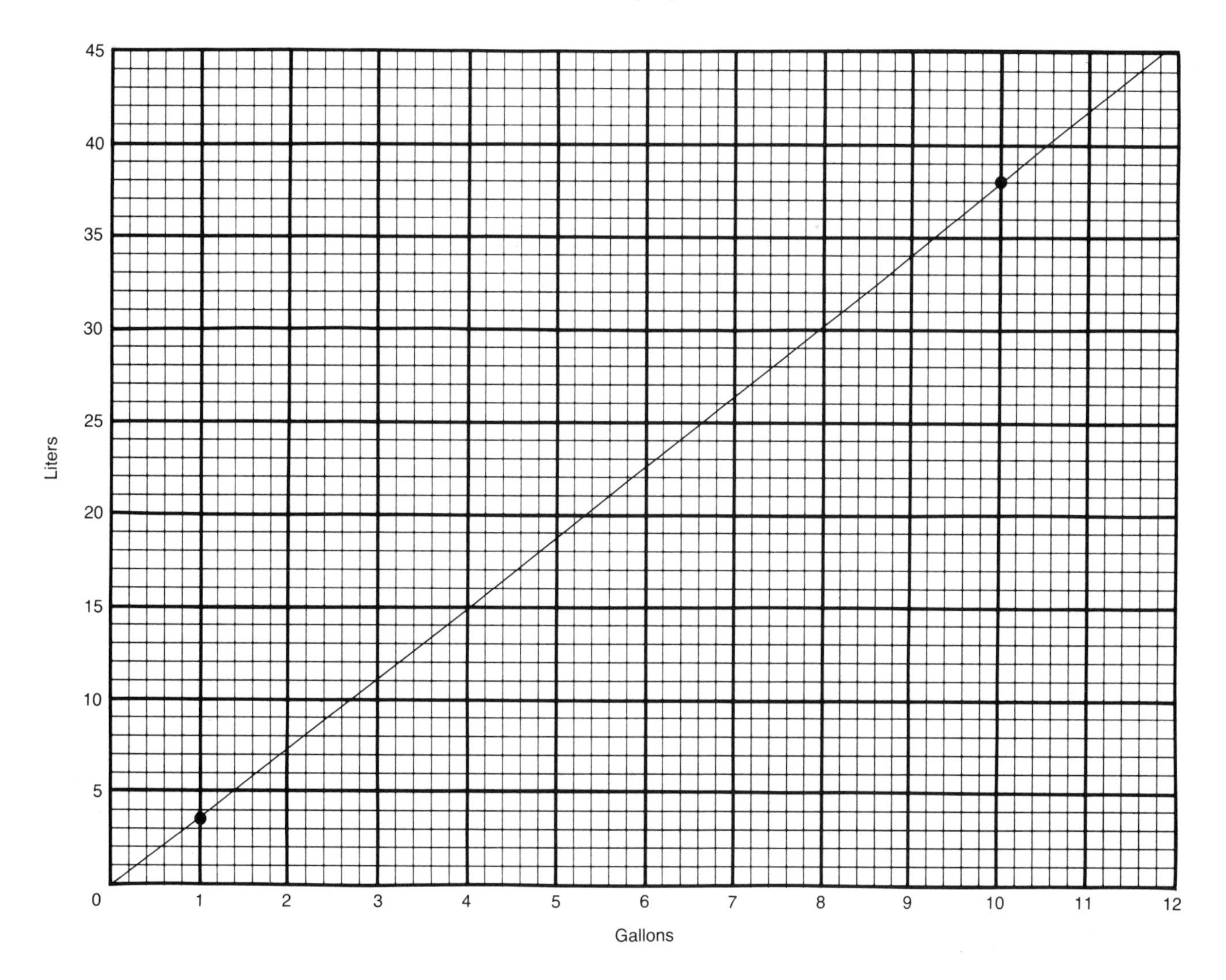

Use the graph to find the following conversions:

1. 11 gallons = ______ liters

2. 6 gallons = ______ liters

3. 2 gallons = ______ liters

4. 5 gallons = ______ liters

5. 19 liters = ______ gallons

6. 26 liters = ______ gallons

7. 30 liters = ______ gallons

8. 42 liters = ______ gallons

(continued)

9. Claudia filled the tank of her Datsun with 34 liters of gas. How many gallons of gas did she buy? ____________

10. Henry filled his Toyota with 11 gallons of gas. How many liters of gas did he buy? ____________

11. If gas costs 34 cents for 1 liter, how much does it cost for 1 gallon? (1 gallon = 3.8 liters) ____________

Next we use a function that converts Fahrenheit temperatures to Celsius. We use the function to construct an input/output table. The input is a Fahrenheit temperature, and the output is a Celsius temperature. A graph on which the temperatures from the table are plotted, and the points are connected, makes a temperature converter that can be used to quickly convert Fahrenheit to Celsius or Celsius to Fahrenheit. The rule for changing temperatures from Fahrenheit to Celsius is

$$\frac{5}{9}(F - 32) = C$$

where F stands for Fahrenheit and C stands for Celsius. You might already know that the freezing temperature in Celsius is 0°, and the boiling temperature in Celsius is 100° (the symbol ° means degrees). We also know that the Fahrenheit temperatures for freezing and boiling are 32° and 212°, respectively. Let's try the rule to see if it works for these points. First, we substitute the Fahrenheit temperature, 32°, for the F in the rule. That gives us

$$\frac{5}{9}(32 - 32) = C$$

Then, perform the operations inside the parentheses: $(32 - 32) = 0$. Thus:

$$\frac{5}{9}(0) = C$$

Since any number times 0 equals 0, 5/9 times 0 equals 0:

$$0 = C$$

Thus, the Celsius temperature is 0° when the Fahrenheit temperature is 32°.

To check the Celsius temperature for boiling using the conversion rule

$$\frac{5}{9}(F - 32) = C$$

first substitute the Fahrenheit temperature for boiling, 212°, in the rule. That gives us the following:

$$\frac{5}{9}(212 - 32) = C \qquad \text{(substitute 212 for F)}$$

$$\frac{5}{9}\left(\frac{180}{1}\right) = C \qquad (212 - 32 = 180)$$

$$\frac{900}{9} = C \qquad \text{(to multiply fractions, multiply numerators and multiply denominators)}$$

$$100 = C \qquad (900 \div 9 = 100)$$

Fahrenheit		Celsius
32°	(freezing)	0°
50°		______
80°	(hot day)	______
98.6°	(body temp.)	______
104°	(ideal hot tub temp.)	______
158°		______
212°	(boiling)	______

Table 2.10

We have converted the Fahrenheit temperature of 212° to the Celsius temperature of 100°. Now use the rule to complete the conversions in Table 2.10.

Mark the points from Table 2.10 on the graph in Figure 2.10. Draw a line connecting the points, then extend the line across the whole grid.

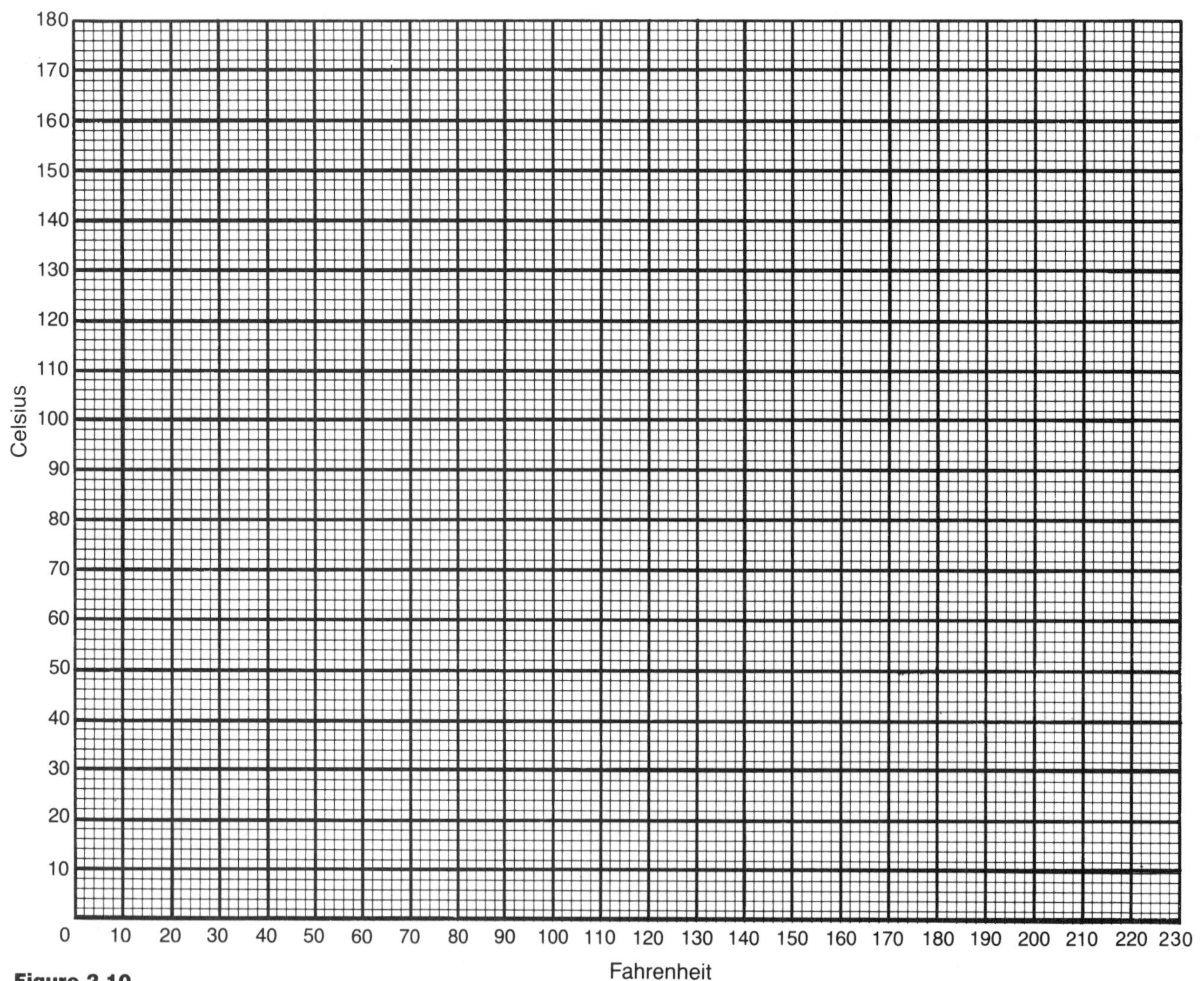

Figure 2.10

Worksheet 2.16

1a. Use the graph in Figure 2.10 to find the approximate Celsius temperature when it is 75° Fahrenheit. Find 75° on the F axis of the graph. Move vertically until you reach the line you drew. Read across to the C axis to find the Celsius temperature.

Try these:

b. 90° F = ______° C

c. 104° F = ______° C

d. 150° F = ______° C

2a. Use the graph to find the approximate Fahrenheit temperature when it is 15° Celsius. Find 15° on the C axis, then move horizontally until you reach the line you drew. Move down to read the answer from the F axis.

Try these:

b. 30° C = ______° F

c. 65° C = ______° F

d. 110° C = ______° F

The following problem can be solved by making tables and reading the answers from their graphs.

PROBLEM: *Sue started a bicycle trip at noon and rode away at 6 miles per hour. Sara tried to catch up with her; she started on her bike at 1:30 and rode at 9 miles per hour. At what time did Sara catch up with Sue and how many miles had they traveled?*

First complete Tables 2.11 and 2.12. Then graph the lines on the grid in Figure 2.11. They will intersect, and the intersection point gives you the answer. Use the graph to tell:

What time Sara caught up with Sue ____________

How many miles each woman had traveled ____________

Sue:

Time	Distance
noon	0
1:00	______
2:00	______
3:00	______
4:00	______
5:00	______

Table 2.11

Sara:

Time	Distance
1:30	0
2:30	______
3:30	______
4:30	______
5:30	______
6:30	______

Table 2.12

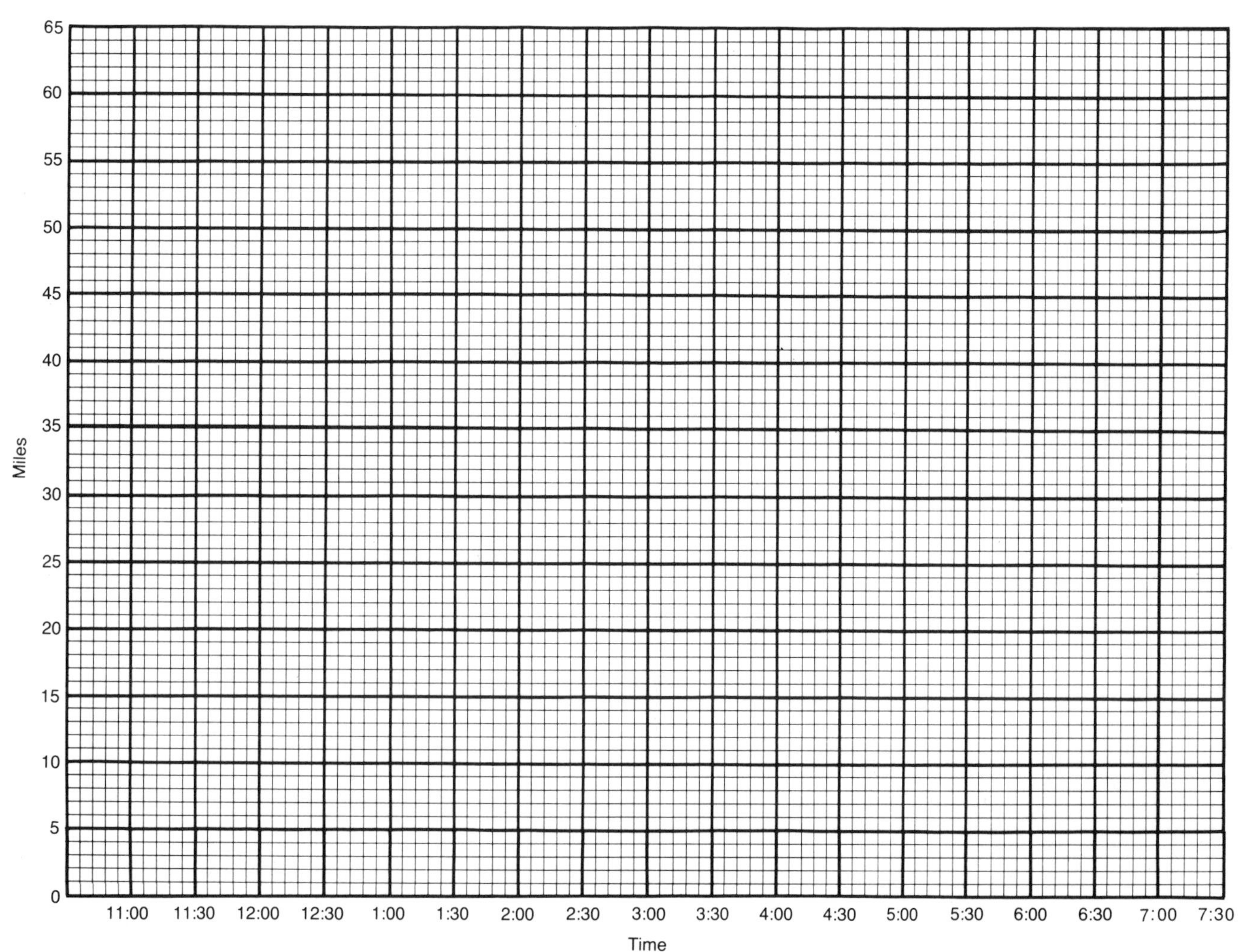

Figure 2.11

Worksheet 2.17

1. Joe started a 10-mile run at 3:00 and finished at 5:30. Richard started the same run at 3:30 and finished at 5:00. At what time did Richard pass Joe, and how many miles had each of them run?

Mark the points (3:00,0) and (5:30,10) on the grid. Connect these points to form a line representing Joe's run. Mark the points (3:30,0) and (5:00, 10), and connect them to form a line representing Richard's run. The intersection point of the two lines will give you the information you need to solve this problem.

Use the graph to tell:

What time Richard passed Joe ____________

How many miles each had run ____________

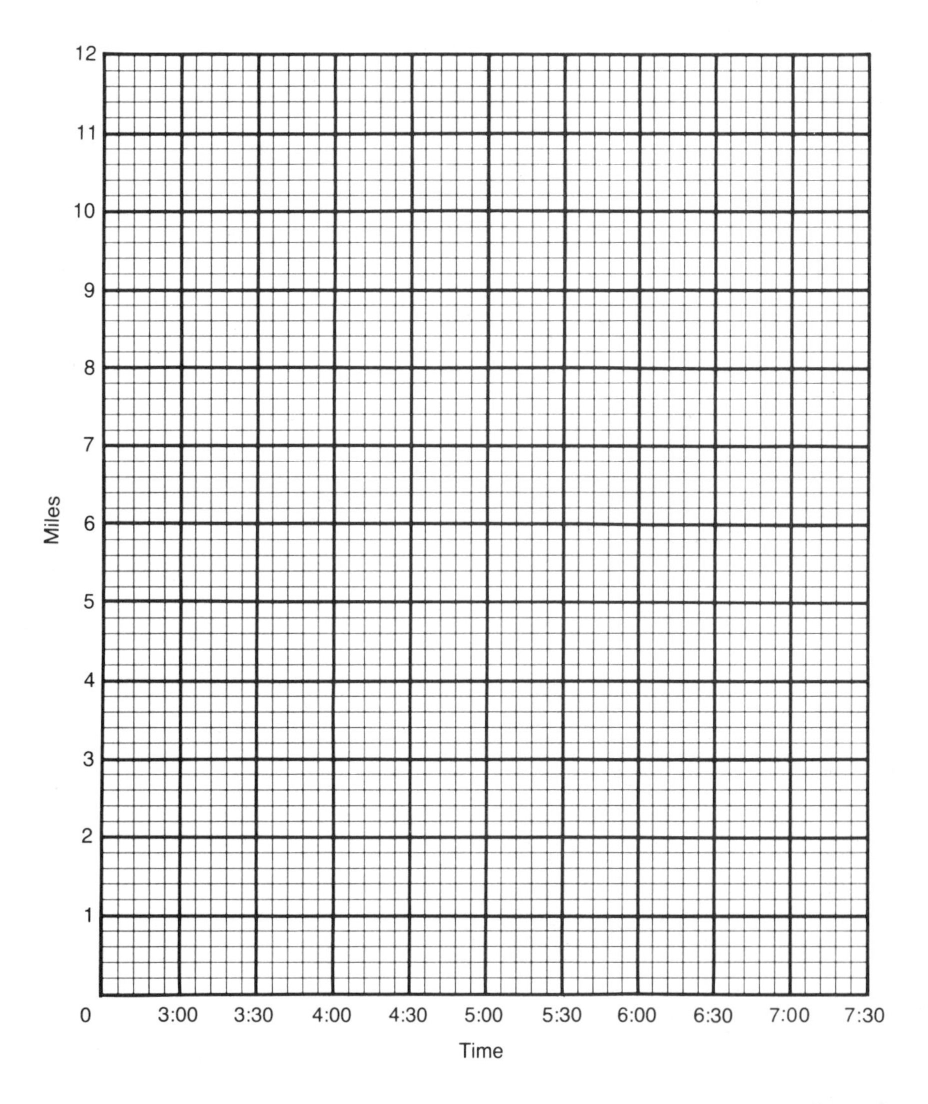

(continued)

2. Nancy and Scott were each driving from Los Angeles to San Francisco, a distance of about 500 miles. Scott left at 8:00 A.M. and drove his beat-up VW at an average speed of 50 miles per hour. Nancy left at 10:30 A.M. and drove her Volvo at an average speed of 75 miles per hour. At what time could they plan to meet for dinner on the road? How many miles had they traveled?

Fill in the tables, graph the points, and draw the lines to find this solution.

Scott

Time	Miles
8:00	0
11:00	______
6:00	______

Nancy

Time	Miles
10:30	0
2:30	______
5:30	______

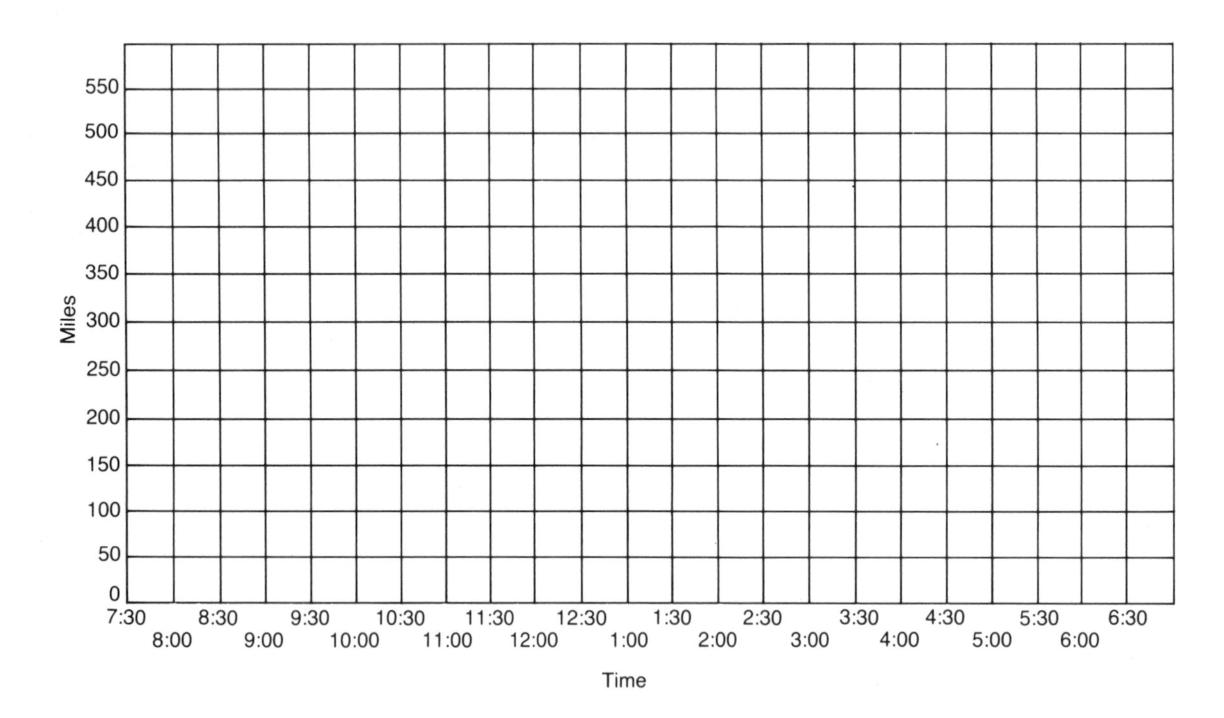

Now we will turn to a problem where we want to find a pair of numbers that fits two functions. Fill in Tables 2.13 and 2.14, then graph both lines. Since there is a point common to both lines, this point of intersection will fit both rules. Name the point, write it in the tables, and check to see if the point does, indeed, fit both rules.

A	$7 - A$
0	7
4	______
5	______
______	______

Table 2.13

A	$A + 3$
0	3
3	______
6	______
______	______

Table 2.14

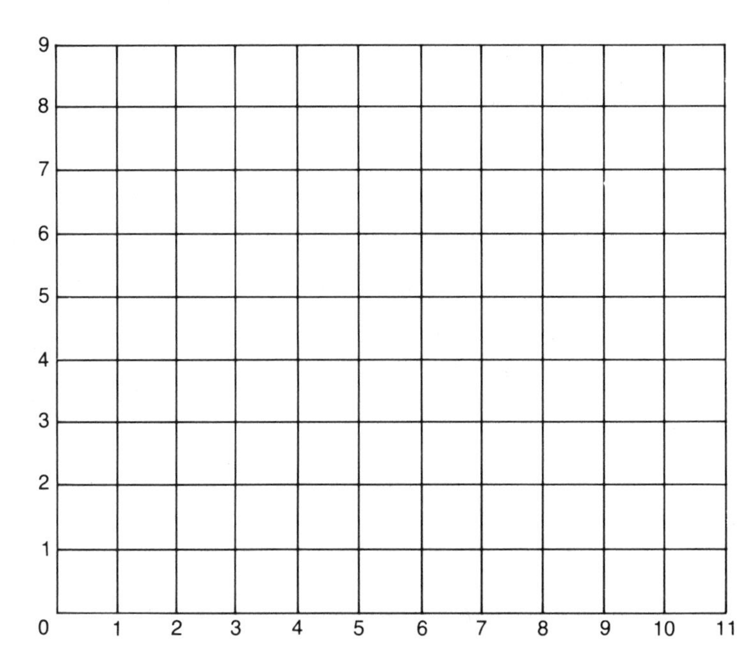

Figure 2.12

Worksheet 2.18

Find the intersection point for each pair of functions. First fill in the tables, then graph the lines. Use your tables to check that the point of intersection on the graph really does fit both rules.

1.

A	$2A - 3$
3	______
5	______
0	______
$^{-}1$	______
______	______

A	$A - 2$
2	______
4	______
6	______
0	______
$^{-}3$	______
______	______

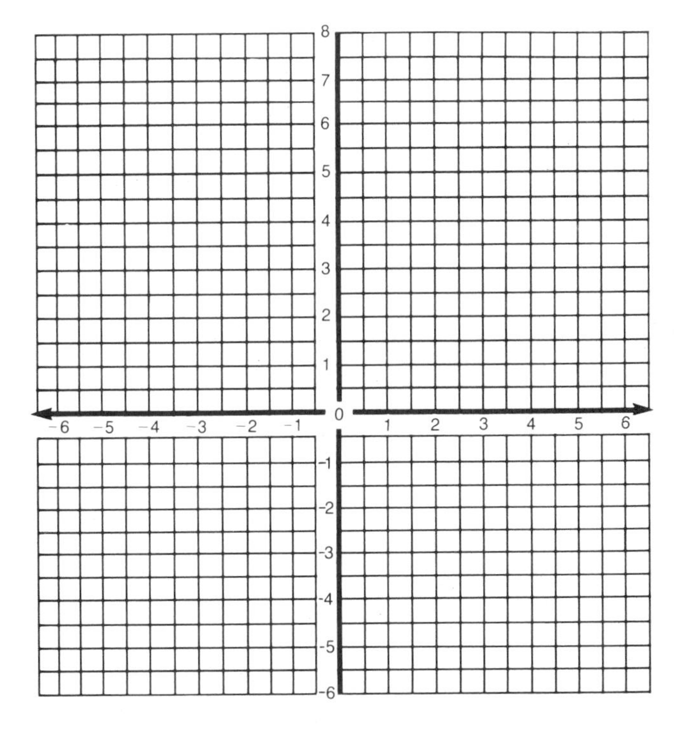

2.

A	$2A - 1$
4	______
3	______
0	______
$^{-}2$	______
______	______

A	$\frac{A}{2} + 2$
4	______
1	______
0	______
$^{-}4$	______
$^{-}6$	______
______	______

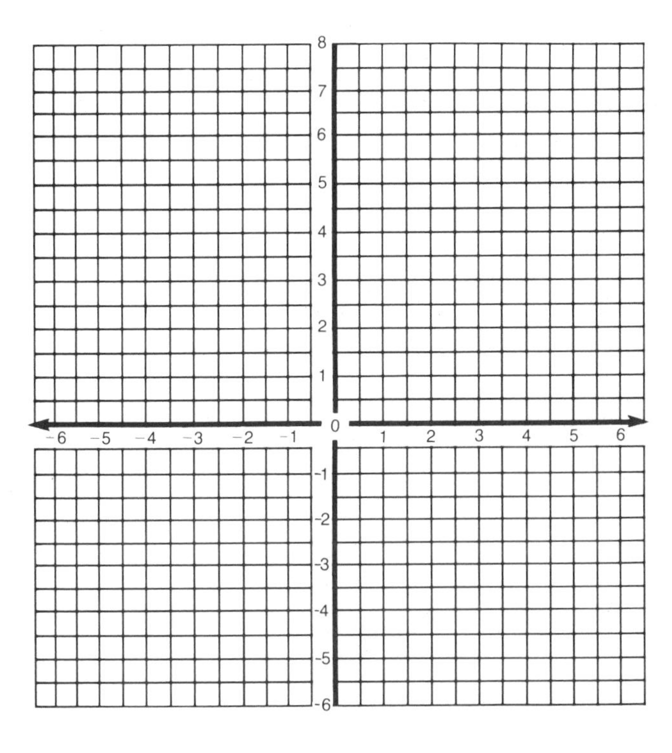

(continued)

3.

A	$5 - A$
0	______
5	______
2	______
4	______
$^{-}1$	______
$^{-}3$	______
______	______

A	$A + 2$
3	______
6	______
5	______
0	______
$^{-}2$	______
$^{-}3$	______
______	______

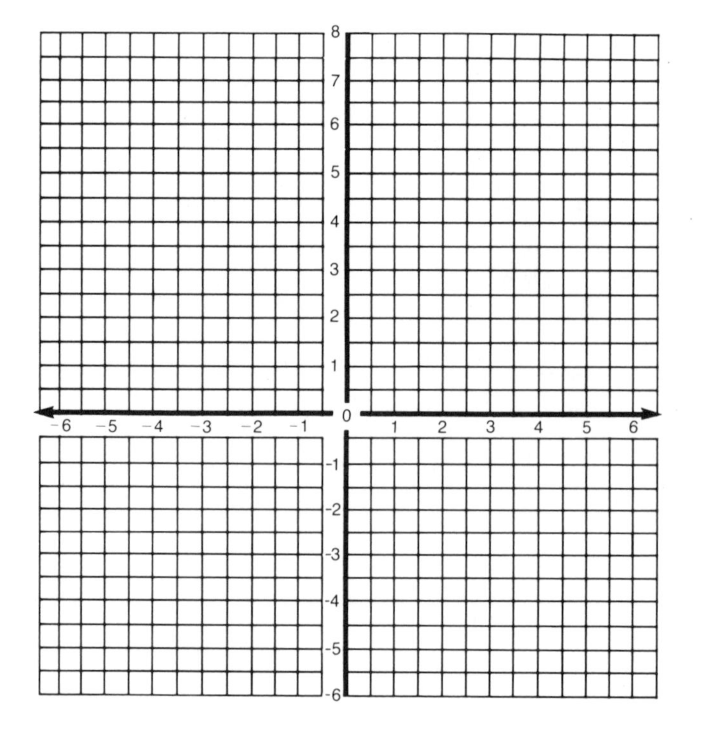

CHAPTER **Three**

Using Your Calculator

This chapter is an introduction to using a calculator. Many people who already have calculators are unaware of some of the things they can do with them. Of course, many models of calculators are available, and some work differently than others. As you work through this chapter, you will find it helpful to refer to the operation manual that comes with your calculator. You will learn some idiosyncrasies of your particular model, and you will also learn some mathematics. You may be surprised at what your calculator can do. Even the simple, inexpensive models have the power to do complicated computations. The material in this chapter is written for simple calculators, not fancy statistical calculators or the calculators used by engineering students.

The price of calculators has fallen dramatically in recent years, and now for less than $10 you can buy one that will be sufficient for the work in this chapter. In 1973 you had to pay an extra $25 for a square-root key. The price of a calculator then was about $75. Now almost any calculator comes with a square-root key—even those that are less than $10.

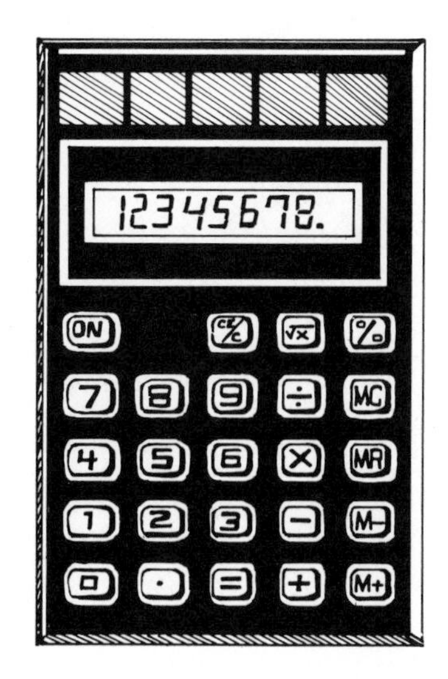

KEYS ON THE CALCULATOR

You are probably familiar with most of the keys. Find the digits 0 through 9, the four operation keys + − × ÷, and the equal sign =.

There is also a decimal point key . . On some calculators, you can determine how many decimal places you wish to show in the answer. Others have a *floating decimal*, which moves across the display and gives different numbers of decimal places depending on the answer. On some models, the numbers are always rounded off to two decimal places.

Try these problems on your calculator, and count the number of digits that come after the decimal point:

.0235 × 3.4 = ______ 95 ÷ 327 = ______

How many decimal places do you see? Does your machine have a floating decimal?

Working the following problems will help you see a pattern in the position of the decimal point when you multiply or divide by powers of 10 (10, 100, 1000, 10000, and so on). This pattern is useful in estimating answers.

325.72 × 10 = ______ 325.72 × 100 = ______

325.72 × 1000 = ______

What happens to the decimal point when you multiply by 10? By 100? By 1000?

46.235 ÷ 10 = ______ 46.235 ÷ 100 = ______

46.235 ÷ 1000 = ______

What happens to the decimal point when you divide by 10? By 100? By 1000?

Look for these keys: C and CE. Some calculators include them both on the same key, separated by a slash, C/CE. Other calculators have two separate keys. The C stands for CLEAR and is used to clear the calculator. It is often used before you start a problem. The CE stands for CLEAR ENTRY, which clears the last number that you have entered and is used when you have made a mistake. If C and CE are on a single key, you usually press the key once for CE and twice for C. Experiment with your calculator to see how it works.

Try this problem: 5 × 3 (do not press the equal sign key yet). Suppose you made a mistake—you really mean 5 × 7. Press the CE key, then press the 7 and the equal sign. The display should show 35. Try this one: 4 × 28—then press CE 2 5 =. The answer displayed should be 100.

The percent key % is very useful. *Percent* means "divided by one hundred." So 25% can also be written as 25/100, as 25 ÷ 100, or as the decimal 0.25. What is 25% of 80? There are three different ways to solve this problem. First, you can change 25% to the decimal 0.25 and multiply by 80. Try it: 80 × 0.25 = ______.

Or you can think of 25% as the fraction 25/100 and multiply by 80. Although calculators have no fractions, you can do this by pressing the following keys: 80 × 25 ÷ 100 =.

Finally, you can use the percent key: 80 × 25 %. (On some calculators you do not need to press the = key.) Write the answer: ______.

The answer using all three methods should be the same: 20.

The (%) key on the calculator is useful and time saving for solving problems like the following:

PROBLEM 1: *You just received an 8% salary increase. If your present pay is $920 per month, how much will be in your new paycheck?*

PROBLEM 2: *The refrigerators at Sears are marked down 18%. What will be the cost of a refrigerator originally priced at $462?*

With most calculators you can solve these problems in just one step. For Problem 1, press these keys: 920 + 8 (%) . Write the answer.

____

On some calculators you do not need to press the (=) key; on others you do. How does your calculator work?

It's a good idea to estimate answers first, so you can recognize a mistake if you accidentally press the wrong keys. Since 8% is nearly 10%, you can figure 10% of $920 in your head. (Do you remember the pattern for 10% from Worksheet 3.1?) The increase will be a little less than 10% of $920, or $92. Adding $90 to $920, we get $1010. The estimated answer, then, is $1010. The exact answer is $993.60. We can assume that the calculator is correct.

Follow these steps to estimate the answer to Problem 2. First, 10% of $462 is about $46, so 20% (twice 10%) is about $92. Since 18% is a little less than 20% we estimate that we will save about $90 at this sale. The sale price will be $462 − $90, or $372. Our estimated cost of the refrigerator is $372.

Now use the calculator. Press the following keys: 462 − 18 (%) . Your answer using the calculator should be $378.84, which is pretty close to our estimate.

Worksheet 3.1

Solve these problems using three different methods. Write the percent first as a decimal, then as a fraction. Finally, solve by using the percent key. Record the keys that you pressed in order to solve the problems.

Problem	Decimal	Fraction	Percent
1. 52% of 500	500 × .52 = ___	500 × 52/100 = ___	500 × 52% = ___
2. 27% of 239	___	___	___
3. 35% of 100	___	___	___
4. 75% of 90	___	___	___
5. 42% of 350	___	___	___
6. 10% of 352	___	___	___
7. 10% of 578	___	___	___
8. 10% of 249	___	___	___
9. 10% of 732	___	___	___

10. Do you notice any patterns when you find 10% of a number?

Worksheet 3.2

First estimate the savings for a 10%, a 20%, and a 30% discount from the regular price. Then use your calculator to find the exact amount of the discount.

	Price	Estimate 10%	Estimate 20%	Estimate 30%	Calculator 10%	Calculator 20%	Calculator 30%
1.	$35.27						
2.	$46.79						
3.	$83.62						
4.	$204.56						
5.	$299.95						
6.	$149.50						
7.	$236.99						
8.	$3562.56						
9.	$4235.95						
10.	$5478.45						

Worksheet 3.3

Solve the following problems using the (%) key. First estimate the answer in your head. Record your estimated answer. Then use your calculator to find the exact answer. Compare your estimated and exact answers.

Problem	Estimate (in head)	Exact Answer (using calculator)
1. What is the sale price of the portable radio?		
2. What is the sale price of the labelmaking kit?		
3. If the regular price for using the Exercise Center is $325 per year, what is the sale price?		

Tune In All the Action With Our Portable Radio

29% Off Reg. 41.95

- *Covers AM, FM and 108–174 MHz VHF-Aviation/Hi Police Band*
- *Automatic AC-to-Battery Switching* • *VHF Squelch Control*

Patrolman-33. Listen to police, fire, aviation, trains, weather or AM and FM anywhere you go! With 3″ speaker, earphone. Built-in AM and telescopic FM/VHF antennas. AFC for drift-free VHF/FM listening 7⅞ × 10 × 3½″. U.L. listed AC operation or four "C" batteries (not incl.)

Complete Labelmaking Kit

17% Off 4.95

- Includes 3 Rolls of Tape

Label your property; self-sticking; waterproof; includes punctuation.

Income Tax Break / Special

40% Off!

Excelsior Exercise Center

- Exercise Classes
- Saunas
- Steam Rooms
- Whirlpool Bath

Hurry!
Offer Ends Soon

Call 555-9080

3000 Muscle Beach St.

(continued)

Problem	Estimate (in head)	Exact Answer (using calculator)
4. What would you pay for the copier on sale if the original price is $1295?		
5. What is the sale price of the ultrasonic alarm?		
6. What will be the actual cost of each of the items in Problems 1–5 if a 6% sales tax is included?		
7. If you leave your $2500 in a savings account for 1 year, how much money will be in your account at the end of that time? (See ad.)		
8. Something about the ad for the hosiery is misleading. Can you find it? What is the regular price of three pairs of style 151 (Sheerest Sheer)? What should the sale price be? Is that what the ad says?		
9. What is the regular price of three pairs of style 151 (Satiny Light Control)? What should the sale price be? Is that what the ad says?		
10. What are the other "irregularities" in this ad?		

Save 15% on a Supercat Copier when you buy one of these copiers.

Ultrasonic Alarm Sale!

14% Off **59.95**

- No Wiring—Just Plug In and Aim
- Ultrasonic Waves Protect 20 x 30-ft. Area

High, High Interest

9.55%

This new account from Maximum Savings pays higher interest than the money market funds. The minimum balance is only $2,500. When you maintain that daily balance, you earn high interest on the entire amount, with no monthly service charges. And all your money is fully insured to $100,000.

Roadrunner Leg Fashions

20% Off Sale

Feb. 23 to March 6

Save now on great fit and silkiness in fashion colors!

Style		Reg.	Sale
151	Sheerest Sheer	3.50	**3/8.40**
	Satiny Light Control	2.80	
181	Silkee Sheer	3.50	**3/8.40**
	All Nude Sandalfoot	2.80	
183	Silkee Sheer	4.00	**3/9.60**
	Control Top Sandalfoot	3.20	

Look for the square-root key on your calculator [√]. This key is very useful, especially in solving problems in statistics. Do you remember how to square a number? Two squared, or 2^2, means 2×2, or 4. Three squared, or 3^2, means 3×3, or 9. The square root of 4 is 2, since 2 squared is 4. The square root of 9 is 3, since 3 squared is 9. Symbolically, we write $\sqrt{4} = 2$ and $\sqrt{9} = 3$.

Squaring and finding the square root are opposite, or *inverse*, operations. Try these problems on your calculator:

$5 \times 5 =$ ______ (25 should be in the display)

Now press the square-root key [√] (5 should be in the display).

7×7 [=] [√] ______

10×10 [=] [√] ______

You probably don't need a calculator to find the square root of numbers like 49 and 100, since they are exact squares. We know that the square root of 20 is somewhere between 4 and 5, since 4×4 is 16, and 5×5 is 25. Press these keys on your calculator— 20 [√] —and 4.4721359 shows in the display. Depending on the problem you are solving, you can round off the answer to as many decimal places as you need.

To reverse the operation of square root, press the [×] key, then the [=] key, with 4.4721359 in the display. In some calculators 19.999999 will show in the display, and in other calculators 20 will show. What does your calculator do? If yours shows 19.999999, you need to round off to 20.0. If you don't get either answer on your calculator, it's probably because it doesn't have a constant feature. If that is the case, to reverse the operation from square root to squared, you must multiply the square root by itself. For this problem you multiply $4.4721359 \times 4.4721359$, and 19.999999 will be displayed.

Rounding off may be necessary in other situations, such as in problems using fractions. For example, we know that the answer to $\frac{1}{3} \times 6$ is 2. However, on some calculators, $\frac{1}{3} \times 6 = 1.9999999$, which must be rounded off to 2.

Many calculators have a key that changes the sign of the number in the display. This key [+/−] will change a positive number to a negative one, and a negative number to a positive one. Enter the number 354 in your display, then press the [+/−] key. Now −354 will show. Press the [+/−] key once more to change it back to the positive number 354.

Some calculators do not have this key. On these, if you press the subtraction operation key, then the number, then the equals key, the negative number will appear ([−] [5] [=]). Or press the [−] [5] [−] , and the negative number will be displayed. Can you think of other ways to obtain a negative number on your calculator? If you don't have the [+/−] key, find out how to show negative numbers on your calculator.

OVERFLOW

Use your calculator to solve the following multiplication problems, and record your answers exactly as they appear in your display.

1. 7 9 3 6 5 2 5 × 8 7 6 2 = ________
2. 8 9 9 2 6 8 4 3 × 6 5 8 9 8 = ________
3. 2 9 6 4 2 7 × 8 9 8 5 6 = ________

Most calculators will show either 8 or 10 digits in the display. The answers to the preceding problems have more than 10 digits. Your calculator probably shows some symbol that indicates that there are more digits in the answer than will fit. An E or a [are common symbols for this.

For example, the Sharp EL-8131 calculator shows the following answers for the problems just given:

1. 695.39832[**2.** 59259.991[**3.** 266.35744[

Notice that for all three answers 8 digits are showing, with the decimal point in different places. The symbol [follows the digits. This calculator divides an answer with more than 8 digits by 10^8—that is, by 10 to the 8th power, or 100,000,000. In order to know how many digits are actually in the answer, we must then multiply the answer in the display by 10^8. We do that by moving the decimal point 8 places to the right. Here are the answers to the problems given, with the decimal point moved to the correct place.

1. 69,539,832,000.
2. 5,925,999,100,000.
3. 26,635,744,000.

We had to add three zeroes in Problem 1, five zeroes in Problem 2, and three zeroes in Problem 3. Of course, we can only add zeroes, since we don't know what the exact digits are. When working with such large numbers, it's usually sufficient to know the number of *places* in the answer without knowing the exact numerals at the end. For example, it's ordinarily enough to know that a project will cost about $250,000,000 (250 million dollars), without knowing its exact cost of $250,132,163.

Different calculators handle the problem of overflow in different ways. Some calculators always place the decimal point in the same place and then display a numeral that indicates how many places you must move it. In this case, the answers to the problems might look like this:

1. 6.9539832 E 10 **2.** 5.9259991 E 12 **3.** 2.6635744 E 10

Move the decimal point the indicated number of places to the right, and notice that the answers match those in the examples.

Find out how your calculator handles the problem of *overflow*. Your answers should have the same number of places as the ones shown, although the actual digits may not all be the same.

Often large numbers are written in scientific notation, using exponents. In this notation, 235,000,000 would be written as 235×10^6, and 460,000 would be written as 46×10^4. Write the scientific notation for 32,530,000,000. ________________

Worksheet 3.4

First estimate, then use your calculator to find the square root of the following numbers. Then square your answers using the calculator.

	Number	Square Root (estimate/calculator)	Square Root (×) (=)*
1.	60	between 7 and 8 / 7.7459666	7.7459666 (×) (=) 59.999999
2.	80		
3.	125		
4.	390		
5.	1000		

* If your calculator does not have a constant feature, change the heading of this column to "Square Root × Square Root."

Worksheet 3.5

Use your calculator to find the answers to the following problems. First write the answer that is displayed, then rewrite the answer with the correct number of decimal places.

Problem	Calculator	Answer
1. 8 9 2 6 4 3 5 × 2 6 6 8 =	238.15728[	23,815,728,000
2. 9 4 8 6 5 2 3 × 8 9 7 5 4 =		
3. 5 6 4 2 3 × 3 5 8 9 6 5 =		
4. 8 9 3 4 7 9 5 2 × 6 9 8 9 3 5 =		
5. 9 8 7 6 5 4 × 6 8 5 2 6 =		
6. 9 9 8 9 9 8 8 9 × 8 8 7 8 8 9 =		

The answers obtained when dividing by fractions and decimals are also large numbers.

Problem	Calculator	Answer
7. 2 3 5 8 9 6 ÷ 0.0 0 0 0 0 7 5 =		
8. 8 7 6 5 ÷ 0.0 0 0 0 0 0 0 5 =		
9. 9 8 9 8 ÷ 0.0 0 0 0 0 0 0 5 =		

Rewrite the following numbers:

10. 345×10^{6} = ______________

11. 762.45×10^{4} = ______________

12. 47.235×10^{5} = ______________

Change the following numbers to scientific notation.

13. 3 5 7 , 0 0 0 = ______________

14. 6 5 9, 0 0 0, 0 0 0 = ______________

15. 4 5 8 , 0 0 0 , 0 0 0 = ______________

ZERO AND DIVISION

Try these problems on your calculator.

$0 \div 5 =$ ______	$5 \div 0 =$ ______
$0 \div 25 =$ ______	$25 \div 0 =$ ______
$0 \div 17 =$ ______	$17 \div 0 =$ ______
$0 \div 19 =$ ______	$19 \div 0 =$ ______

Note that the problems in the second column cause an error symbol to be displayed. Some calculators will display the E or [alone; others show the symbols preceded by a zero and decimal point (0.E or 0.[). Your calculator may have even a different way of alerting you to the fact that something is wrong. In this case, the problem is that we asked the calculator to do something it cannot do—divide by zero. We can *never* divide by zero.

We know that $12 \div 4 = 3$ means that the opposite is also true, $3 \times 4 = 12$. Also, $10 \div 2 = 5$, and we know that $5 \times 2 = 10$. But if we assume that $10 \div 0 = 0$, then it should follow that $0 \times 0 = 10$, which we know is not true.

This is an example of proving something by contradiction. We found a contradiction—something that cannot possibly be true—and so we must change our original assumption. Since the assumption $10 \div 0 = 0$ leads us to a contradiction, we know it cannot be true, and we must conclude that 10 divided by 0 is not equal to 0 ($10 \div 0 \neq 0$).

USING THE MEMORY

Many inexpensive calculators today come equipped with a memory, which not too long ago was a specially added, more expensive feature. The memory allows you to keep track of numbers in it, separate from the display screen. Press the following sequence of keys, and notice the display at each step.

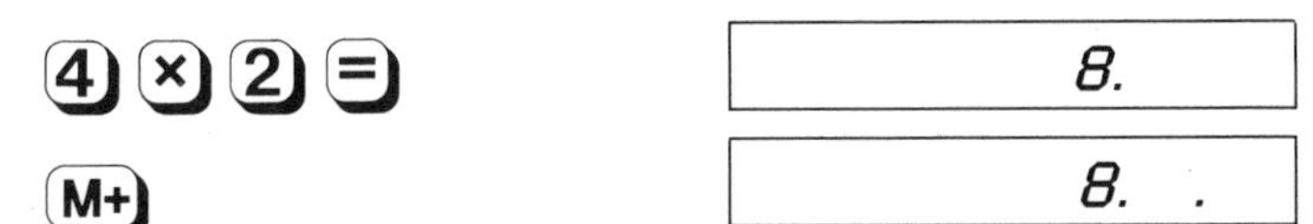

There should be some indication that the memory is in use. Often a small M or a second decimal point will be displayed. Now press the following keys:

Keys	Display
C	0. .
5 × 2 =	10. .
M+	10. .
RM	18. .

The first time we pressed (M+) an 8 was displayed, and the second time a 10 was displayed, giving us a total of 18 in the memory. Continue:

Keys	Display
(C)	0.
(2) (5) (×) (3) (=)	75.
(RM)	18.

The memory is still holding the 18.

Keys	Display
(2) (×) (3) (=)	6.
(M−)	6.
(RM)	12.

The memory is now holding 12, (18 − 6 = 12).

Keys	Display
(CM)	12.
(RM)	0.

Now there is nothing in the memory.

By now you may have discovered how the memory keys work:

Press (CM) to *clear* the memory;
(RM) to *read* the memory;
(M+) to *add* to the memory;
(M−) to *subtract* from the memory.

Locate the memory keys on your calculator.

Worksheet 3.6

Look at the following sequence of keys, and predict what will show in your display. Then check your predictions by pressing the keys on your calculator.

	Prediction	Display
1. 3 × 2 =		
M+		
5 × 2 =		
4 × 2 =		
RM		
3 × 3 =		
M+		
C		
RM		
CM		
RM		

	Prediction	Display
2. 4 + 3 =		
M+		
C		
RM		
4 + 1 =		
M−		
RM		
C		
RM		
CM		
RM		

CONSTANT FEATURE

Many calculators have a *constant* feature. The way it works depends on the calculator. Try the following steps on your calculator. Record what shows in your display. Check your operation manual to find out how its constant feature works. Press these keys: [2] [+] [5] [=] . Now Press [=] again.

What is the result of [2] [+] [5] [=] [=] ? ______ What will happen when you press the equals key once again? ______ Which addend is the constant? ______

Try these problems:

3 + = = = = ______

4 + = = = = ______

10 + = = = = ______

And this:

2 + 3 = ______ 8 = ______ 7 = ______ 25 = ______

Here are some problems using the constant in subtraction:

50 − 10 = = = ______

20 − 4 = = = ______

Now try this:

9 − 2 = ______ 12 = ______ 8 = ______ 10 = ______

Do you see how the constant feature works for subtraction?

Here are some problems using multiplication:

2 × 5 = = = ______

5 × 2 = = = ______

Which factor is the constant for multiplication in the preceding problems? Try:

2 × = = = ______

10 × = = = ______

What seems to be happening? ______________________

The constant feature is very useful in solving problems in which there are *exponents*, such as 2^3, which means $2 \times 2 \times 2$. Using the constant feature, we can save some steps: 2^3 can be found by pressing these keys: [2] [×] [=] [=] . Use this method for the following problems:

5^2 = ______

4^3 = ______

10^3 = ______

2^5 = ______

The constant feature helps us save steps when we wish to multiply several different numbers by the same factor, as in the following problems:

4 × = ______ 7 = ______ 9 = ______ 10 = ______

Finally, try some division problems:

1000 ÷ 5 = = = ______ and 360 ÷ 2 = = = ______.

And these: 50 ÷ 2 = ______ 60 = ______ 78 = ______.

ORDER OF OPERATIONS

Solve this problem on your calculator:

3 + 5 × 2 − 1 = ______

On many calculators, a 15 will be seen in the display. However, that is incorrect; the correct answer is really 12. If your calculator displayed a 12, it has an extra feature—it uses the *order of operations*. This rule tells us that the multiplication and/or division operations must be performed before the operations of addition and/or subtraction. In the given problem, then, you must first multiply 5 × 2, then work the problem from left to right: 3 + 5 × 2 − 1 = ; 3 + 10 − 1 = ; 13 − 1 = 12.

Press These Keys	Display
5 × 2 =	10.
M+	10. .
3 + RM − 1 =	12. .

Let's work the same problem using the memory on your calculator. Follow these steps. We now know, because of the order of operations, that the multiplication must be done first. Put that answer in the memory. Now work the problem from the left, using the RM key to read the memory. The correct answer, 12, should be in the display. Clear the memory.

Here is another example:

$1045 - (18^2 + 711) =$ ______

Press These Keys	Display
1 8 × =	324.
+ 7 1 1 =	1035.
M+	1035. .
1 0 4 5 −	
RM =	10. .

Perform the operations inside the parentheses first. Put that sum in the memory. Work the problem from the left. The answer is 10. If you press the RM key now, the 1035 will still be in the memory. Press CM to clear the memory.

Worksheet 3.7

Try to solve these problems by doing all the work on your calculator, using the memory. Don't write down partial answers as you work, if you can help it. There is usually more than one way to work each problem. Try several ways to see if your answers check.

Remember: multiplication/division *before* addition/subtraction. Be sure to clear the memory (CM) after each problem.

1. $12 + 9^3 - 375 =$ ____________

2. $13 \times 146 - 13 \times 52 =$ ____________

3. $17 \times 35 + 14 \times 26 =$ ____________

4. $25 + (14 \times 17 - 35) =$ ____________

5. $15^3 - (135 + 8 \times 231) =$ ____________

6. $758 + 18^3 =$ ____________

CHAPTER Four

Geometry and Measurement

This chapter includes the topics of area, perimeter, volume, and surface area, drawn from geometry and measurement. The goal is to develop an understanding of the concepts that underlie these topics rather than to stress the memorization of formulas. With this understanding you will find everyday applications easier to approach.

MATERIALS

Most of the activities in this chapter should be done with manipulable, "hands-on" materials. Moving and visualizing these objects are parts of the learning process. In many cases, a difficult problem will be simplified by using these objects. The following materials should be used.

Square Tiles or Paper Squares. Tiles can often be found as remainders in building and supply stores. A copy of the graph paper on page 281 in the Appendix can be cut into squares. Use construction paper or another stiff paper.

Graph Paper. See page 281 in the Appendix for a master copy.

Cubes. Use wooden cubes or sugar cubes.

Geoboards, Rubberbands, and Dot Paper. A geoboard can be made from a 10-inch square piece of wood. Twenty-five nails are arranged in five equally spaced rows, with 2 inches between each nail and a 1-inch border, as in Figure 4.1. Geoboards are also available from math supply dealers. A master for dot paper can be found on page 284 in the Appendix.

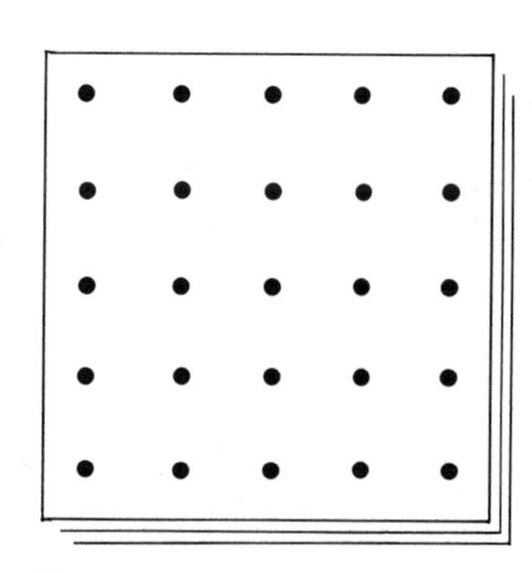

Figure 4.1

String. You will need a piece of string about 12 inches long.

AREA

You will need a set of square tiles or paper squares for this section. Take 12 tiles or squares. Arrange the squares to form a rectangle. Remember that a rectangle has L-shaped corners with 90° angles and opposite sides of equal length (Figure 4.2).

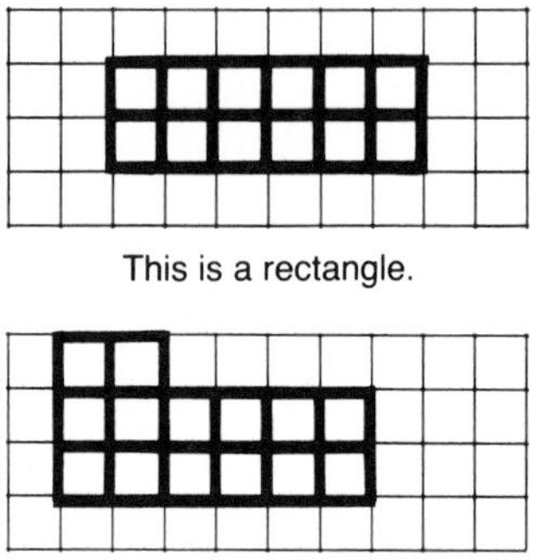

This is a rectangle.

This is not a rectangle.

Figure 4.2

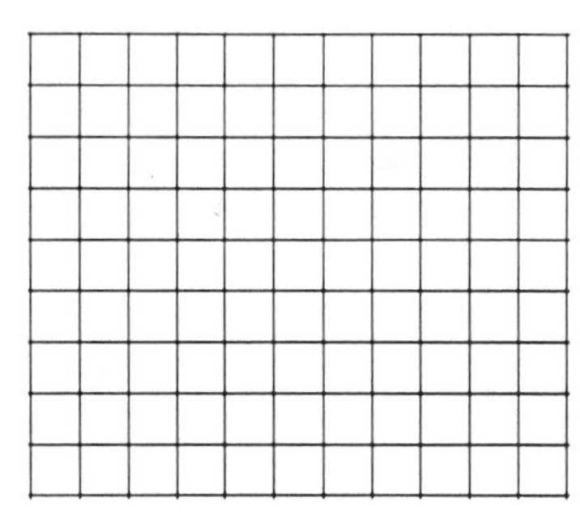

Figure 4.3

Draw your rectangle on the graph paper in Figure 4.3. Is this the only rectangular shape you can make with 12 squares? ____________ Try to make another. Again, record your results. Look around. Has anyone made a different rectangle?

Here is a record of the rectangles according to their dimensions (length and width):

3 squares by 4 squares
2 squares by 6 squares
1 square by 12 squares

What about 4 squares by 3 squares? 6 by 2? 12 by 1? We will say that a 2-by-6 rectangle is the same as a 6-by-2 rectangle. Mathematicians say that these rectangles are *congruent*—that is, that they have the same size and shape. Thus, for 12 squares, we have 3 different rectangles.

What can be done with 8 squares? Record your results on the graph paper in Figure 4.4.

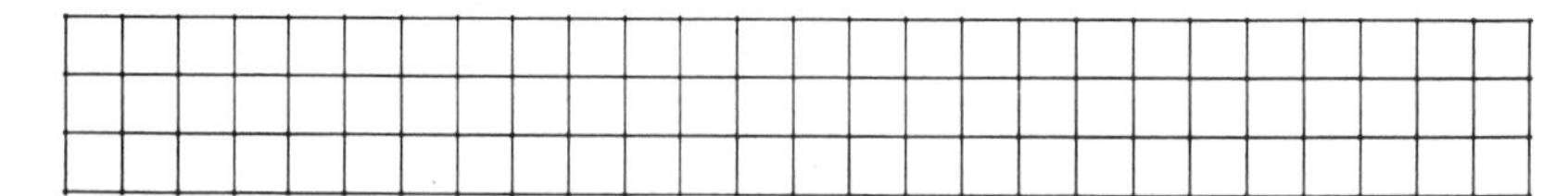

Figure 4.4

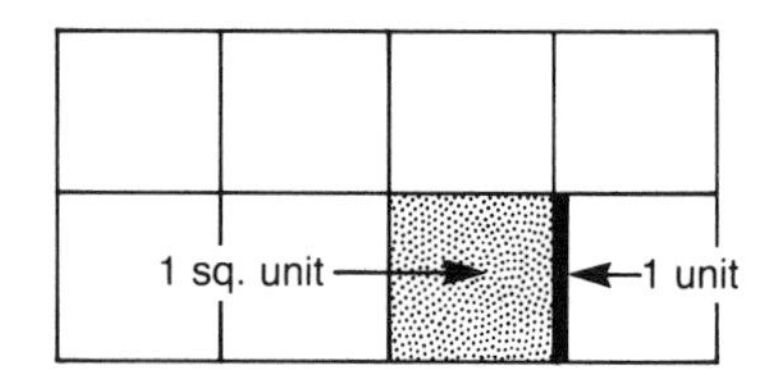

Figure 4.5

When we make a rectangle with 8 squares or tiles, we are making a rectangle with an area of 8 square units. *One unit* is the length of the side of 1 of the squares. *One square unit* is equal to 1 of these squares (see Figure 4.5).

When the squares are 1 inch on a side, the area of the rectangle is 8 square inches; when the squares are 1 centimeter on a side, the area is 8 square centimeters.

Area measures how many square units it takes to cover a surface. For example, when you want to buy a tablecloth or rug, you need to know the dimensions, the length and width, of the object you want to cover. Knowing just the length of the room does not provide enough information for you to buy the right-sized rug. List some objects that you need to measure in square units: ______________________________

____

Worksheet 4.1

Make as many rectangles as you can from 6, 9, 10, and 11 squares. Record your results, and label each rectangle with its area and dimensions, length and width, as in the first example.

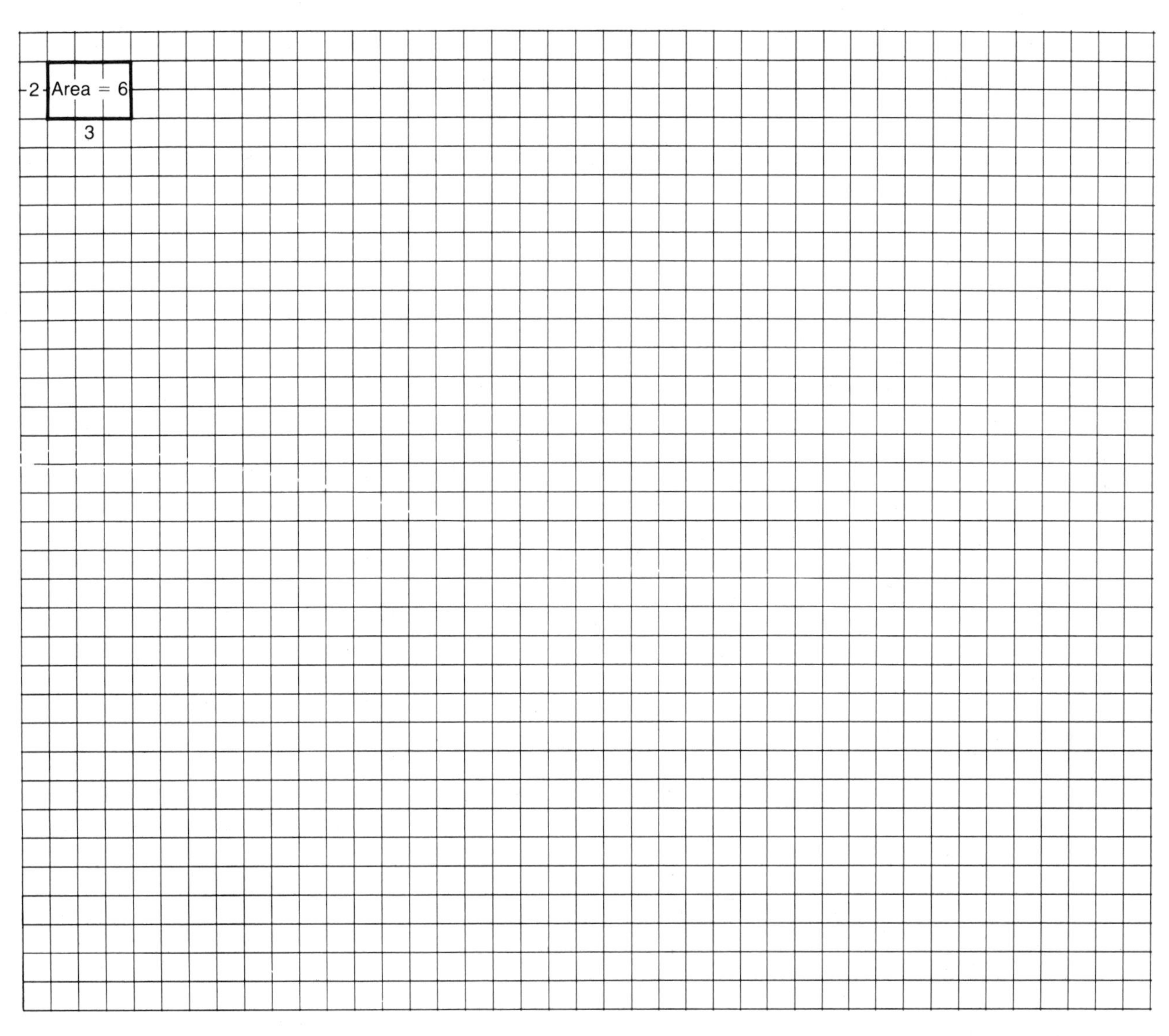

Did you notice any unusual results? ____________

What happened when you used 9 squares on this worksheet? Only certain numbers will make a square. (Note that a square is a special kind of rectangle that has all four sides equal.) Find some other numbers that make square areas. List them: ______________________________.

Worksheet 4.2

Find the dimensions of all possible rectangles for each number (area in square units). If possible, work with a partner or in small groups in class. Each group can do part of the numbers. If you wish, draw the rectangles for each number on graph paper, cut them out, and post them under their areas on a larger chart. The first three numbers are completed for you.

2 SQ. UNITS	3 SQ. UNITS	4 SQ. UNITS	5 SQ. UNITS	6 SQ. UNITS	7 SQ. UNITS	8 SQ. UNITS	9 SQ. UNITS	10 SQ. UNITS	11 SQ. UNITS	12 SQ. UNITS	13 SQ. UNITS
1 × 2	1 × 3	1 × 4 2 × 2									
14 SQ. UNITS	**15 SQ. UNITS**	**16 SQ. UNITS**	**17 SQ. UNITS**	**18 SQ. UNITS**	**19 SQ. UNITS**	**20 SQ. UNITS**	**21 SQ. UNITS**	**22 SQ. UNITS**	**23 SQ. UNITS**	**24 SQ. UNITS**	**25 SQ. UNITS**
26 SQ. UNITS	**27 SQ. UNITS**	**28 SQ. UNITS**	**29 SQ. UNITS**	**30 SQ. UNITS**	**31 SQ. UNITS**	**32 SQ. UNITS**	**33 SQ. UNITS**	**34 SQ. UNITS**	**35 SQ. UNITS**	**36 SQ. UNITS**	**37 SQ. UNITS**
38 SQ. UNITS	**39 SQ. UNITS**	**40 SQ. UNITS**	**41 SQ. UNITS**	**42 SQ. UNITS**	**43 SQ. UNITS**	**44 SQ. UNITS**	**45 SQ. UNITS**	**46 SQ. UNITS**	**47 SQ. UNITS**	**48 SQ. UNITS**	**49 SQ. UNITS**

Look at the results on Worksheet 4.2. Do you see any patterns?

____

Which areas (numbers) have the most rectangles? ______________

Which numbers have only one rectangle? ______________

What is the relationship between the dimensions (length and width) of the rectangles and their areas? ______________

The area of a rectangle is the product of its length multiplied by its width. Mathematicians write $A = l \times w$, where A stands for area, l stands for length, and w stands for width.

When we start with a given number of squares, we find that we usually can make only a few rectangles. We must find pairs of whole numbers whose products are equal to the number of squares in the given area. For example, when we start with an area of 13, we can find only one pair of numbers whose product is 13: 1×13. For an area of 12, we find: 1×12, 2×6, and 3×4. The numbers 1, 2, 3, 4, 6, and 12 are called *factors* of 12. They divide 12 evenly. What happens when you try to make a rectangle with 9 squares? 16 squares?

The numbers with only one rectangle have a mathematical name. They are called *prime numbers*. They have only two factors: 1 and the number itself. The numbers with more than one rectangle are called *composite numbers*.

Look back at your results again. How many of the numbers between 2 and 49 are prime numbers? ______________

Which number or numbers had the most rectangles? ______________

Which number or numbers from 50 to 100 do you think have the most rectangles? Work with a friend to check your ideas. What is the next prime number after 47?

Mathematicians have been looking for years for a formula that always predicts the next prime number. Only recently has anyone reportedly solved this problem—Arnold Arnold of England—and very few people have seen the solution.

Worksheet 4.3

Use the formula for area: $A = l \times w$. Find the missing values for the rectangles below, and record them in the table. (Hint: given an area of 27 and a length of 9, we know that $9 \times w = 27$. Look for the number that will work for w.)

	Length	Width	Area
1.	______	______	______
2.	______	______	______
3.	______	______	______
4.	______	______	______
5.	______	______	______
6.	______	______	______
7.	______	______	______

1. 18

12 A=___

2. 100

3 A=___

3. 9

___ A=27

4. 25

2 A=___

5. 45

15 A=___

6. ___

7 A=49

7.

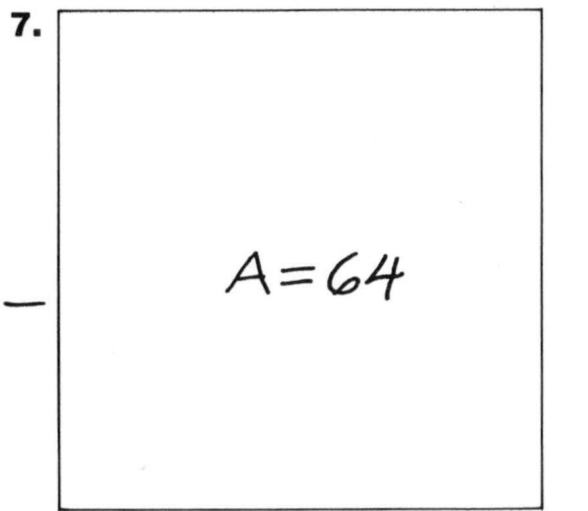

PERIMETER

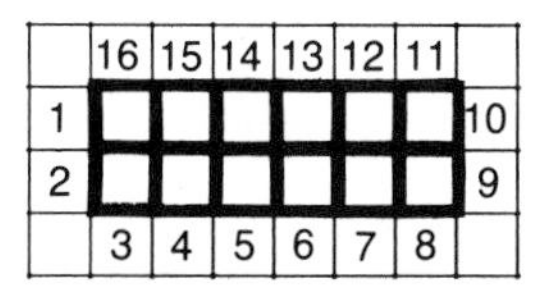

Figure 4.6

In the previous section, we made rectangles with various areas. Now we will look in a new way at the rectangles that have an area of 12 square units. Use your squares or tiles to make a 2-by-6 rectangle.

Suppose we want to put a fence or edging around this rectangle. How many units long would it be? We need to know the distance around the rectangle (called the *perimeter*) in order to find what length of fencing to buy. The units of length are counted in Figure 4.6. We would need 16 units of fencing for this rectangle.

We say the *perimeter* of this rectangle is 16 units. The perimeter is the distance around an area and is a *linear* measurement. In this example, if each square were 1 meter long, the perimeter would be 16 meters.

Use the graph paper in Figure 4.7 to draw the other two rectangles that have an area of 12 square units. Find their perimeters. Record the perimeters for all three rectangles:

1 by 12; perimeter = ____________________

2 by 6; perimeter = ____________________

3 by 4; perimeter = ____________________

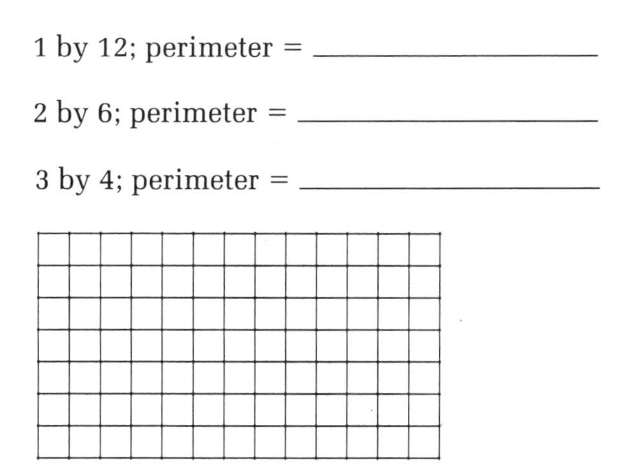

Figure 4.7

Suppose we are working with squares that are 1 foot on a side. How many feet of fencing would we need for a 2-by-6-foot rectangular plot? ____________ If fencing costs $10 per foot, how much would this cost? ____________

How many feet of fencing would we need for a 3-by-4-foot rectangle? ____________ How much would this cost? ____________

How many feet would we need for a 1-by-12-foot rectangle? ______ How much would this cost? ____________

As you can see, the price for fencing varies a great deal according to the arrangement of the 12 units of area.

We found a formula that helps us find the area of a rectangle when we know the length and width. As mathematicians say, we can express the area in terms of the length and width of the rectangle. Consider the

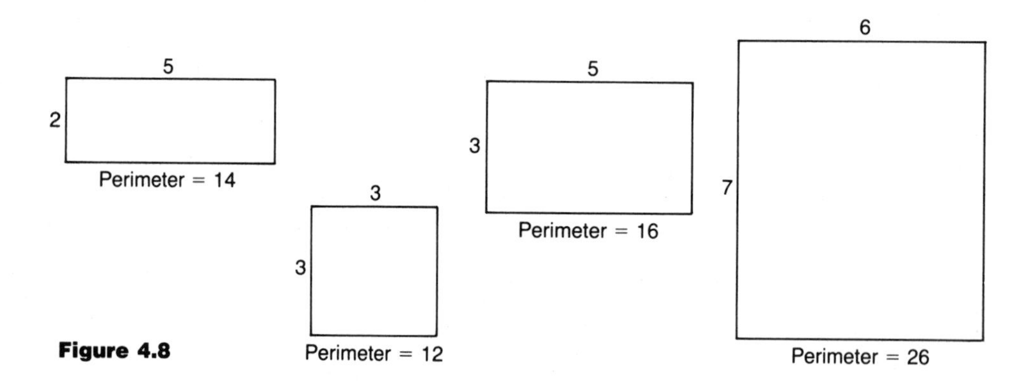

Figure 4.8

rectangles and their perimeters in Figure 4.8. Can you think of a formula for the perimeter of a rectangle in terms of its length and width? Work on this question with another person. After the next worksheet, we will discuss the answer.

Worksheet 4.4

Construct all the rectangles that have the following areas: 4, 8, 16, 24.
Find the perimeter of each rectangle. Record your work in the table.

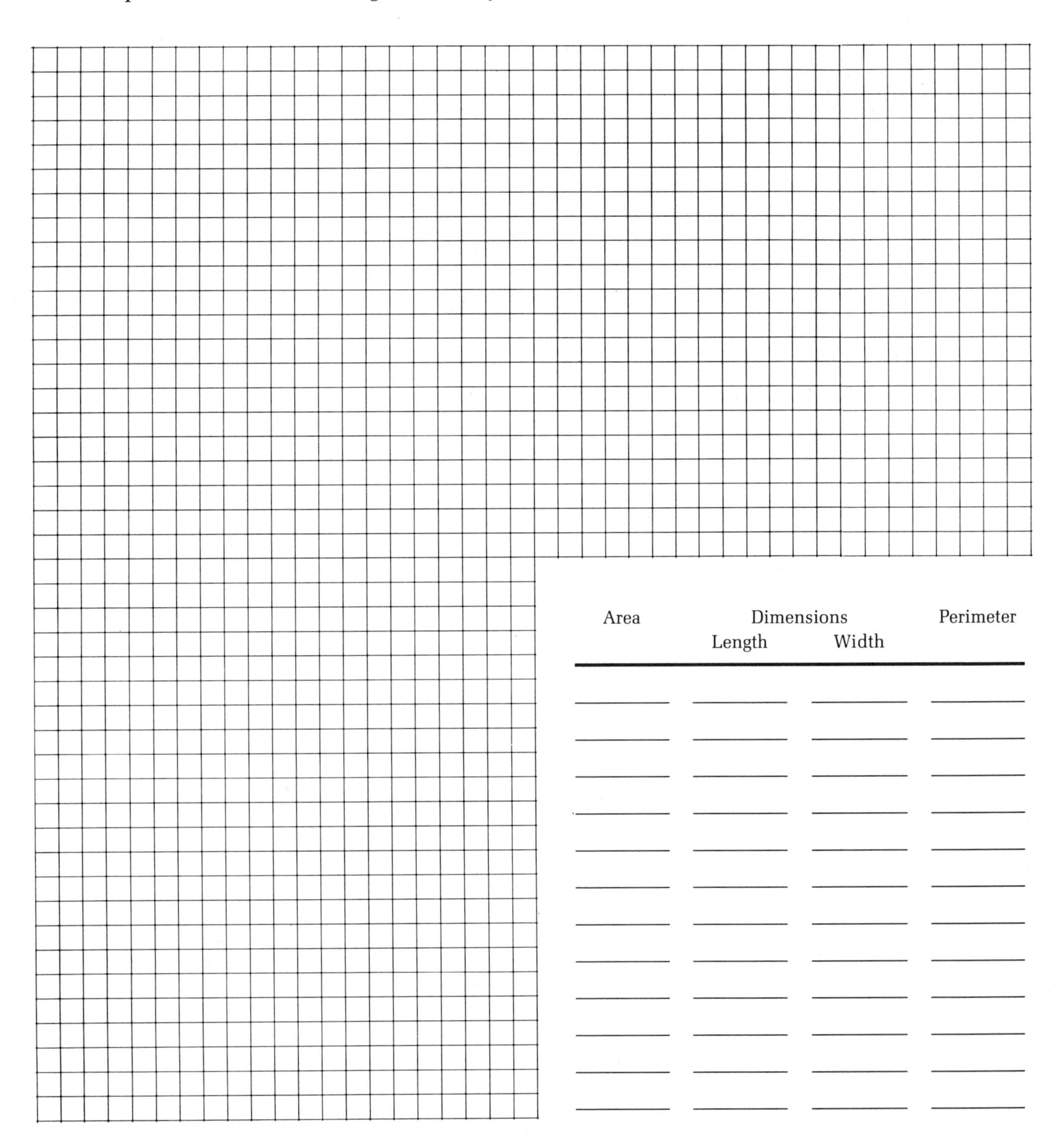

Area	Dimensions		Perimeter
	Length	Width	

Did you find a formula for perimeter? Look at the rectangle with its length and width labeled in Figure 4.9.

To find the perimeter, we add the "lengths" of all of the sides. We have $w + l + w + l$, or $2w + 2l$, which is the same as $2(l + w)$. To see

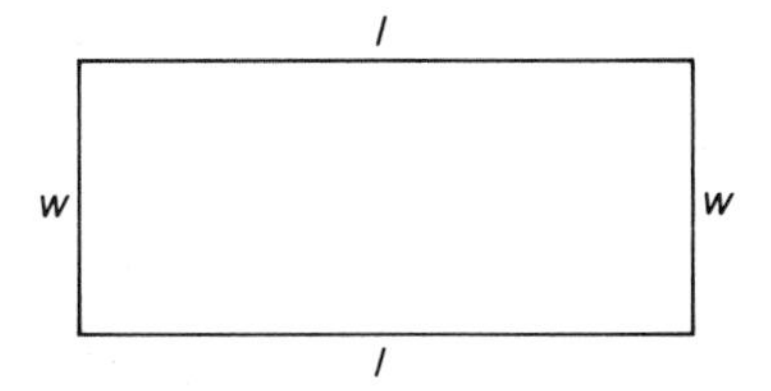

Figure 4.9

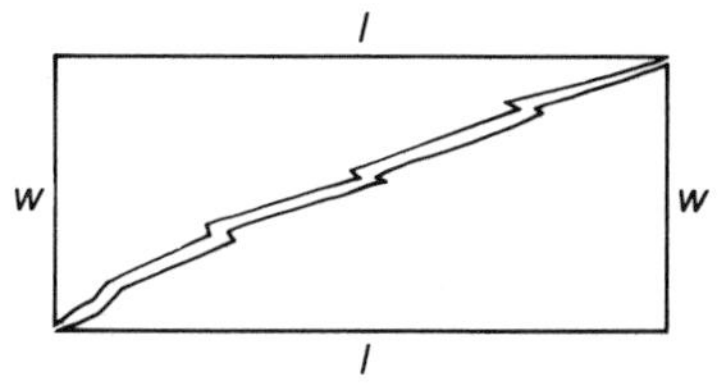

Figure 4.10

this, suppose we add the length and width together on each half of the rectangle (Figure 4.10). From each half, we get $l + w$. Thus, we can write:

$$\text{perimeter} = 2(l + w) = 2l + 2w$$

(Note: it is a common convention to omit the multiplication sign that you would expect between the 2 and the w and between the 2 and the l.)

If the rectangle is a square, how will the formula for the perimeter be affected? ______________________________

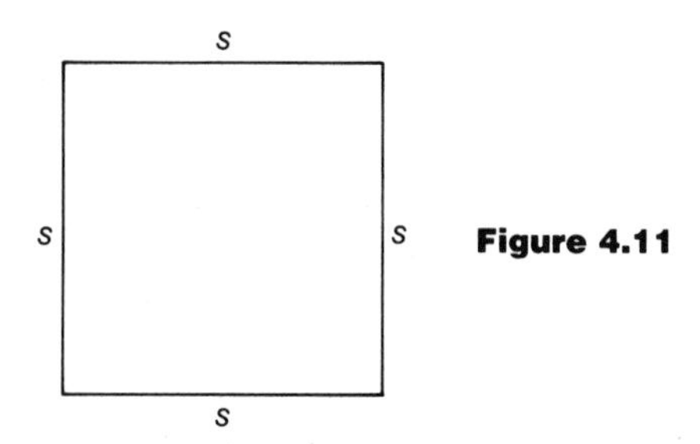

Figure 4.11

In a square (Figure 4.11), the length and width are equal and are usually referred to as the *sides*, s. Using the formula for perimeter, we would have:

$$\text{perimeter} = 2s + 2s = 4s$$

Look at your table on Worksheet 4.4. What conclusions can you draw about the dimensions of rectangles that have the shortest perimeters for given areas? ______________ The longest perimeters? ______________

If you want a rectangular garden with a certain amount of area, how can you save money on fencing? For each fixed area, the rectangle that was a square—or the closest to a square when it wasn't possible to make a square—had the shortest perimeter. Up to this point, we have only considered rectangles with sides whose lengths are whole numbers.

Suppose we allow fraction or decimal lengths. Is it possible to make a square with an area of 24 square units? About how long would each side have to be? ______________ (Remember that the two sides multiplied together must equal 24.) Note that $5 \times 5 = 25$ and $4 \times 4 = 16$. So the side length is between 4 and 5, probably closer to 5 than 4. Try 4.8. Use your calculator or multiply by hand to find $4.8 \times 4.8 =$ ____________. About 23? Try 4.85 and 4.9 to see which gives an answer closer to 24.

$4.85 \times 4.85 =$ ____________

$4.9 \times 4.9 =$ ____________

Which is closer? ____________ 4.9 is quite close. Mathematicians say that 4.9×4.9 is approximately equal to the square root of 24 and write:

$$4.9 \approx \sqrt{24}$$

Suppose you can have any shape you wish for your garden. Is there a shape that would give a perimeter that is even shorter than the perimeter of a square? Discuss this question with another person or group of students. The question will be discussed later in the chapter.

Worksheet 4.5

Find the approximate length of the sides of the squares with the following areas: 2, 5, 12, 30, and 72 square units. Show your work as in the first problem, which has been started for you. Also give the perimeter for each square. Use your calculator if you wish to help in finding the approximation. *Then* check using the square root key.

For a square with an area of 2:
the length of a side, $\sqrt{2}$, is between 1 and 2.

$1 \times 1 = 1 \qquad 2 \times 2 = 4$

Thus $\sqrt{2}$ is closer to 1.

We try: $1.2 - 1.2 \times 1.2 = 1.44$

and $1.5 - 1.5 \times 1.5 = 2.25$

Now we try: $1.4 - 1.4 \times 1.4 = 1.96$

$\sqrt{2} \approx 1.4$

perimeter ≈ 5.6

Worksheet 4.6

Find the areas and perimeters of the shapes given below. Notice that all of the shapes can be "cut up" into rectangles. Remember that the perimeter is the distance around the outside of the shape and that the area is the number of square units it covers.

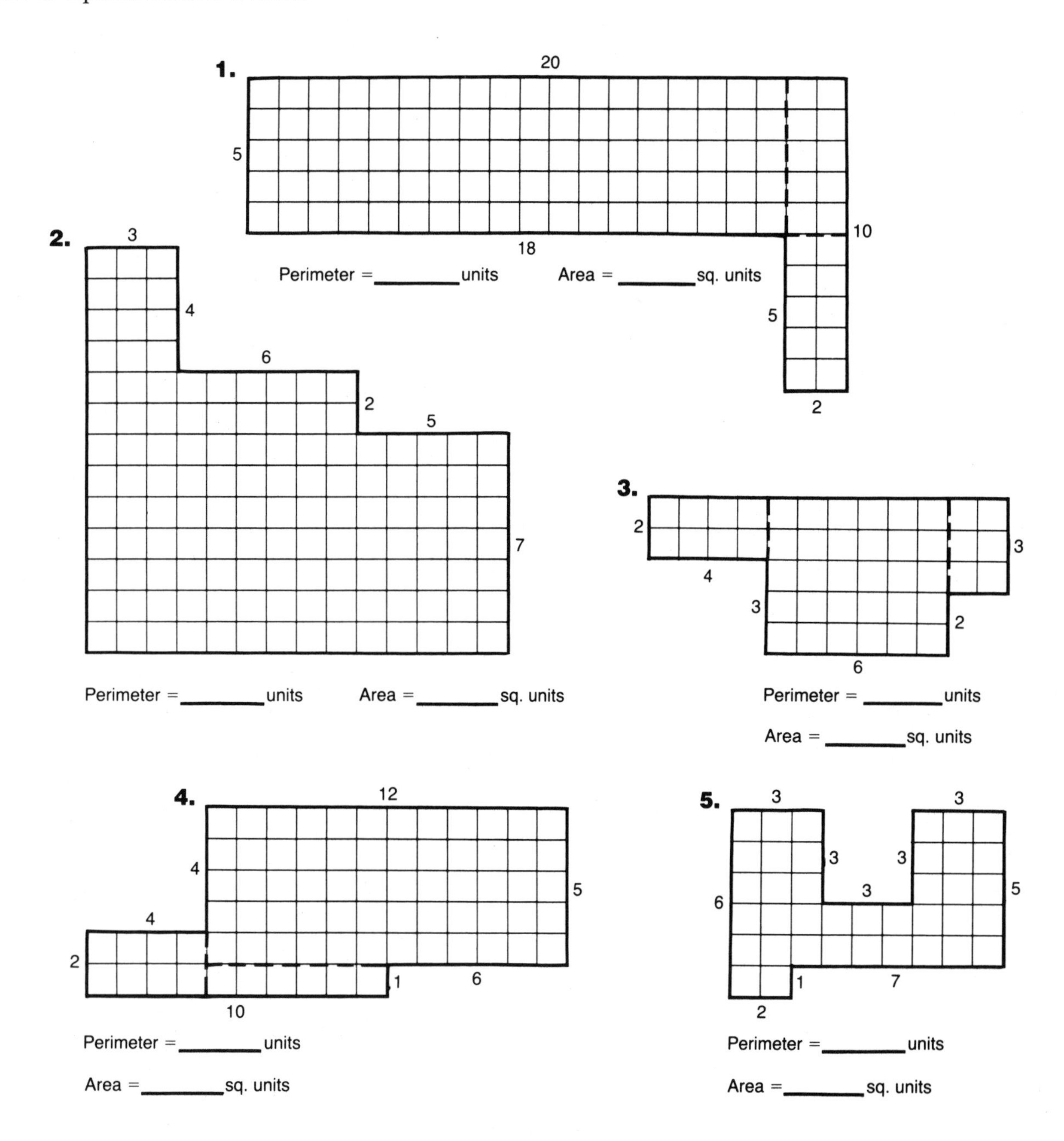

Worksheet 4.7

Each line in the table describes a different rectangle. Find the missing information, and record it in the table. Draw a sketch for each problem.

	Length	Width	Area	Perimeter
1.	7 in.	2 in.	________	________
2.	________	4 ft	20 sq. ft	________
3.	8 mi	________	________	22 mi
4.	________	________	36 sq. yd	24 yd
5.	L ft	W ft	________	________
6.	________	10 mi	________	60 mi

Earlier we looked at shapes that gave us the shortest, or minimum, perimeter for a fixed area. Now suppose we have a fixed amount of fencing, say 14 yards, and that we want to find the rectangle that will give us the most area. If the perimeter is 14 yards, then halfway around the rectangle, or a length plus a width, is 7 yards. Thus, we should look for pairs of lengths and widths that add up to 7, such as 1 and 6 (illustrated in Figure 4.12). A 1-by-6 rectangle does have a perimeter of 14. What are the other possible rectangles with a perimeter of 14 (ignoring sides of fractional lengths)?

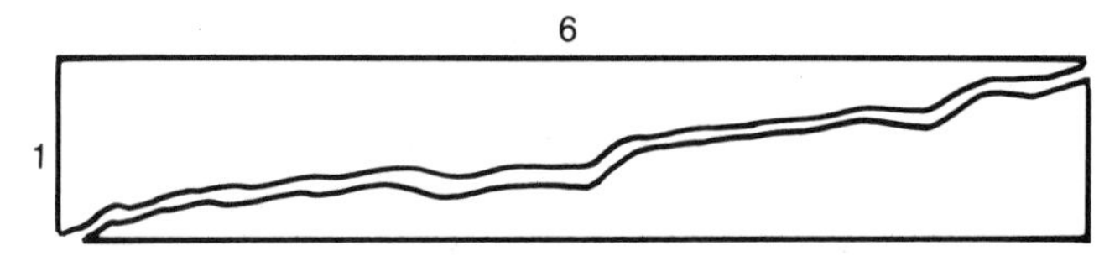

Figure 4.12

Worksheet 4.8

Use the graph paper below to draw all the rectangles (with length and width of whole numbers) that have a perimeter of 14 units. Indicate which has the largest area. Then do the same for rectangles with perimeters of 12, 18, and 24 units. Summarize your results in the table.

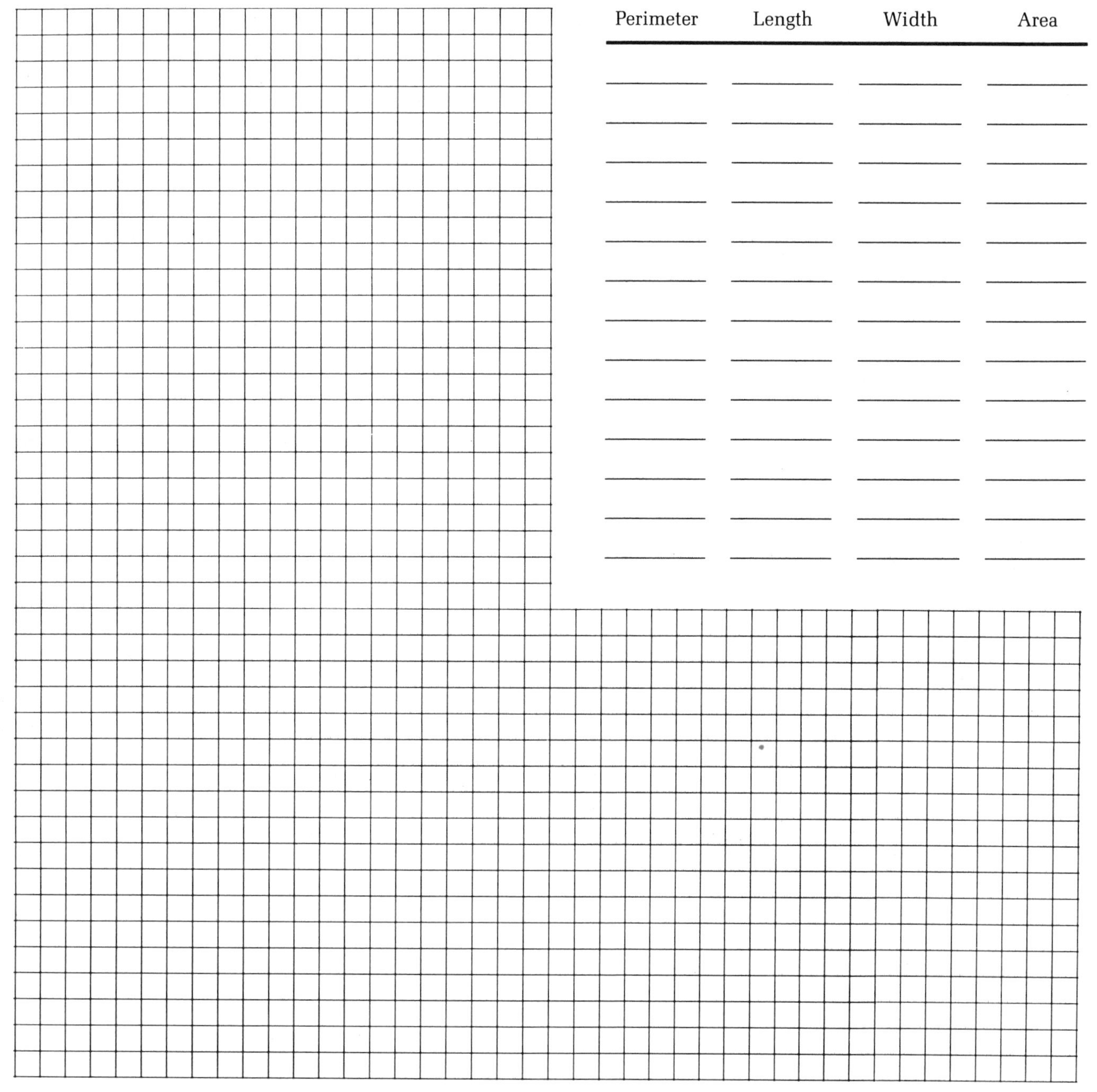

Perimeter	Length	Width	Area

Did you develop any pattern for making the rectangles? ____________

Explain it to someone else.

Did you think of any shape that would give you a shorter perimeter than a square for a fixed area? We can also ask a similar question about a shape with a fixed perimeter. Sometimes, to help ourselves think about such questions, we express them using particular numbers. We can rephrase the two questions as follows:

If we were allowed to make any shape with an area of 16 square units, would we be able to make one with a shorter perimeter than a 4-by-4 square?

If we were allowed to make any shape with a perimeter of 24 yards, would we be able to make one with more area than a 6-by-6 square?

The answer to both questions is a circle.

These types of questions are commonly found in algebra II and calculus courses and are referred to as *maximum/minimum* problems. Using drawings on graph paper, we have been able to reach a conclusion that is the general solution to many of these problems. We will not give formulas for the area and perimeter of a circle here. But we will check this conclusion using estimation and graph paper.

A circle with an area of 16 square units is drawn in Figure 4.13. Place a string around the outside of the circle. Measure the string along the graph paper to find the perimeter, called the *circumference*. (Remember that the length of the side of each square on the graph paper is 1 unit.) What is the circumference of the circle? ____________

Draw a square with 16 square units of area next to the circle (Figure 4.13). What is its perimeter? ____________ Which has the shorter perimeter, the circle or the square? ____________

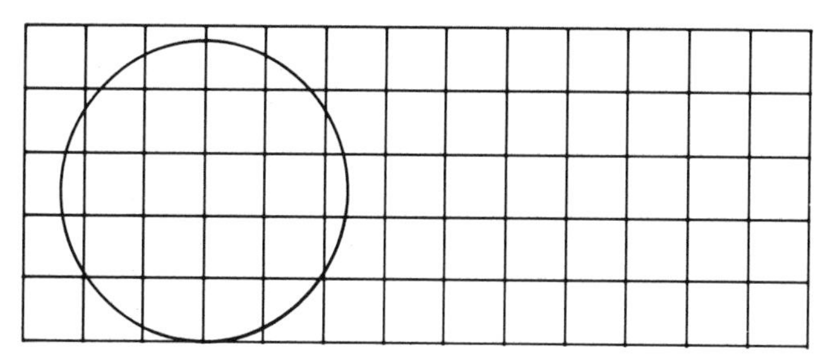

Figure 4.13

A 6-by-6 square has a perimeter of 24 units and an area of 36 square units. The circumference of the circle in Figure 4.14 is 24 units. (Check with string.) We want to know whether its area is larger than 36 square units. We will use two methods to estimate the area of this circle and then compare their results.

Method 1. Count the whole squares. Then estimate the area covered by partial squares by counting *all* of the partial squares and dividing by 2.

No. of whole squares ____________

Estimated no. of partial squares

____

Total ____________

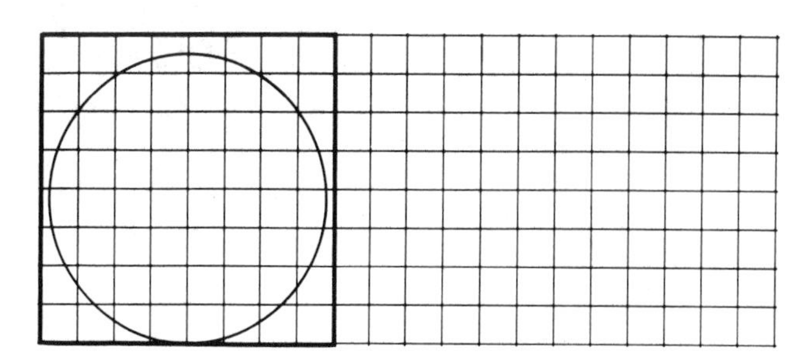

Figure 4.14

Method 2. Draw a rectangle or square around the circle. The area of the circle is the area of this (large) square less the extra unit squares outside the circle. This method is called the *subtractive method*.

Area of large square ____________

less area outside circle ____________ =

Area of circle ____________

Look at the two answers you found for the area of the circle to decide on a single estimate for this area. How does this estimate compare with the area of a 6-by-6 square? ____________

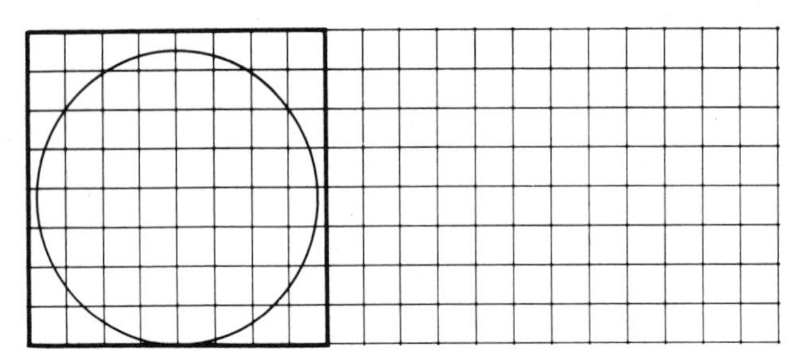

Figure 4.14 (repeated)

Worksheet 4.9

We can use the previous methods to estimate the areas of irregular shapes. Find the areas of the shapes below by first estimating the number of squares inside the shape and then using the subtractive method. Record your results below each figure.

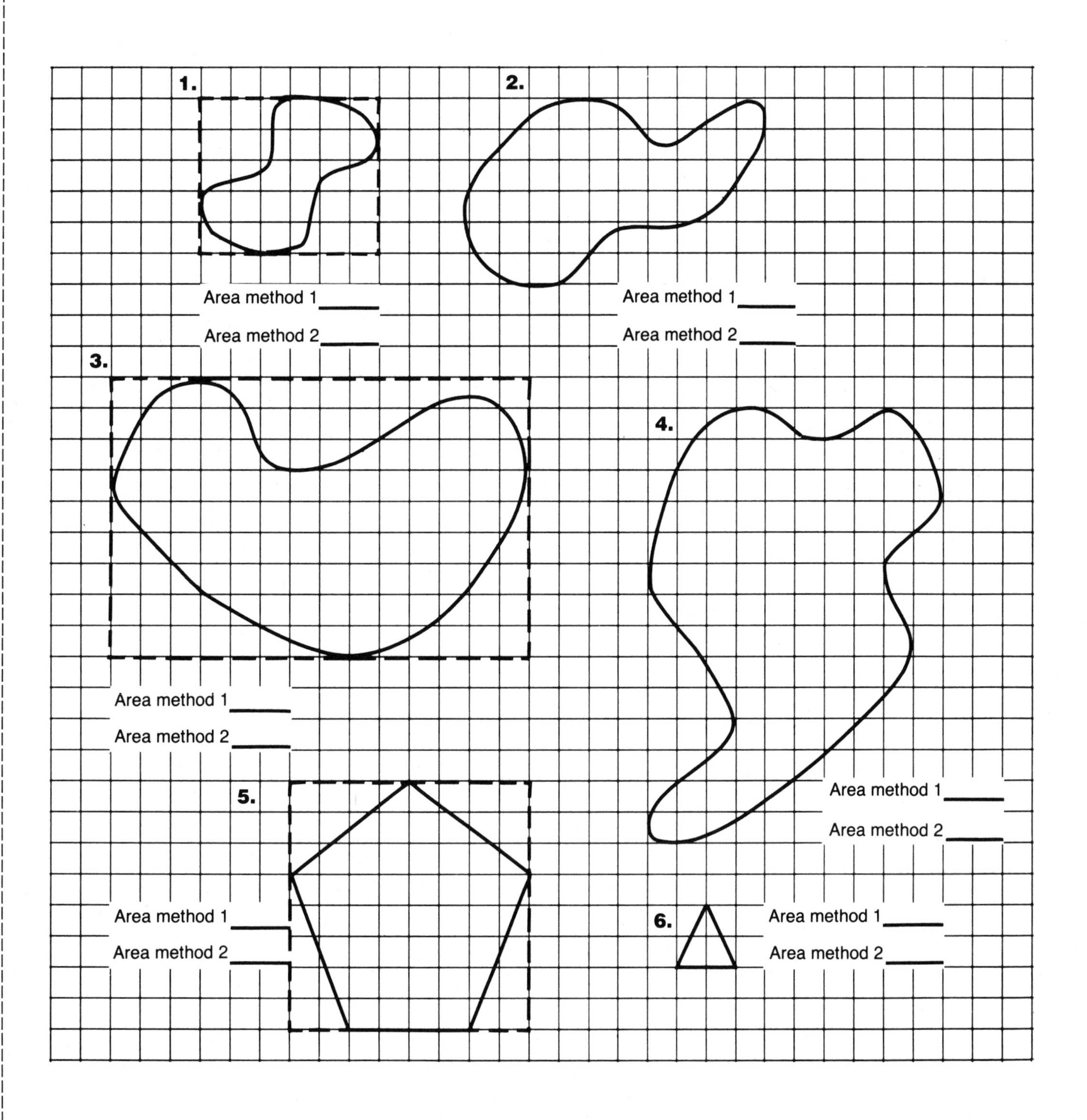

USING THE GEOBOARD TO FIND AREA

For this section you need a geoboard, rubber bands, paper squares (the same size as the squares on your geoboard), and dot paper for recording your work (see Appendix page 284). If you don't have a geoboard, the problems can be done using paper squares and dot paper.

You have learned that area is measured in square units. Make the smallest square with a rubber band on the geoboard. The area of that square is 1 square unit. One paper square should fit into that space. Using one rubber band, make a shape that has 4 square units of area. See the example in Figure 4.15. Again using only one rubber band, make a different shape that has 4 square units of area.

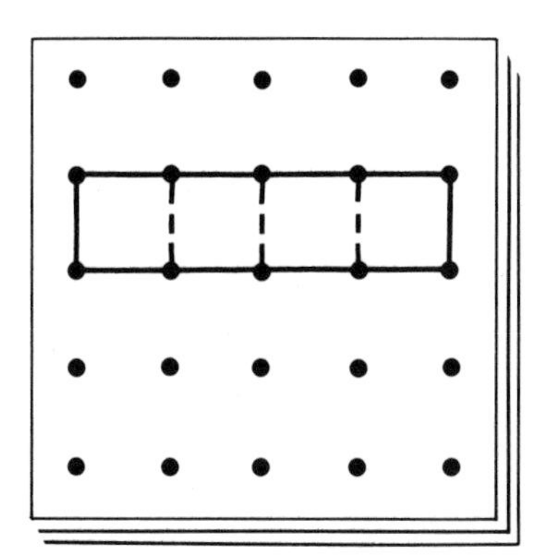

Figure 4.15

A shape with one inside region is called a *simple* shape. The shape in Figure 4.16 is simple; the shape in Figure 4.17 is not simple. In this chapter we will be making simple shapes; that is, the rubber band cannot cross itself.

The shapes in Figure 4.18 are *congruent* because they are the same shape and size. One shape, if it were rotated and/or flipped, would fit on top of the other. For our purposes, we will consider these shapes the same.

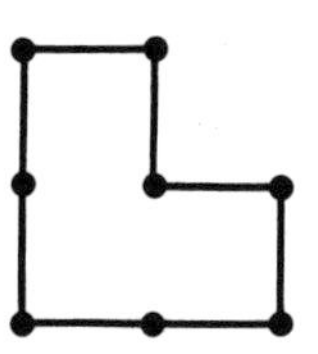

Figure 4.16

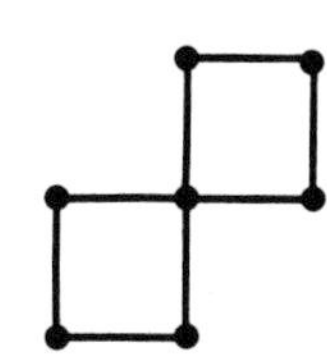

Figure 4.17

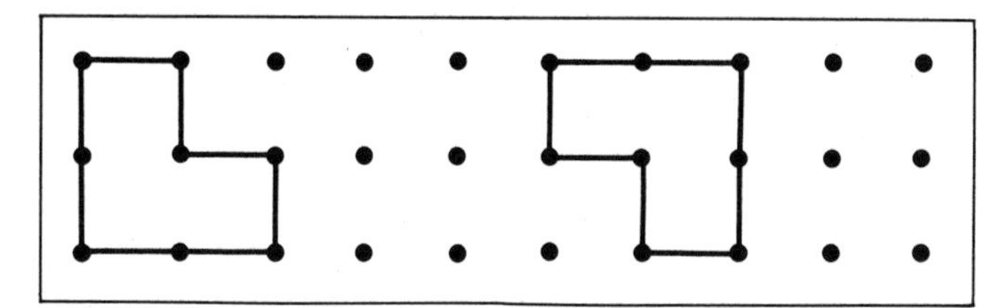

Figure 4.18

Worksheet 4.10

Using a geoboard, make some shapes that have 5 square units of area. The shapes may look different, but they all should have the same area of 5 square units. Put paper squares into each shape to make sure that exactly 5 squares fit. Record the shapes on the dot paper below. Twelve different shapes can be made; the shape that is 5 squares long will not fit on the geoboard. If you do not have a geoboard, use paper squares to make the shapes.

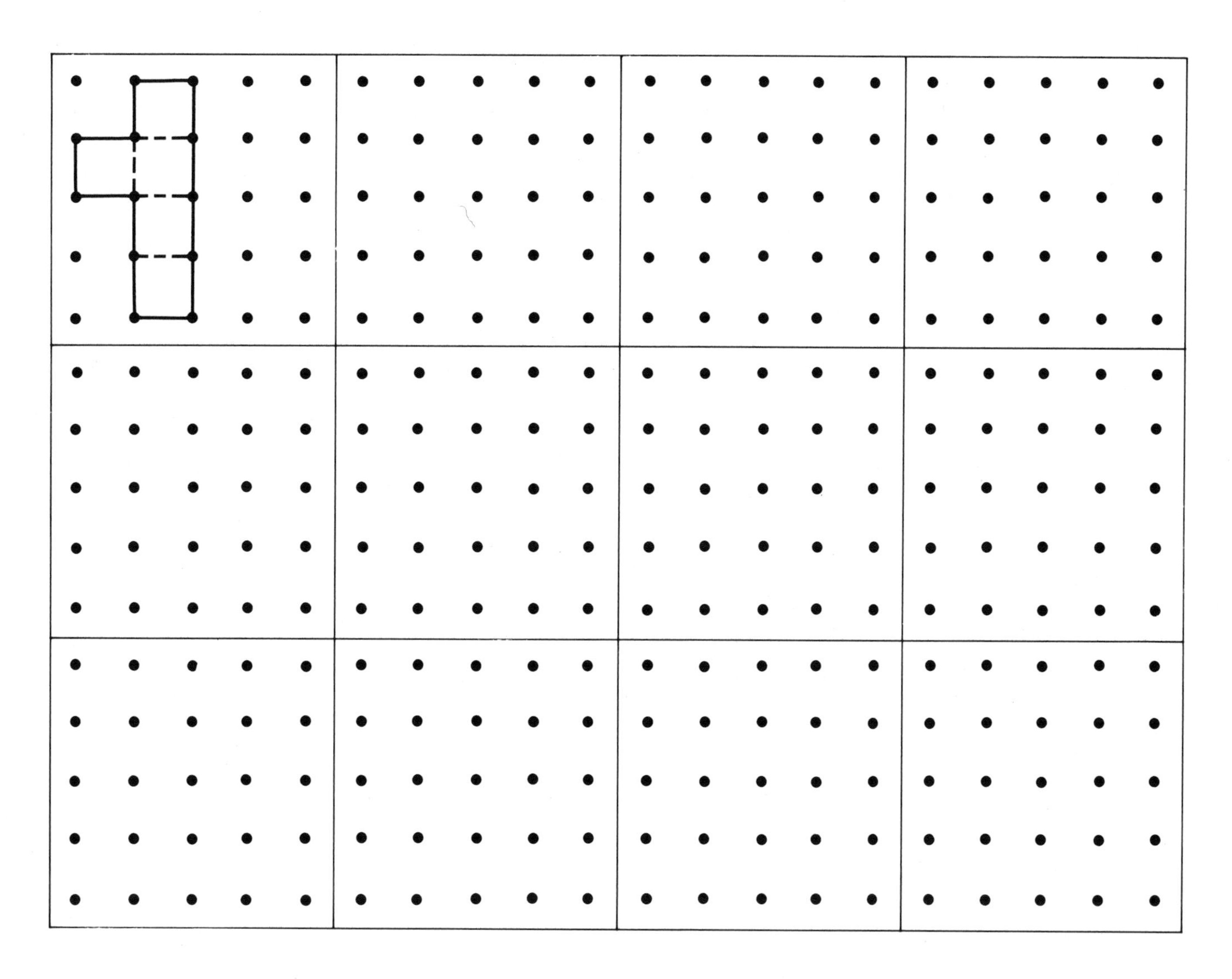

Fold a paper square along the diagonal, then cut along the fold. Each triangle is one-half of a whole square. On the geoboard the diagonal of the triangle must connect opposite corners of the square.

The shaded triangle in Figure 4.19 is one-half of the square unit.

Figure 4.19

The shaded triangle in Figure 4.20 is *not* one-half of the square unit.

Figure 4.20

The area of the shape in Figure 4.21 is 4 square units. Three whole squares and 2 half squares make a total of 4 whole squares.

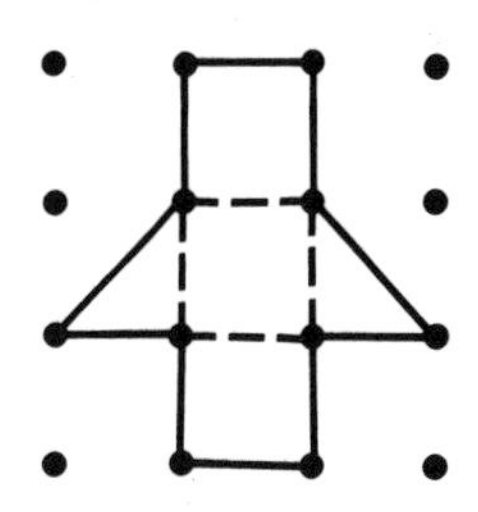

Figure 4.21

Copy the shapes in Figure 4.22 on your geoboard. Place your paper shapes (wholes and halves) inside the rubber band to help you figure out the areas.

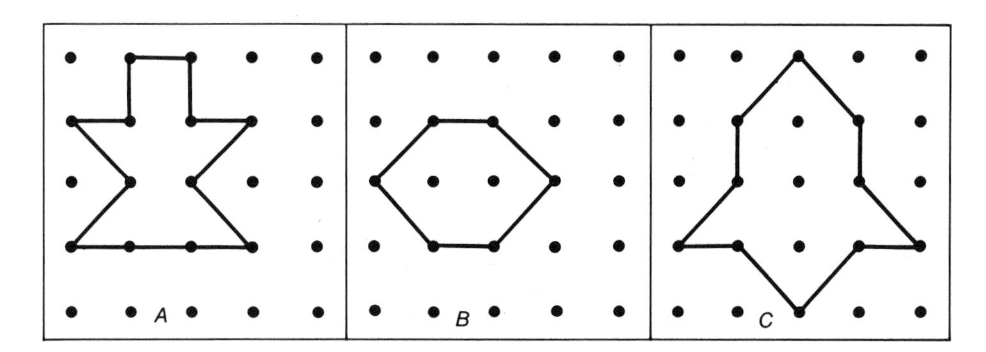

Figure 4.22

The area of shape *A* is 5 square units; the area of shape *B* is 4 square units; the area of shape *C* is 7 square units.

Worksheet 4.11

Make some interesting shapes on your geoboard with areas of 4 square units. Fit the paper squares and triangles inside your shapes to check their areas. Record each shape on the dot paper below. If you don't have a geoboard, use paper shapes.

Worksheet 4.12

Copy these shapes on your geoboard. Figure out the areas, and record your results.

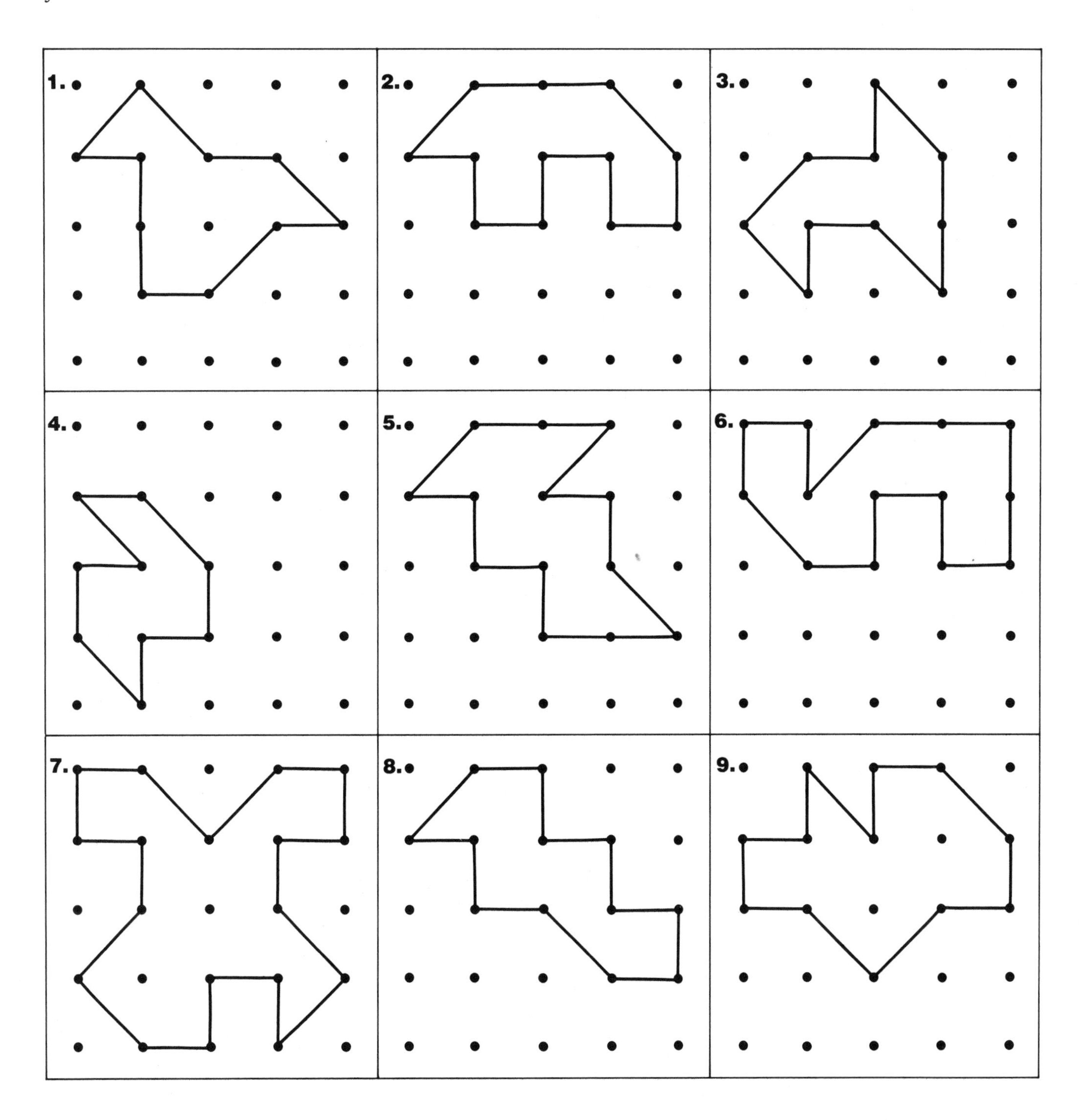

Make several different triangles on your geoboard. Copy them on the dot paper in Figure 4.23.

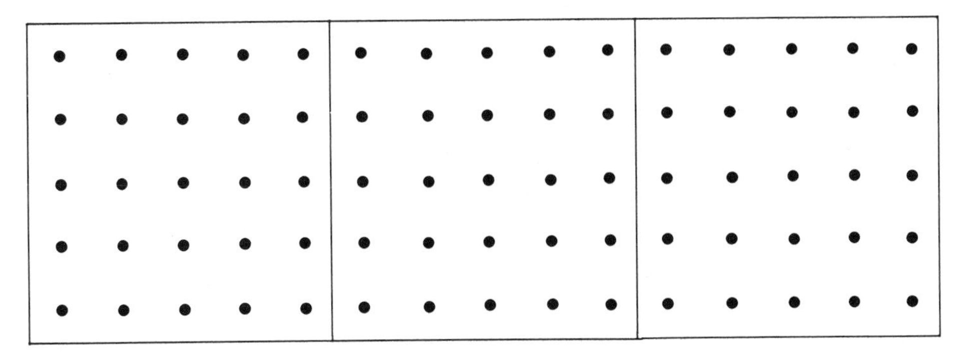

Figure 4.23

Do any of your triangles have an L-shaped corner like those in Figure 4.24? These corners are called *right angles* and measure 90°. Triangles that have a 90° angle are called *right* triangles.

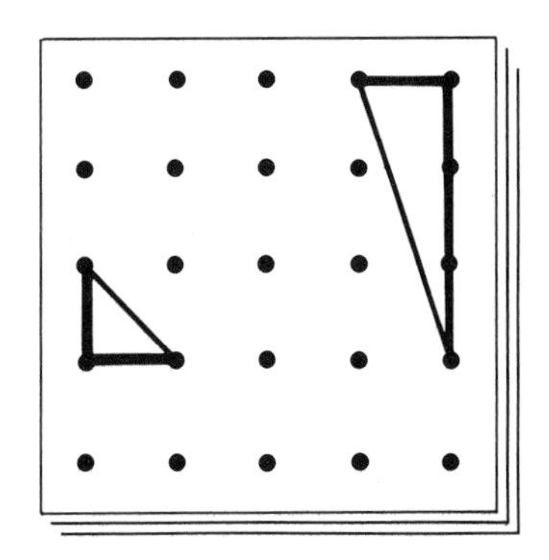

Figure 4.24

Figure 4.25

Copy right triangle *ABC* in Figure 4.25 on your geoboard. The paper squares and half squares will not fit—try them. Notice that the long side of the triangle (called the *hypotenuse* in a right triangle) extends from *A* to *B*. Using a different colored rubber band, make a rectangle around the triangle. Notice that the line from *A* to *B* is the diagonal of this rectangle. The whole rectangle measures 4 square units of area. The diagonal cuts the rectangle in half, so each triangle has an area of 2 square units.

Worksheet 4.13

Copy the right triangles on your geoboard. Make a rectangle around each triangle, using a rubber band of a different color. Then measure and record the area of the triangles.

Make up more right triangles on your geoboard. Measure their areas, and record your results.

1.

2.

3.

4.

5.

6.

7.

8.

9.

To find the area of the shape in Figure 4.26, cover part of it with squares and half squares. The area of the rest can be figured out by completing the rectangle around the remaining triangle. The problem is worked out step by step.

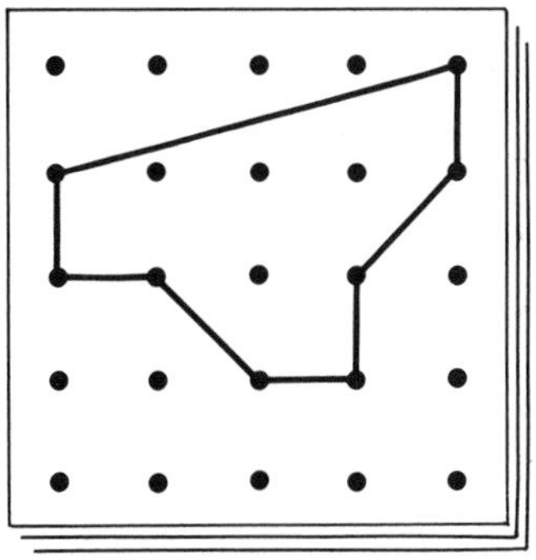

Figure 4.26

Step 1: Fit whole squares (marked by Xs) into the shape. There are 4 whole squares.

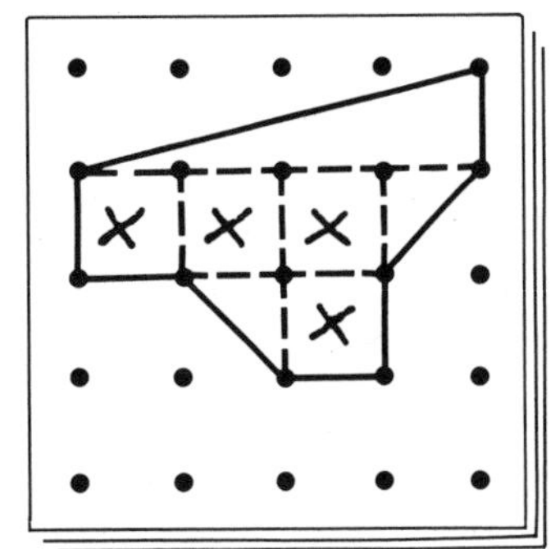

Figure 4.27

Step 2: Place half squares in the shape. There are 2 half squares.

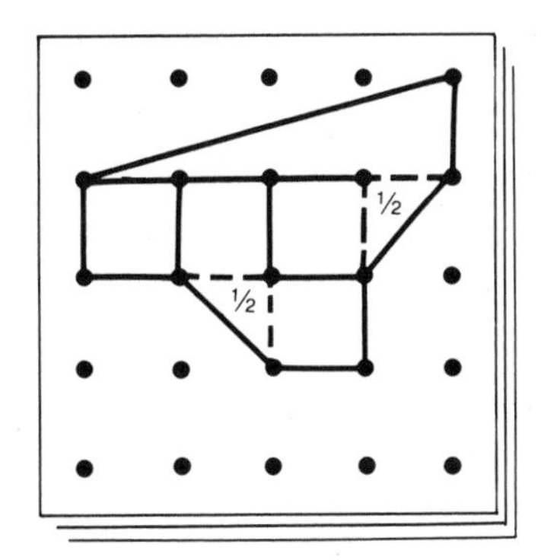

Figure 4.28

Step 3: The remaining area can be measured by completing the rectangle. The whole rectangle measures 4 square units; therefore, the triangle measures 2 square units.

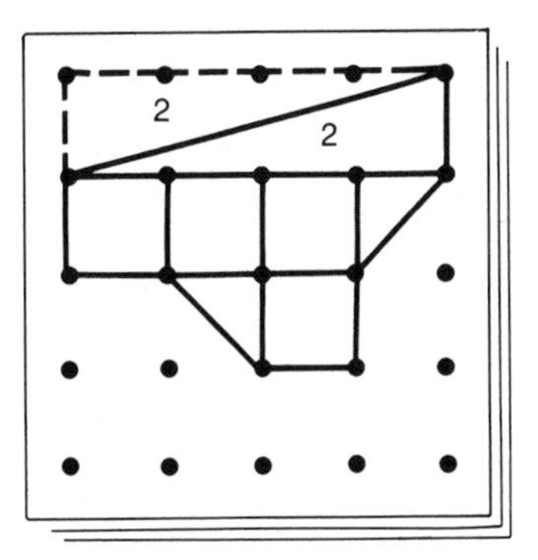

Figure 4.29

Step 4: The shape has a total area of 7 square units: 4 whole squares, 2 half squares, and a triangle that measures 2 square units.

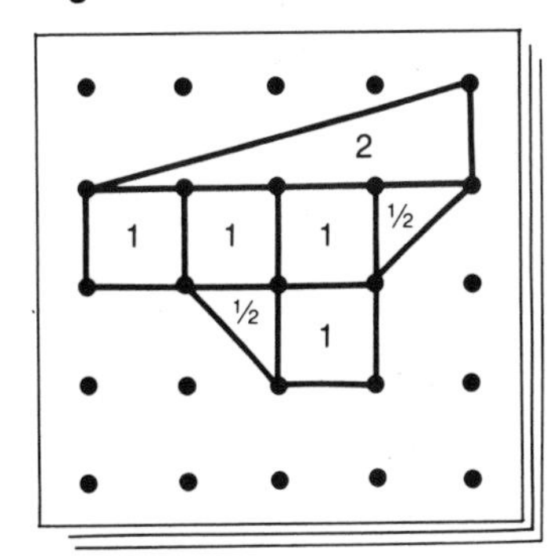

Figure 4.30

Worksheet 4.14

Find the areas of the following shapes. Work them out on a geoboard, and record the areas under each shape.

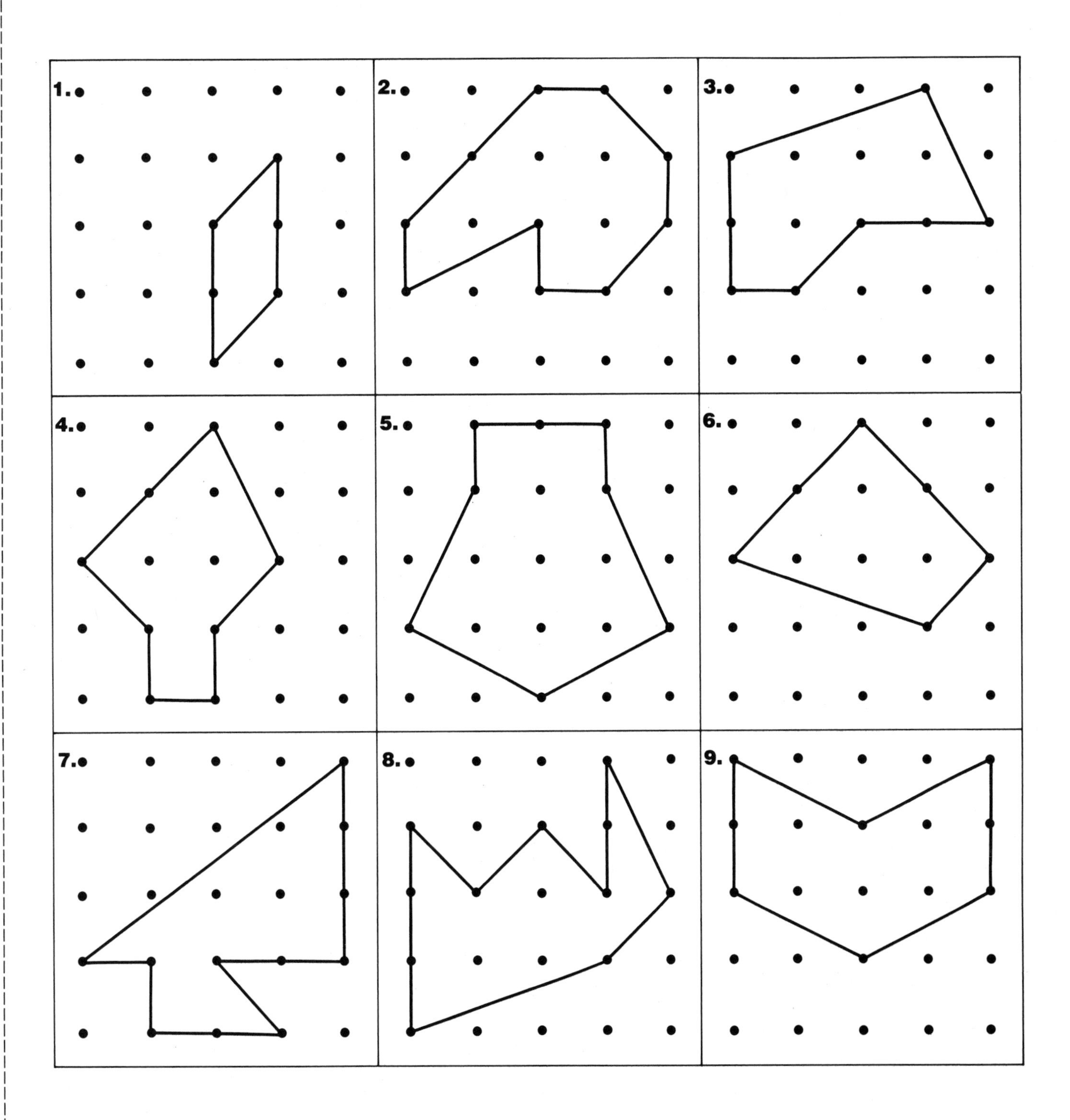

You will find the methods we've been using to find area don't work for the triangle in Figure 4.31. Whole squares and half squares don't fit. There are no right angles to help in making rectangles. We need to learn one more method—called the *subtractive* method—to help us measure this area.

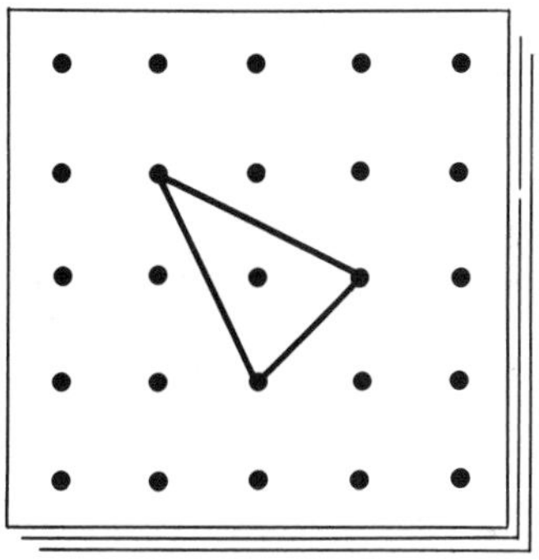

Figure 4.31

Step 1: Make a rectangle or square around the triangle. The square measures 4 square units. If we can find the area of the shaded parts and subtract that from 4 (the area of the square), we will have the area of the triangle.

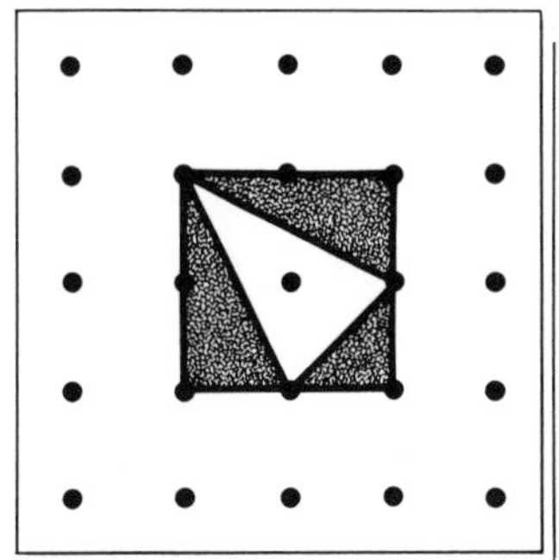

Figure 4.32

Step 2: One half square fits into the bottom corner. That leaves two right triangles.

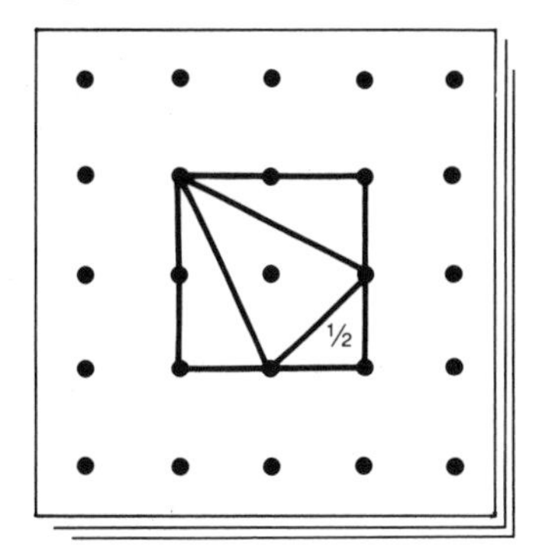

Figure 4.33

Step 3: Make rectangles around the right triangles. These rectangles each have an area of 2 square units; therefore, these triangles each have an area of 1 square unit.

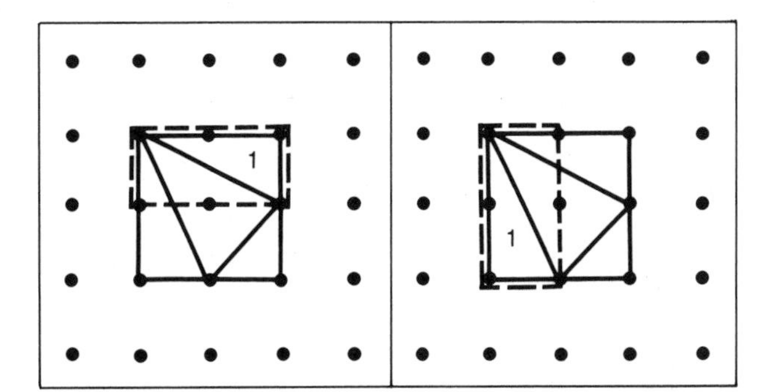

Figure 4.34

Step 4: We have two right triangles, each with an area of 1 square unit. We also know that there is a half square unit in the corner. This makes a total area of $2\frac{1}{2}$ square units that are inside the square but outside the original triangle. Subtract this $2\frac{1}{2}$ from 4. The area of the original triangle is $1\frac{1}{2}$ square units.

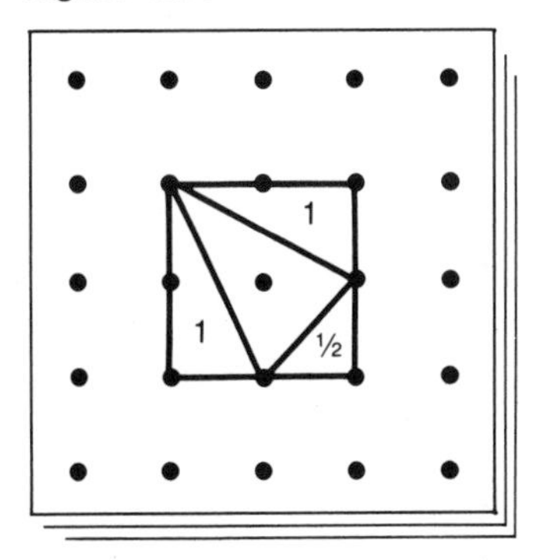

Figure 4.35

Worksheet 4.15

Measure the areas of these shapes. First copy the shapes on a geoboard. Use rubber bands to help you find the areas. Record your work on this page.

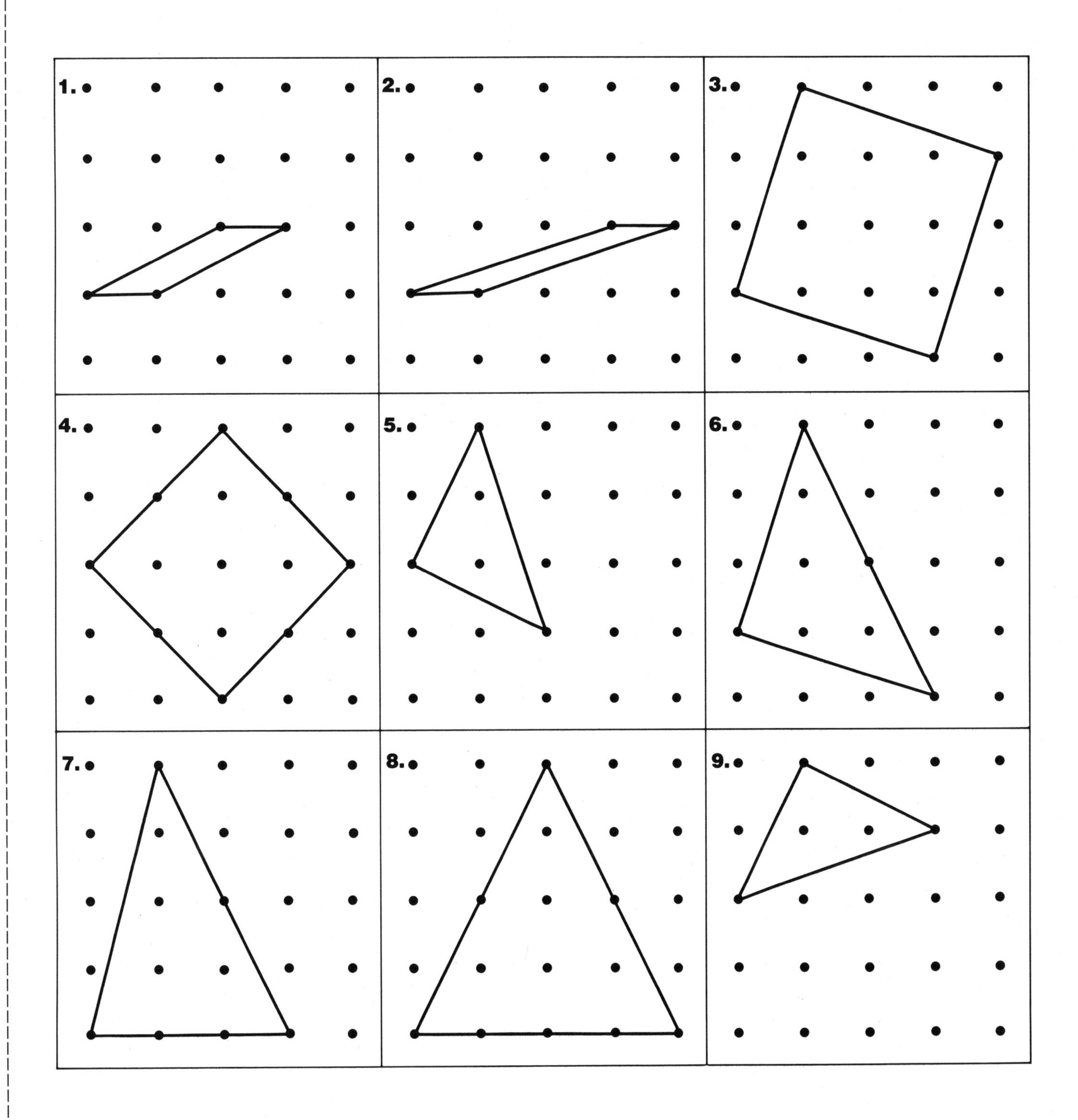

Often more than one method can be used to measure areas. Two ways are described to find the area of the shape in Figure 4.36.

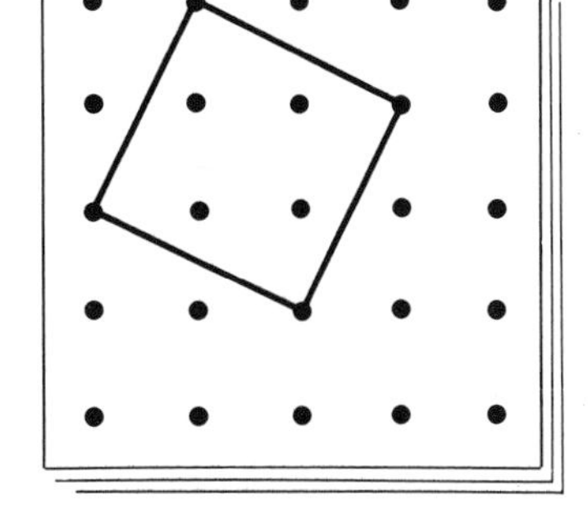

Figure 4.36

First, one whole square fits into the center, and rectangles can be made around the four remaining triangles. (See Figure 4.37.) Each of these triangles measures 1 square unit. One whole square plus four 1-unit triangles makes a total of 5 square units.

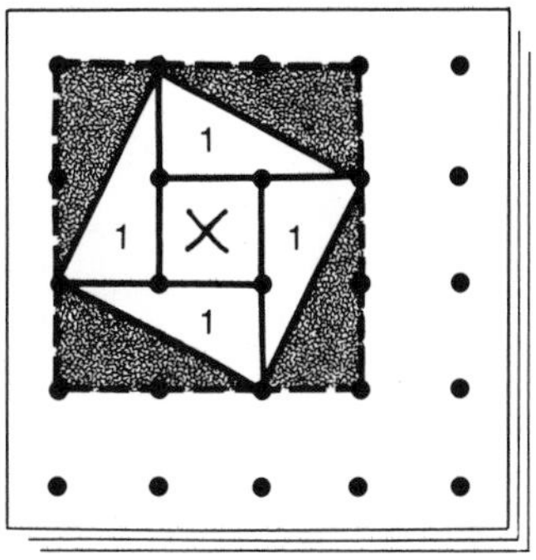

Figure 4.37

Alternatively, we can make a large square surrounding the entire shape. (See Figure 4.38.) This large square measures 9 square units. Subtract the four shaded triangles, each of which measures 1 square unit. Nine minus 4 leaves the original square of 5 square units.

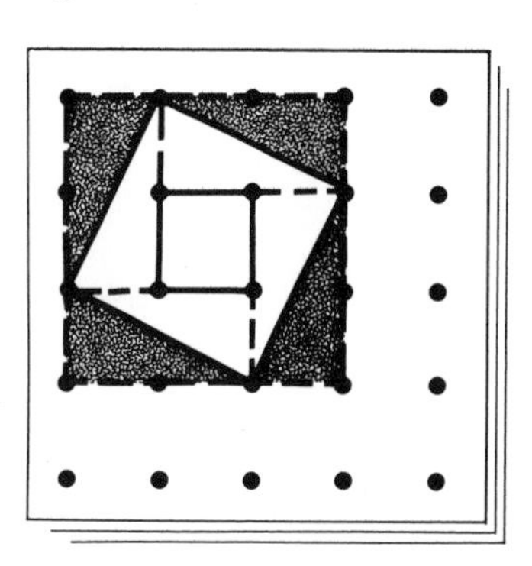

Figure 4.38

We have shown that the area of a *right triangle* measures one-half the area of the rectangle that completes it. Perhaps you remember the formula for finding the area of triangles: one-half the base times the height—$\frac{1}{2} \times b \times h$, or $\frac{1}{2}bh$. Earlier in this chapter we called the sides of a rectangle *length* and *width*. When we talk about triangles, we use the terms *base* and *height*.

What is the relationship between the right triangle and the rectangle in Figure 4.39? The area of the triangle is one-half the area of the rectangle. If we relabel the rectangle, calling the length the base and the width the height, we can see that the area of the right triangle is one-half of the base times the height, or $\frac{1}{2}bh$.

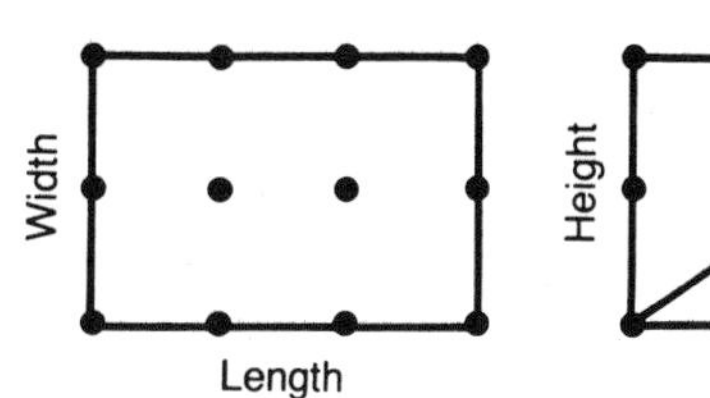

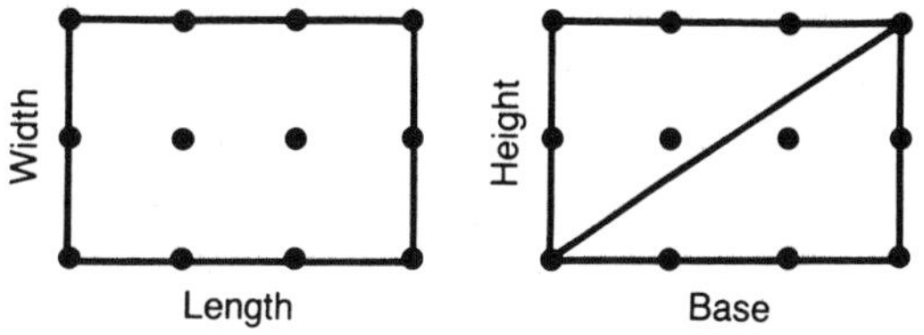

Figure 4.39

Worksheet 4.16

To complete this page, first draw a right triangle with the given dimensions. Then find the area using two methods. First, complete the rectangle to find the area. Second, use the formula ½*bh*. Both methods should give the same area.

	Base	Height	Area of Rectangle	Area of Triangle	Formula ½ × *b* × *h*
1.	2	3	6	3	½ × 2 × 3 = 3
2.	1	4			
3.	2	4			
4.	3	1			
5.	3	4			
6.	4	2			

1. 3 3 3 2

2.

3.

4.

5.

6.

Worksheet 4.17

Triangles can be classified according to the length of their sides. If all three sides are equal, they are called *equilateral*. Triangles with two equal sides are called *isosceles*, and those with no equal sides are called *scalene*. Classify the triangles, then find their areas. Use a geoboard method, then check with the formula.

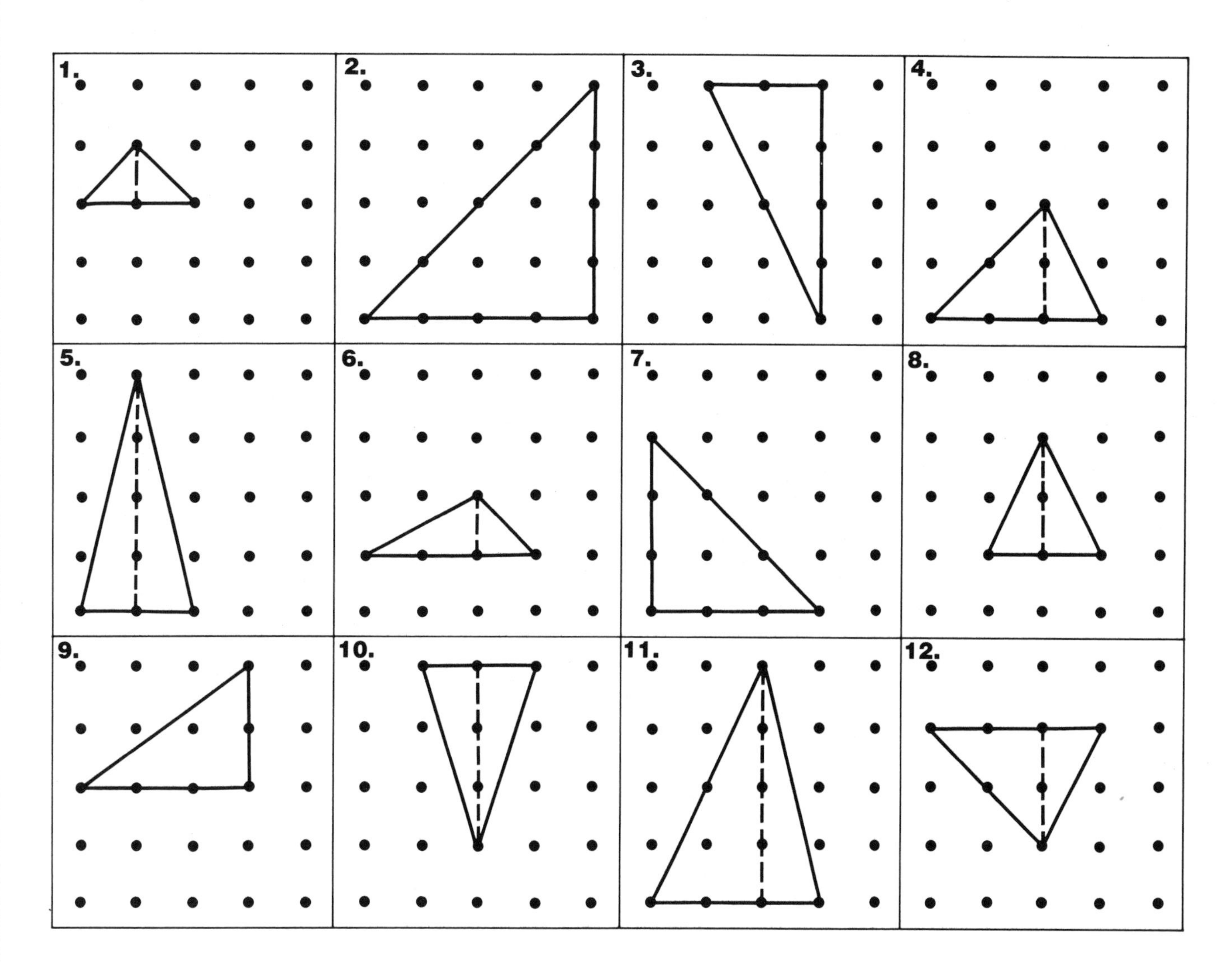

We can also find some patterns and rules to help find the areas of *polygons* (shapes with straight sides) on the geoboard. There is a relationship between the number of nails inside the shape, the number of nails touching the rubber band, and the area. Some examples are presented in Figures 4.40, 4.41, and 4.42.

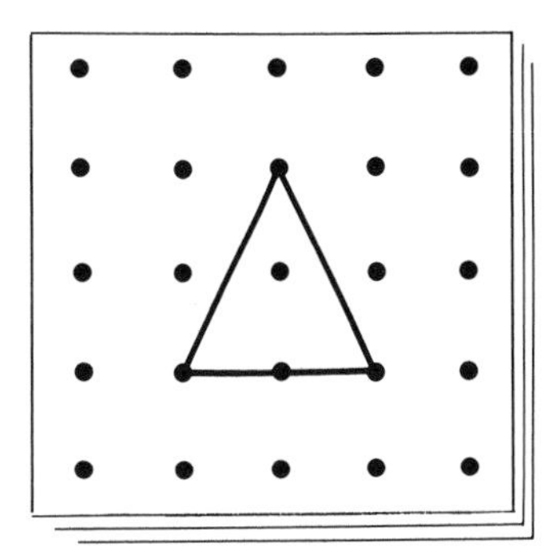

Figure 4.40 This shape has four nails touching the rubber band and one nail inside.

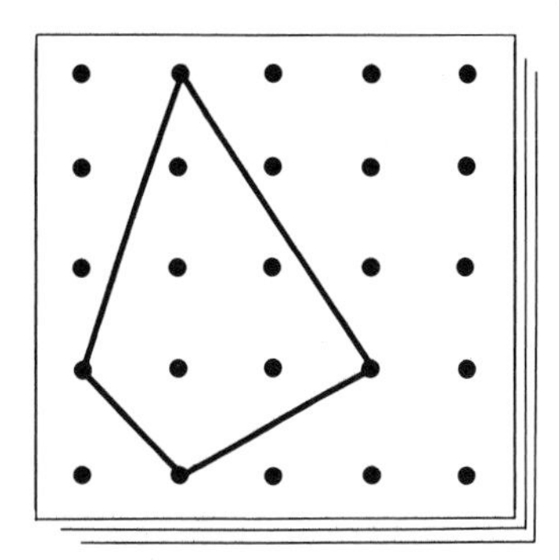

Figure 4.41 This shape has four nails touching and five nails inside.

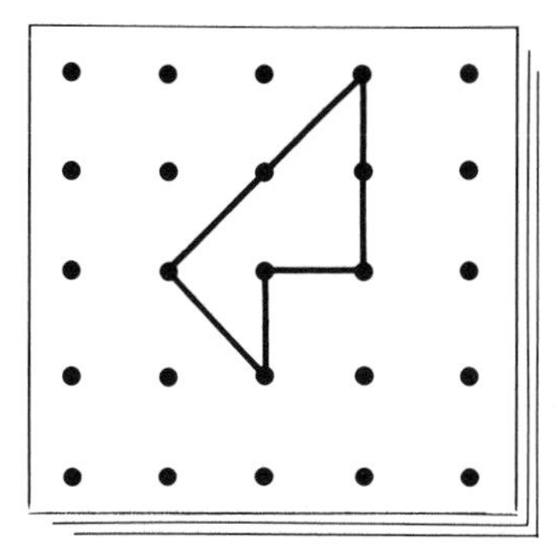

Figure 4.42 This shape has seven nails touching and zero nails inside.

Worksheet 4.18

Make several shapes with no nails inside and three nails touching. Record the area. Next make shapes with four nails touching, and then with five nails touching. Fill in the rest of the first table. Do the same for the other tables. Do you see a pattern? Can you discover a rule for finding the area for each table?

1. Zero Nails Inside

Touching	Area
3	______
4	______
5	______
6	______
7	______
•	
•	
•	
10	______
T	$T \div 2 - 1$

Describe the rule in words:
Divide the number of
nails touching by 2,
then subtract 1.

2. One Nail Inside

Touching	Area
3	______
4	______
5	______
6	______
7	______
•	
•	
•	
10	______
T	______

Describe the rule in words:

____

____

____

Use your rules to answer these questions about shapes that cannot fit on the geoboard.

3. What is the area of a shape that has:

a. 0 nails inside and 56 nails touching? ____________

b. 0 nails inside and 100 nails touching? ____________

c. 1 nail inside and 68 nails touching? ____________

d. 1 nail inside and 100 nails touching? ____________

(continued)

4. Two Nails Inside

Touching	Area
3	______
4	______
5	______
6	______
•	
•	
•	
10	______
T	______

Describe the rule in words:

____

____

____

5. Three Nails Inside

Touching	Area
3	______
4	______
5	______
6	______
•	
•	
•	
10	______
T	______

Describe the rule in words:

____

____

____

6. What is the area of a shape that has:

a. 2 nails inside and 74 nails touching? ________

b. 2 nails inside and 100 nails touching? ________

c. 3 nails inside and 54 nails touching? ________

d. 3 nails inside and 100 nails touching? ________

Worksheet 4.19

This chart consolidates the information from Worksheet 4.18. Fill in all the blanks. Make the shapes on the geoboard to help you. Are there patterns to help? Can you state a general rule?

Nails Touching

Nails Inside	3	4	5	6	7	8	9	10
0	1/2	1	1 1/2	2	2 1/2	3	3 1/2	4
1	1 1/2			3				
2	2 1/2		3 1/2					
3		4						7
4								
5								
6								
7								

Use your general rule to answer the following questions. What is the area of a shape that has:

1. 25 nails touching and 82 nails inside? ____________

2. 57 nails touching and 100 nails inside? ____________

3. T nails touching and I nails inside? ____________

VOLUME AND SURFACE AREA

For three-dimensional objects, the concepts of *volume* and *surface area* parallel the concepts of area and perimeter. Just as area fills in the region of a two-dimensional shape, volume fills in the space of a three-dimensional object, such as a box. Just as perimeter is the distance around the outside of a two-dimensional shape, surface area is the area that covers the outside of a three-dimensional shape. Imagine filling a shoe box with cubes. The number of cubes it takes to fill the box is its volume (in cubic units). The amount of paper it would take to cover the box is its surface area (in square units).

The following activities using small cubes (such as sugar cubes or wooden cubes) will help to clarify these concepts.

Build a structure using 12 cubes. Then build a different structure using another 12 cubes. One structure may be taller or wider than the other, but they both have the same volume, 12 cubic units.

Now count the square faces of the cubes that are on the outside of your structure. Mark each face with an *X* to help keep track of them. Be sure to count the faces on the bottom as well. Different structures can have different surface areas, even though they are made from the same number of cubes.

The surface area of the structure in Figure 4.43 is 18 square units. The surface area of the structure in Figure 4.44 is 16 square units. Be sure to count all six faces of your structure. Some of the *X*s don't show in the pictures. Both structures have the same volume, 4 cubic units.

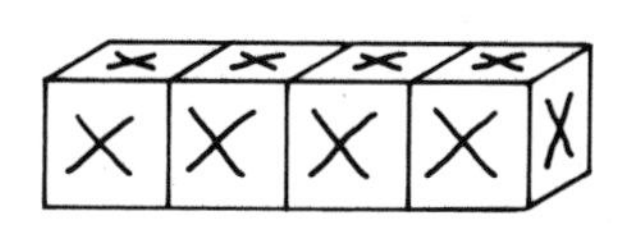

Figure 4.43

Figure 4.44

Worksheet 4.20

Make several different rectangular shapes with 24 cubes. What are the dimensions of these solids? Sketch your structures, and fill in the dimensions and surface area for each.

Shape	Length	Width	Height	Surface Area
2 × 3 × 4	2	3	4	two 2-by-4 faces = 16 sq. units two 3-by-4 faces = 24 two 2-by-3 faces = 12 Total = 52 sq. units

The volume for each of these solids is the same, 24 cubic units. Although the structures may look different, they all have the same volume.

Build as many rectangular structures as you can with 8 cubes. Which shape has the largest surface area? __________ Which shape has the smallest surface area? __________ Build rectangular structures with 27 cubes. Which one has the largest surface area? __________ Which has the smallest surface area? __________

Note that a cube is the shape with the smallest surface area for these examples. If we built structures with 20 or 24 cubes, we could not build a cube shape; the most compact structure would be the one with the smallest surface area.

A structure with dimensions 2 by 2 by 2 has a volume of 8 cubic units. A shape with dimensions of 3 by 3 by 3 has a volume of 27 cubic units. Both 8 and 27 are called *cubic numbers*. Name the next three cubic numbers: ______, ______, ______.

Square numbers and cubic numbers can be written using *exponents*. A square that has dimensions 4 by 4 is written as 4×4, or 4^2. We read 4^2 as "4 squared." A cube with dimensions 5 by 5 by 5 is written as $5 \times 5 \times 5$, or 5^3. This is read as "5 cubed."

Worksheet 4.21

Find the surface area and volume of the following structures. Build the structures with cubes. Sketch in lines to show the individual cubes.

	Volume	Surface Area
1.	__________	__________
2.	__________	__________
3.	__________	__________
4.	__________	__________

1.

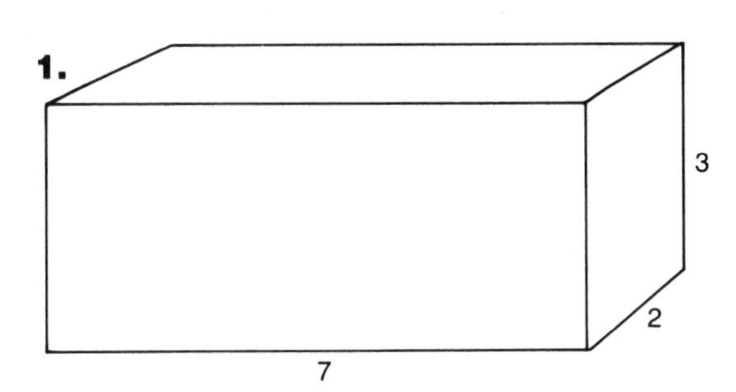

2.

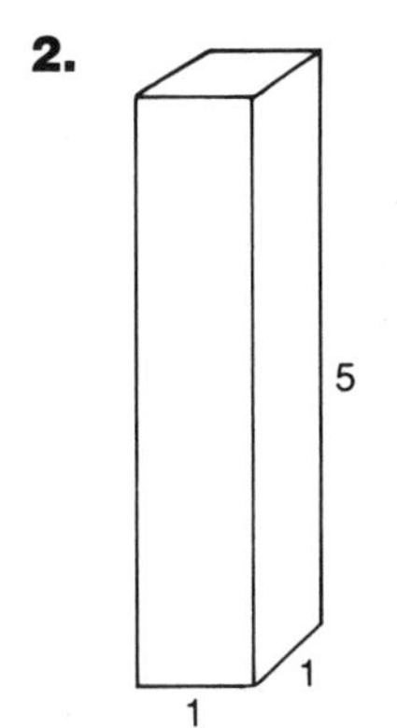

3.

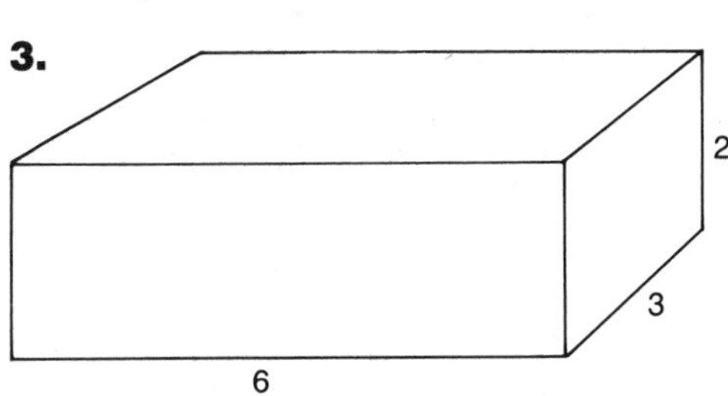

4.

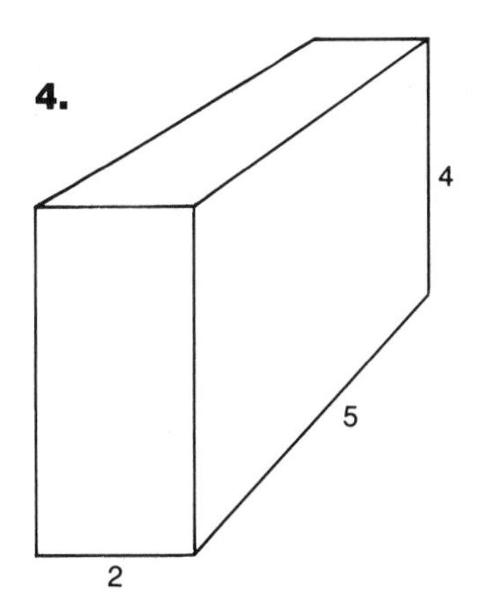

Worksheet 4.22

Sketch and then build these structures. Find their volumes and surface areas.

Length/Width/Height	Sketch	Volume	Surface Area
1. 3 2 4			
2. 1 4 3			
3. 5 2 3			
4. 2 4 2			
5. 3 3 3			

APPLICATIONS

The concepts in this chapter have many practical uses. As a consumer, you can apply them to a variety of situations. Can you figure out what size of rug will fit into a room? Do you know how much fencing to buy? How many rolls of wallpaper or cans of paint will you need to redecorate your living room? How much will it cost for cement to resurface your driveway? "Which is the better buy?" is a question we ask ourselves every day, and answering this question requires real problem-solving skills.

One important strategy for attacking these problems is to draw sketches that illustrate the given information. Often these drawings will help to put the whole problem into proper perspective and bring you closer to the solution.

PROBLEM: *Joanne wants to put new tile on her kitchen floor, which is sketched in Figure 4.45.*

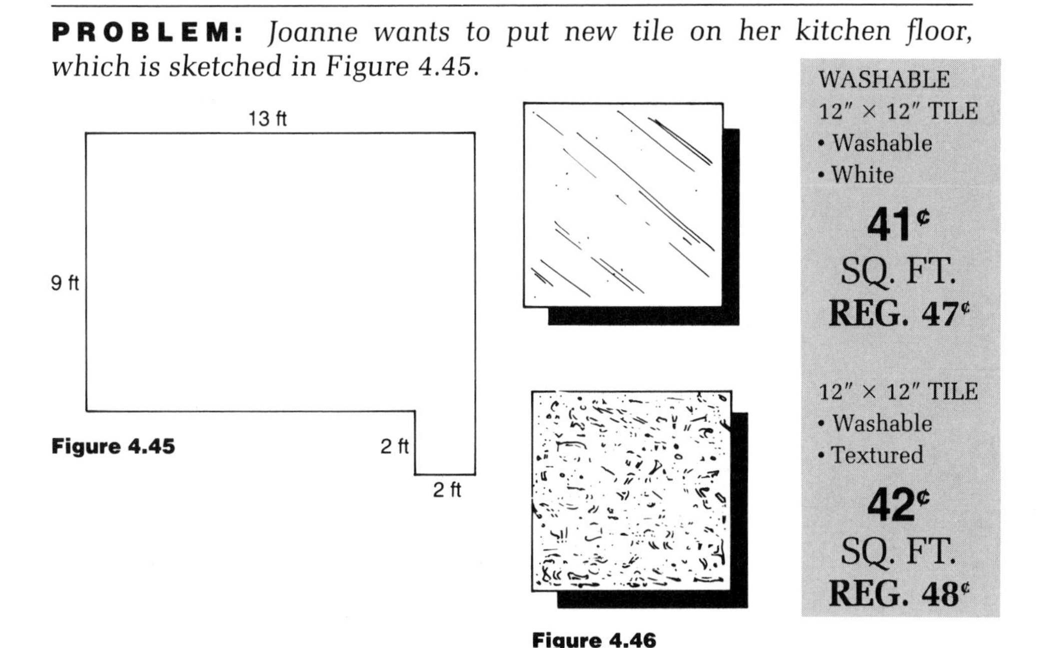

Figure 4.45

Figure 4.46

To find out how many tiles she needs (as advertised in Figure 4.46), we need to find the area of her kitchen.

The kitchen can be thought of as a 9-by-13-foot rectangle plus a 2-by-2-foot square. The total area is 117 square feet plus 4 square feet, or 121 square feet. Since each tile is 12 inches by 12 inches, or 1 square foot, she needs 121 tiles.

If she buys the washable white tiles, she saves $0.06 on every tile from the regular price, for a total of 121 × $0.06, or $7.26. How much will she save from the regular price if she buys the washable textured tiles?

How much will she save if she buys the washable white instead of the textured tiles?

Worksheet 4.23

Solve these problems.

1. Fencing a Yard

a. How many rolls of split bamboo fencing would you need to buy to enclose a rectangular yard that is 24 feet long by 17 feet wide?

b. How much would this fencing cost?

c. How much would it cost to use the galvanized wire fencing instead?

Galvanized Wire Fence

2″ x 4″ mesh. 36″ high. Save on all your fencing needs.

13[95]

25′ Roll

Split Bamboo Fencing

Split bamboo adds decorative accent to patios and gardens. Adds privacy and wind protection.

5[95]

6′ x 15′

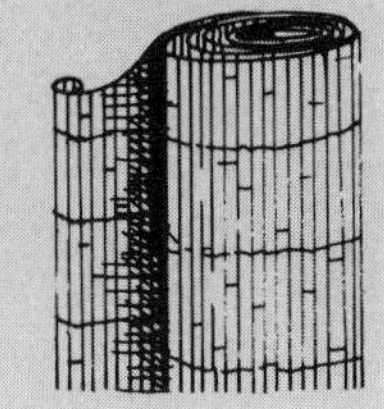

2. Painting a Room

a. How much would it cost to paint a room (four walls and the ceiling) with Scrape-Less if you want a thick coat of paint? The size of your room is 12 feet by 15 feet by 9 feet.

b. How much would you save if you used a thin coat of paint instead?

Scrape-Less Acrylic Paint

Add a deep, stucco-like texture to your walls that you can't get with paint. Dover White. Great crack filler.
Thin coat covers 60 Sq. Ft.
Thick coat covers 20 Sq. Ft.

12[99]

2-Gal. pail

3. Filling Some Planters

a. How many cubic feet of gravel are there in a cubic yard?

b. How many cubic centimeters of compost are there in a cubic meter? (There are 100 centimeters in a meter.)

c. How many cubic inches of soil are there in a cubic foot?

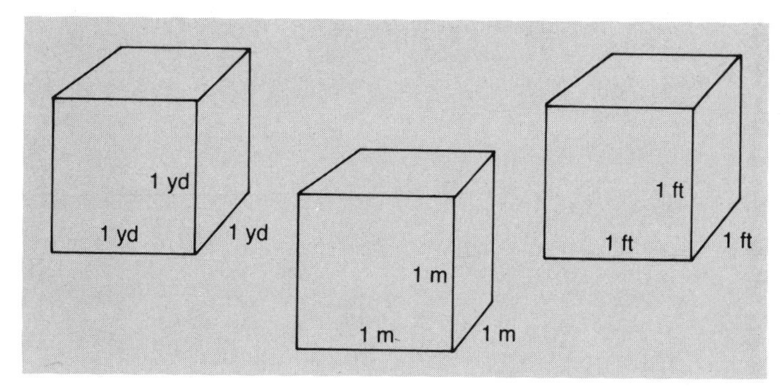

Suppose you have three window boxes that are each 28 inches long by 10 inches wide by 9 inches deep. You need to fill them with soil to a height of 6 inches.

d. How much Ferti-Soil do you need to buy?

e. How much will it cost?

f. How much do you save by buying the large size?

Ferti-Soil

Ready to use!—a complete growing medium for indoor or outdoor use. Steam sterilized.

6.79 2 Cu. Ft

3.79 1 Cu. Ft

FERTI SOIL

The field of real estate also uses the concepts of area and perimeter. Here is an example of a problem that was adapted from a real estate course manual.

PROBLEM: *If a rectangular lot with a 34-foot frontage contains 1870 square feet, how many feet deep (long) is it? (A sketch for this problem is illustrated in Figure 4.47.)*

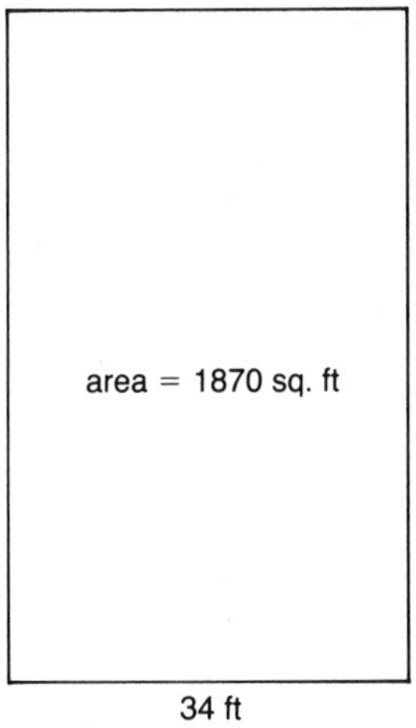

area = 1870 sq. ft

34 ft

Figure 4.47

We know that the frontage, or width, of the lot is 34 feet and the area is 1870 square feet. Since length times width equals area, we know that $34 \times ? = 1870$. Dividing 1870 by 34 will give us the answer for the depth of the lot.

Worksheet 4.24

Make a sketch to help you solve these problems.

1. A rectangular lot is valued at $6.50 per square meter. The lot is 300 meters deep (long) and is sold for its value of $200,000. Often property value is expressed per foot of frontage (front width). How would you value this lot by its frontage?

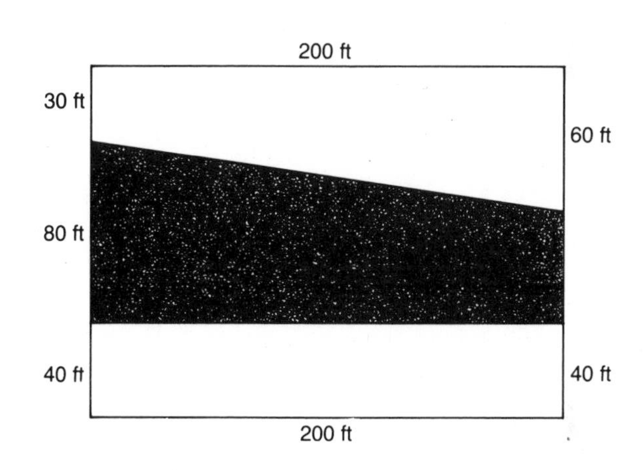

2. What is the area of the shaded region in the diagram? Apply your geoboard experiences to this problem, and try to solve it in more than one way.

3. About how wide is a road that is 1 mile long and contains 3 acres of area? (Hint: there are 43,560 square feet in an acre and 5,280 feet in a mile.)

4. What is the approximate square footage of the house in the sketch?

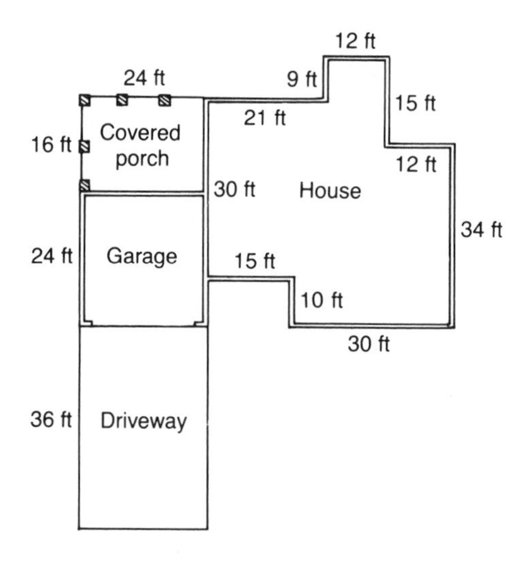

5. If concrete costs $13.00 per cubic yard, how much would you pay to put concrete 4 inches deep in the driveway?

6. How much would it cost to tile the covered porch?

a. With vinyl tiles? ____________

b. With brick tiles? ____________

c. How much more would it cost to use the oak parquet instead of the brick tiles?

____

Commercial Grade
Extra Thick
Vinyl Tiles **69¢**

⅛″ extra thick 12″ x 12″ commercial grade tile in a famous pattern. Its extra thickness will provide longer-lasting floor. In beige color. Excellent Buy!

Best!
Brick Tiles **1 09**

The sunny floor that shines without waxing! Rich embossed surface maintains its high gloss indefinitely. Every time you mop it—it looks just-waxed! Self-adhesive—12″ x 12″.

Special Purchase!
Grade 'A' Pre-Finished Oak Parquet
- *Smooth Finish*
- *Texture Finish*

1 79 Sq. Ft.

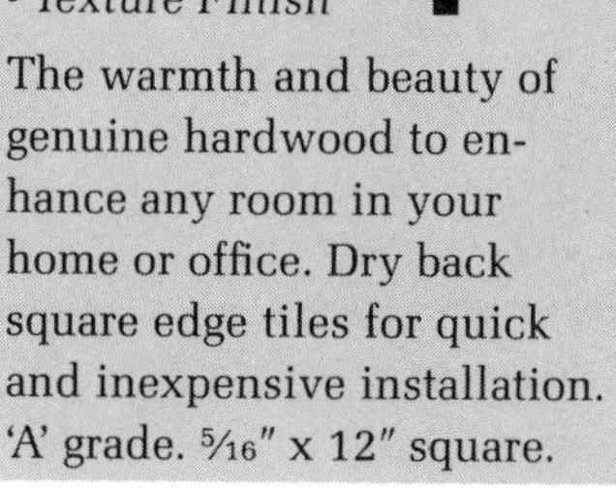

The warmth and beauty of genuine hardwood to enhance any room in your home or office. Dry back square edge tiles for quick and inexpensive installation. 'A' grade. 5⁄16″ x 12″ square.

CHAPTER Five

Word Problems

As you have already seen, many different approaches can be used for solving problems. In fact, the same problem can often be solved in a variety of ways. In other chapters we use such techniques as looking for patterns, making lists, and making tables or charts.

In this chapter, we emphasize drawing pictures and using guessing as techniques to organize the information given in word problems. These techniques are very important but are often avoided. Perhaps people do not want to learn them because of their experimental nature or because of the possibility of making a wrong guess. As you work on the problems in the first sections, you may wish to remember the following advice: "Draw a picture and write down everything you know." This quote from the father of one of the authors has stood her in good stead through the years.

USING PICTURES

The first few problems will demonstrate how to get a handle on the information in a word problem by organizing it in a sketch and writing down what you know.

PROBLEM 1: *The Interstate Highway runs due east and west. The town of Concord is 200 miles west of Hillsdale. Lafayette is 40 miles west of Hillsdale. Bowling Green is 60 miles east of Concord. How far is Bowling Green from Lafayette?*

How do you react when you read this problem? Do all your thinking processes cease? Do you look at the problem and decide to add because there are so many numbers?

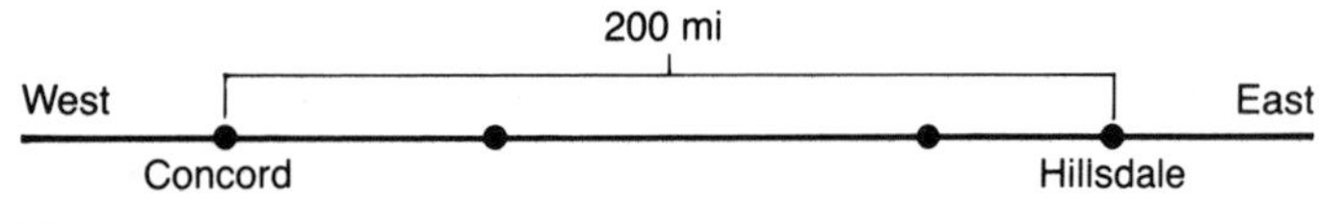

Figure 5.1

This problem is not an easy one to keep track of in your mind. To help, we will make a picture of the information. Make a sketch of your own as you follow along in the book. (See Figure 5.1.) First, we are told that Concord is 200 miles west of Hillsdale. Label Concord and Hillsdale on your sketch, and note the distance between them.

Next, in Figure 5.2, we fill in Lafayette and its distance from Hillsdale. Then we locate Bowling Green according to its distance from Concord.

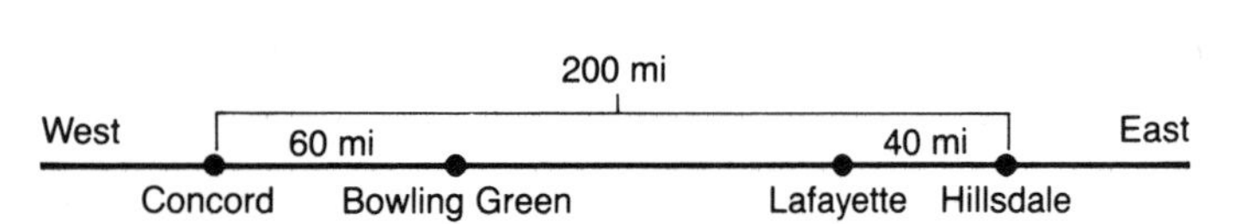

Figure 5.2

How can we find the missing distance from Bowling Green to Lafayette? We subtract both 60 and 40 miles from 200 miles, leaving 100 miles.

Here is a similar problem for you to try on your own. Use Figure 5.3 to make a sketch.

North

South

Figure 5.3

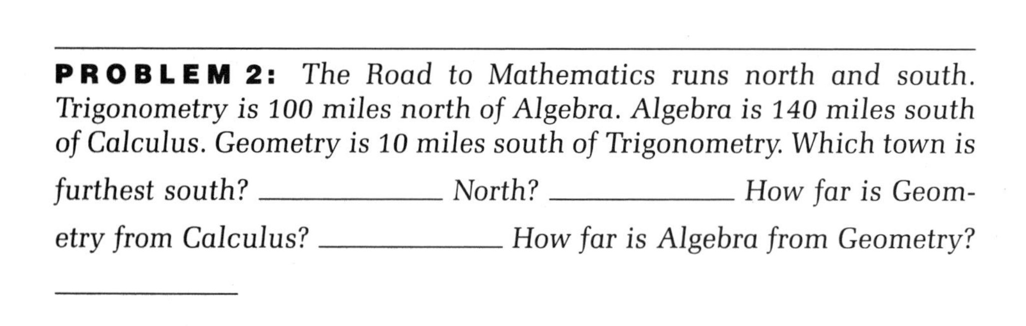

PROBLEM 2: *The Road to Mathematics runs north and south. Trigonometry is 100 miles north of Algebra. Algebra is 140 miles south of Calculus. Geometry is 10 miles south of Trigonometry. Which town is furthest south?* __________ *North?* __________ *How far is Geometry from Calculus?* __________ *How far is Algebra from Geometry?* __________

The next two problems also involve finding a position in space.

PROBLEM 3: *In the Tug-of-War Game, there is only one marker for two players to use. The marker is placed in the start box on the board in Figure 5.4. The first player, Anne, rolls a die and moves the marker the corresponding number of places to the right. The second player, George, rolls a die and moves the marker the corresponding number of places to the left. The first player to move off the board wins.*

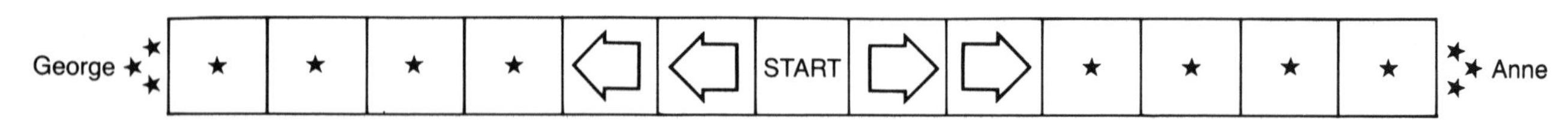

Figure 5.4

Round	Anne	George
1	2	4
2	3	1
3	6	5
4	1	4
5	1	3

Table 5.1

Look at the record of rolls in Table 5.1

Has anyone won yet? ____________

After which round was the marker closer to Anne? ____________

To George? ____________

Who was closer to winning after five rounds? ____________

Who do you think will win? ____________

Why? ______________________________

____

In a children's activity called a Penny Hike, you start to walk north from a particular intersection. Whenever you come to a corner, you toss a penny: if it is heads, you turn *right* and walk to the next corner; if it is tails, you turn *left* and walk to the next corner. The game continues until you get tired.

Look at the sketch in Figure 5.5 for the sequence heads, heads, tails, tails. After this pattern, our hikers are 2 blocks east and 1 block north of their starting point.

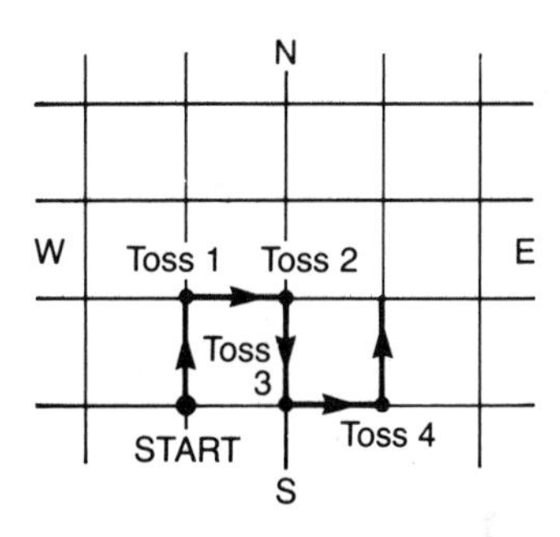

Figure 5.5

PROBLEM 4: *Use graph paper to help you find out how far east or west and north or south you would be after following the paths indicated by the sequences in Figures 5.6–5.9. (Note that it is easier to draw a picture if you turn your graph paper as you "follow the path.")*

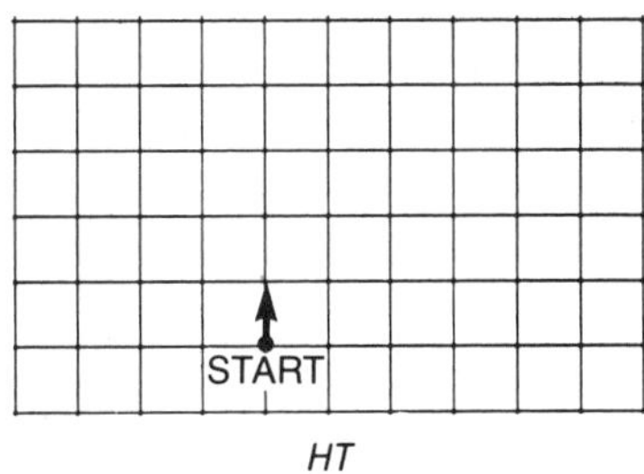

HT

Figure 5.6

START

HTHTHT

Figure 5.7

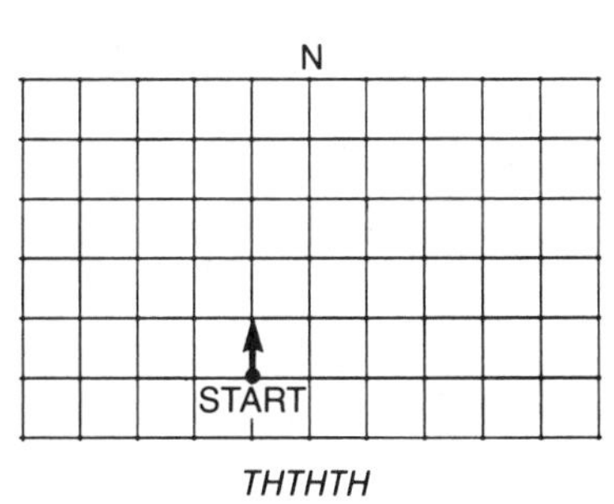

THTHTH

Figure 5.8

N

START

HHTTTTH

Figure 5.9

Write a sequence of heads and tails that will get you back to your starting point. ____________ Is there only one? ____________ If not, write another one. ____________

What is the shortest sequence that will get you back to the start? Is there just one? ____________

Write a sequence that will take you 2 blocks north and 2 blocks west of your starting point. ____________

Is there only one? ____________ What is the shortest sequence you can find to this point? ____________

If you want to get to the intersection 2 blocks east and 2 blocks south of your starting point, how many blocks, on the average, do you think you would have to walk to get there? ____________

PROBLEM 5: *Wayne is building crayfish traps. He needs 2-by-3½-foot rectangles cut from heavy wire mesh. The hardware store has a strip of mesh on sale that is 2 feet wide and 21 feet long. How many rectangles can be cut from this strip? If the store charges $1.50 for each cut, how much extra must Wayne pay to have the rectangles cut at the shop?*

The wire mesh strip is sketched in Figure 5.10.

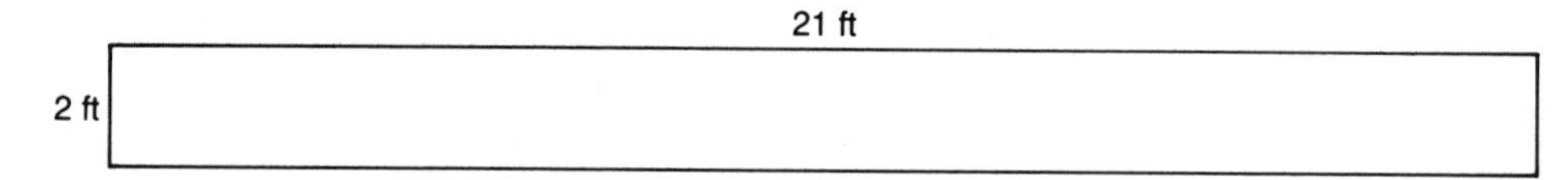

Figure 5.10

The width is just right. How many 3½-foot pieces will fit along the strip? Two 3½-foot pieces are 7 feet long; thus, three of these pairs will fit into 21 feet. Wayne can cut six rectangles from the strip. Count the cuts in Figure 5.11. Are you surprised?

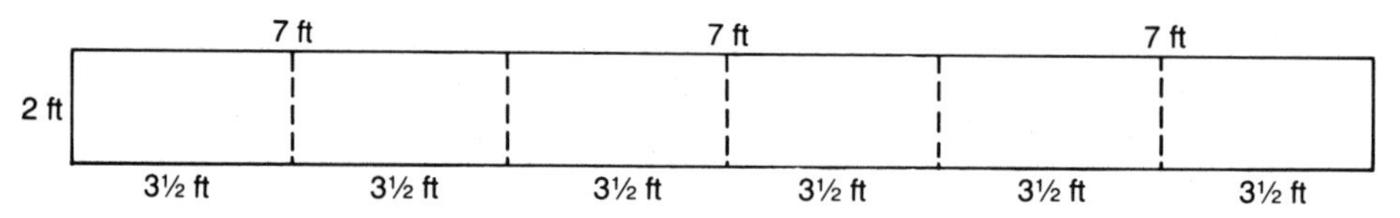

Figure 5.11

The extra cost for the five cuts will be 5 × $1.50 or $7.50.

Worksheet 5.1

Solve the following problems. Draw and label a picture or diagram to help you with each problem. Use a calculator if you wish.

1. Susan has 2 yards of special Japanese fabric that is 1 foot wide. She plans to make place mats from it.

a. Draw a picture of the material, and label the dimensions.
b. If each mat is 1 foot by 1½ feet, how many place mats can she make?
c. How many cuts will she have to make in the fabric?

2. Carol and Virginia are putting together a draft of their book to send to the publisher. They will use red construction paper for the covers and chapter dividers. So far, the book has six chapters.

How many pieces of red construction paper do they need? Draw a picture to help solve this problem.

3. The Greens are building a fence with 2½-foot posts. The lumberyard sells wood for fence posts in 15-foot lengths.

a. How many posts can they cut from one 15-foot length?
b. If the lumberyard charges $1.00 per cut, how much will it cost to have four 15-foot lengths cut into the 2½-foot posts they need?

4. The Dow Jones Average of the New York Stock Exchange dropped 9 points on Monday, from 1205 to 1196. On Tuesday it gained 22 points. On Wednesday it lost 1 point. On Thursday it gained 11 points, and on Friday it gained 6 more points. Fill in the table to help you answer the following questions. (Note that the starting average for any one day is the same as the preceding day's closing average.)

Day	Opening Average	Loss/Gain	Closing Average
Monday	1205	−9	1196
Tuesday	1196	+22	______
Wednesday	______	−1	______
Thursday	______	+11	______
Friday	______	+6	______

a. What was the closing average on Wednesday? ____________ On Friday? ____________

b. Was there an overall drop or gain for the week? ____________ Of how much? ____________

c. Which day had the highest closing? ____________ The lowest? ____________

d. Which morning would have been best for buying? ____________ For selling? ____________

(continued)

5. During another week the Dow Jones Average gained 7 points on Monday. On Tuesday it lost 20 points. On Wednesday it gained 5 points. On Thursday it gained 12 points, and on Friday it lost 3 points. Complete the table to help you answer these questions.

Day	Opening Average	Loss/Gain	Closing Average
Monday	______	+7	______
Tuesday	______	−20	______
Wednesday	______	+5	______
Thursday	______	______	______
Friday	______	______	______

a. Was there an overall gain or loss in that week?

b. Which day had the highest closing average?

____________ The lowest? ____________

c. If the opening average was 1150 on Monday, what was the closing average on Thursday? ____________

d. If the closing average on Wednesday was 978, what was the opening average on Monday? ____________

The closing average on Friday? ____________

6. Follow the rules for the Penny Hike in Problem 4. Use graph paper to find how far east or west and how far north or south you would be from your starting point after following each of the sequences below. Remember that you start by walking north 1 block and *then* toss your penny.

a. HHH **b.** TTT **c.** HHTTT **d.** HHTHHH **e.** TTTHHT

f. Write a sequence that will take you 2 blocks west and 2 blocks south of the start.

g. Write a sequence that will take you 2 blocks east and 2 blocks south of the start.

h. What is the relationship between the last two sequences?

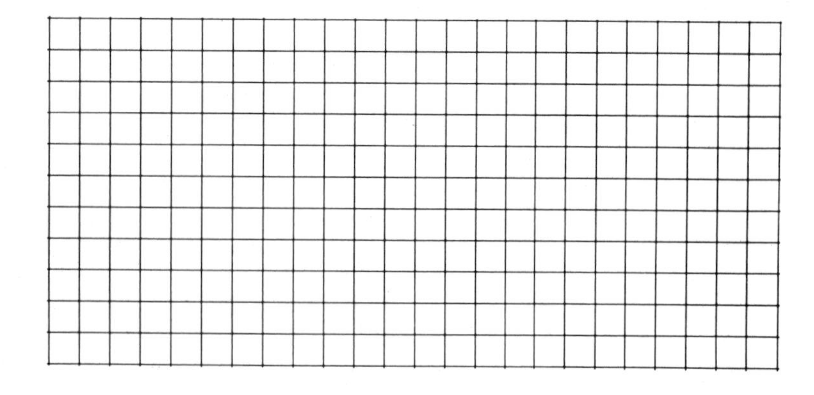

PICTURES FOR FRACTIONS

Using pictures and diagrams to solve fraction problems may seem unusual to you. You may be surprised to learn that drawing a picture often helps to reveal the answer. When thinking about problems that involve fractions, we must first establish the *whole* amount. Often what we call *one*, meaning "one whole," is very arbitrary. One-half of a tractor-trailer is much larger than one-half of a compact car, yet the meaning of *one-half* remains the same. The truck and the car are of quite different sizes, yet both represent one whole.

Pictures will help you solve the following problems. Rectangles are a good representation of the *one whole* because they are easy to draw.

PROBLEM 6: *If ¾ pound of sweet butter costs $1.80, how much does the whole pound cost?*

We start by drawing a picture of 1 pound (the one whole) and separate it into fourths (4⁄4, or four-fourths, equals one whole). (Figure 5.12). We know that each equal section, or fourth, must cost the same amount. Since three-fourths (¾) of a pound costs $1.80, then each one-fourth (¼) must cost $0.60. The whole pound of butter is made up of four-fourths, each costing $0.60. Thus, the whole pound costs $2.40.

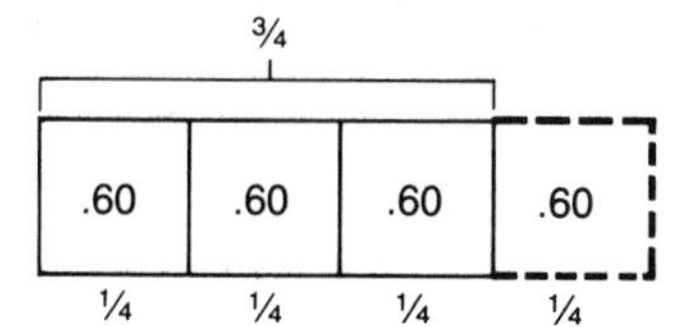

Figure 5.12

Here are some problems for you to try. Think about the information in each problem. Often, with a minimum of computation you'll *see* the answer.

PROBLEM 7: *If ⅗ box of chocolate costs $4.50, how much does the whole box cost?*

First draw the whole box (Figure 5.13). Then divide it into fifths. How much does one-fifth of the box cost, if three-fifths costs $4.50? ____________

How much does the whole (5⁄5) cost? ____________

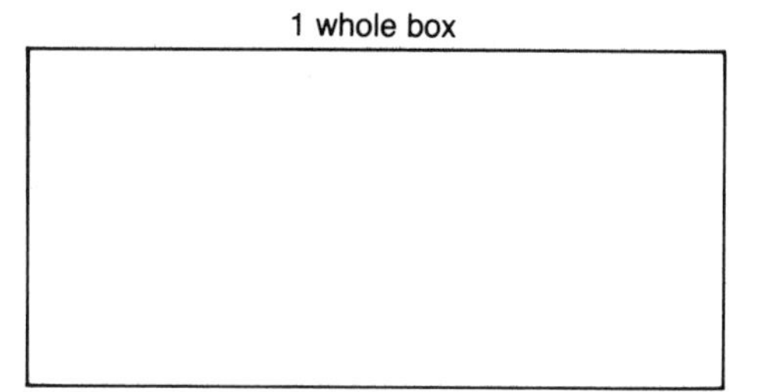

Figure 5.13

PROBLEM 8: *What is the price of walnuts per pound, if ⅔ pound costs $1.40?*

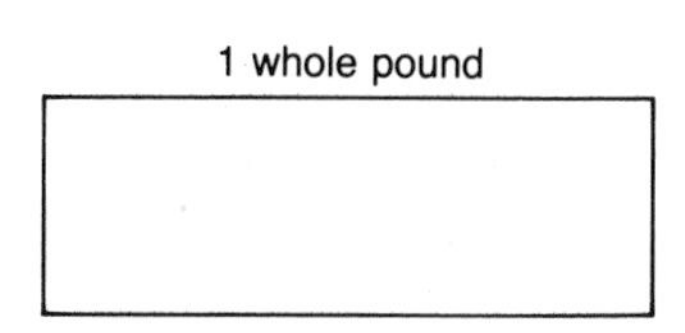

Figure 5.14

Pictures can often help to solve problems about profits, sale prices, and original prices.

PROBLEM 9: *Harold bought a suit at a ¼-off sale. If he paid $120 for the suit, what was the original price?*

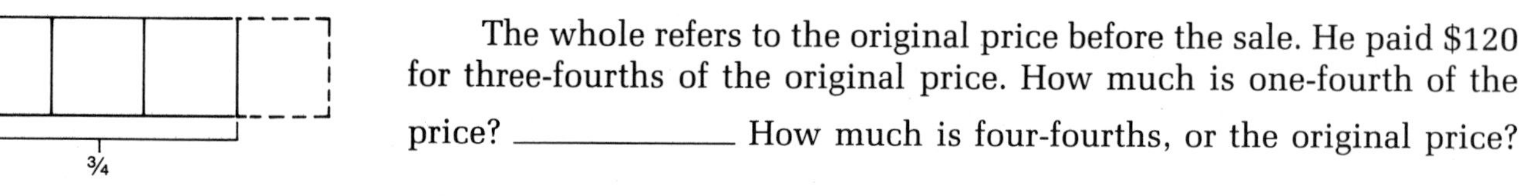

Figure 5.15

The whole refers to the original price before the sale. He paid $120 for three-fourths of the original price. How much is one-fourth of the price? ____________ How much is four-fourths, or the original price? ____________

Worksheet 5.2

Draw pictures to help you solve these problems.

1. If $\frac{5}{6}$ bag of potting soil weighs 10 pounds, how much does the whole bag weigh?

2. After 18 walnuts were used to bake some brownies, $\frac{3}{4}$ package was left. About how many walnuts does the package hold?

3. The pickle barrel was $\frac{2}{3}$ full. After 23 pickles were sold, it was $\frac{1}{3}$ full. About how many pickles does the barrel hold?

4. If $1\frac{1}{2}$ pounds of nails cost $1.74, how much does 1 pound cost?

5. Alice bought a pair of cross-country skis for $90 at a $\frac{1}{4}$-off sale. What was the original price?

PICTURES FOR ALGEBRA

Pictures can be used to solve some algebra problems. Here is part of an algebraic word problem.

PROBLEM 10: *Mary's investment earned four times as much as Peter's.*

What do we know so far? Whose investment earned the least? Peter's. We will draw a box to represent Peter's earnings: ☐ To represent Mary's earnings, we need to draw four boxes the same size as Peter's, as in Figure 5.16.

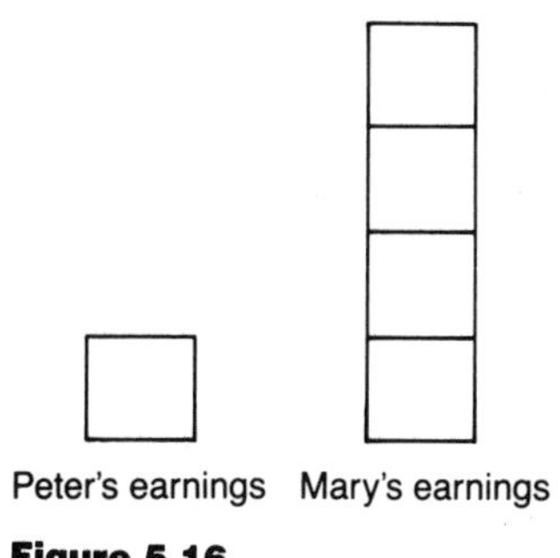

Figure 5.16

Here is the next part of the problem:

In June, the total of their earnings was $350. How much did they each earn?

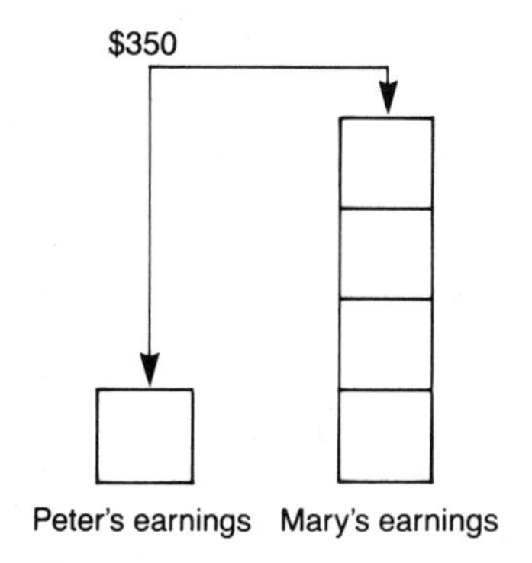

Figure 5.17

The sketch in Figure 5.17 represents all of our knowledge. Altogether there are five *equal-sized* boxes—and we know that their earnings total $350. Writing $350 over the drawing will help you keep the total in mind. How much of the earnings are represented by one box? We find this by dividing the total $350 by 5 (the number of boxes) and obtaining an answer of $70 for each box in the sketch. Write $70 in each box. How much did Peter earn? ____________ How much did Mary earn? ____________

PROBLEM 11: *Helen has three times as many math books as literature books.*

Which type of book does she have the least of? ____________ If we draw a box to represent those books, how many boxes do we need to draw to represent the others? ____________ Draw a sketch to represent Helen's books. Label the math books and the literature books.

Altogether she has 128 books. How many literature books does she have? How many math books does she have?

Write the total number of books over your sketch, and find the answers.

Here is the beginning of another problem:

PROBLEM 12: *John has half as many music tapes as Clyde.*

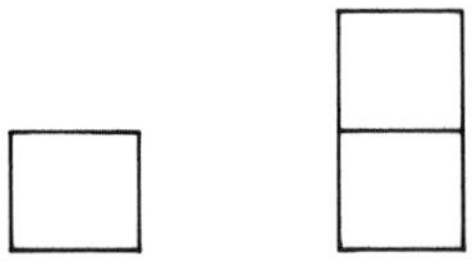

John's tapes Clyde's tapes

Figure 5.18

How can we represent their tapes in a picture? Who has the fewest tapes? John. If we draw one box to represent John's tapes, how many should we draw for Clyde's? ____________

The rest of the problem states:

Altogether the men have 33 tapes. How many does each man have?

Write the total number of tapes over the drawing. This time we have three boxes for 33 tapes. When we label the boxes, we find that John has 11 tapes and Clyde has 22.

Here is the first part of another type of problem:

PROBLEM 13: *Jan has 4 more golf balls than Betty.*

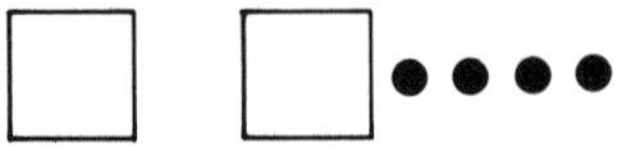

Betty's golf balls Jan's golf balls

Figure 5.19

Who has the smaller number of golf balls? We draw a box to represent Betty's golf balls: □. For Jan, we draw a box and 4 loose balls: □ ●●●●

Here is the rest of the problem:

Altogether the women have 28 golf balls. How many golf balls does Betty have? How many golf balls does Jan have?

To solve this problem, we need to find the number of golf balls in the boxes. Of the 28 balls, 4 are not in either box. That leaves 24 golf balls to be divided evenly between the two boxes in the picture; that is, 12 in each box. We write 12 in each box, and we can see from the sketch in Figure 5.19 that Betty has 12 balls and Jan has 12 + 4, or 16 balls.

PROBLEM 14: *Laura is 5 years younger than Joan.*

Laura's age Joan's age

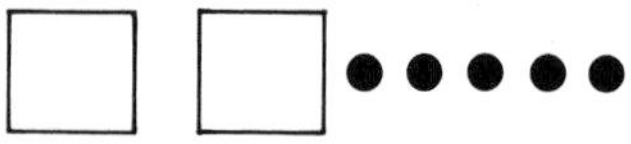

Figure 5.20

Before we draw a picture, we have to ask who is younger. Here is a sketch that depicts Laura's and Joan's ages. Note that, even though age is abstract, we can still use a box to represent Laura's unknown age.

If we say Laura is 5 years younger than Joan, that is equivalent to saying that Joan is 5 years older than Laura—and that is what our drawing illustrates.

The rest of the problem says:

The total of their ages is 65 years. How old is each woman?

If we subtract the extra 5 years from the total of 65, how many are left to put in each box? Write that number in the boxes. We can easily see now that Laura is 30 years old and Joan is 35.

PROBLEM 15: *The sum of three consecutive numbers is 66. Find the numbers.*

First, what does *consecutive* mean? The dictionary says, "following one another in order," like 4, 5, 6.

How can we draw a picture to represent our three consecutive numbers? If we draw a box for the smallest of the numbers, we draw a box "plus one" for the middle number and a box "plus one plus one" for the largest of the three numbers, as in Figure 5.21.

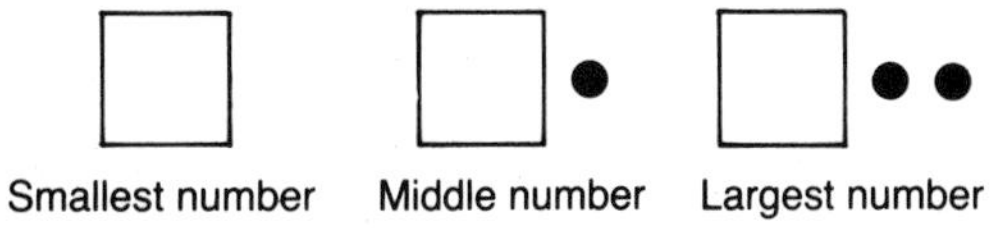

□   □ ●   □ ● ●

Smallest number   Middle number   Largest number

Figure 5.21

If we subtract three ones from 66, how much would each box represent? What are the three consecutive numbers?

You may have noticed that in all of the problems in this section we have used a box to represent the smallest number we are looking for. If we know that Jessica has three more raisins than peanuts, it is easy to draw a box □ to represent the peanuts and a box with three small circles □ ● ● ● to represent the raisins. However, it would be much harder to draw a box for the raisins and a box missing three peanuts for the peanuts.

A similar difficulty occurs in the problem that states that Greg has three times as many dimes as quarters. It is quite easy, on the one hand, to draw one box □ to represent the quarters and three boxes □ □ □ to represent the dimes. But if we start by drawing one box for the dimes, we would have to draw one-third of a box for the quarters, which could lead to errors or, at the least, to considerably harder arithmetic when we try to find the answer.

In the worksheets that follow, determine which quantity is the smallest, and use one box to represent that in your drawing. Be sure to label your drawings.

Worksheet 5.3

Solve these problems, drawing a picture for each one. Use a calculator if you wish.

1. A board 21 feet long is cut into two pieces. One piece is 5 feet longer than the other. How long is each piece?

2. A certain number is 6 more than another number. Their sum is 42. Find the numbers.

3. A certain number is 6 times as big as another number. Their sum is 42. Find the numbers.

4. A notebook costs $1.50 more than a pencil. Together they cost $2.10. How much does the pencil cost?

(continued)

5. The sum of four consecutive numbers is 50. Find the numbers. Remember that *consecutive* means "following one another in order."

6. At the Mendocino County Fair, Jane won twice as many ribbons as Kris. Kris won twice as many ribbons as Elizabeth. Together the women won 196 ribbons. How many ribbons did each woman win?

7. A jacket costs three times the price of a pair of shoes, and a shirt costs half the price of the shoes. Altogether these three items cost $180. How much does each item cost?

8. At the Las Flores Cafeteria, a burrito with extra cheese costs 30 cents more than a plain burrito; and a plain burrito costs three times as much as milk. For lunch with a friend, John spent $4.30 on a plain burrito, a burrito with extra cheese, and two milks. How much did each item cost? (Hint: which item cost the least?)

Worksheet 5.4

Solve these problems. Use a calculator if you wish.

1. Two numbers differ by 5. (This means that one number is 5 more than the other.) Their sum is 55.

a. Draw and label a picture to represent this information.

b. Find the two numbers.

2. The sum of two numbers is 55. The smaller number divides the larger evenly, with an answer (quotient) of 10. (In other words, the larger number is 10 times as big as the smaller.)

a. Draw and label a picture to represent this information.

b. Find the two numbers.

3. The Lopez family lives on a triangular plot of land with a perimeter of 180 feet. The first side of their lot is 10 feet *shorter* than the second side. The third side is 10 feet *longer* than the second side.

a. Which side is the shortest?

b. How much longer is the third side than the first?

c. Draw a picture to represent the information in this problem.

d. Find the length of each side of the lot.

4. Two times a number is 4 less than 20.

a. If we use a box to represent the number in this problem, why do we need to add four circles to the picture to make the total equal to 20?

□ □ ● ● ● ●

b. What is the number?

(continued)

5. Three times a number is 5 less than 20.

a. Draw a picture to represent this information.

b. Find the number.

6. Nine times a number is 1 less than 100. What is the number?

7. Henry has six times as many rock records as classical records. He has 16 more jazz records than classical records. Altogether he has 96 records.

a. Draw a picture to represent his record collection.

b. How many records does he have of each type?

8. A number is added to 4. The *total* is multiplied by 3, giving a result of 33.

a. Draw a picture to represent the information in the first sentence of this problem.

b. Draw a picture to represent the information in the second sentence.

c. Find the number.

9. Make up a problem, check it, and give it to a partner to solve.

TRANSLATING WORDS AND NUMBERS

One important skill in solving word problems is translating words or phrases into mathematical symbols. Let's look at some phrases.

"Four more than five" can be written as "$5 + 4$."

"Six less than 11" translates to "$11 - 6$."

"Twice as large as six" is "2×6."

"Twice the sum of five plus three" is "$2 \times (5 + 3)$."

For the last phrase we need to use parentheses. Without them, the translation would read "$2 \times 5 + 3$." Because of the order of operations, the 2×5 would be multiplied before the 3 is added on, giving us an incorrect answer.

"One-half of ten" can be written in two ways, as a multiplication problem, "$\frac{1}{2} \times 10$," or as a division problem, "$\frac{10}{2}$" or "$10 \div 2$."

Worksheet 5.5

Translate the phrases into mathematical expressions, then translate the mathematical expressions into phrases.

	Phrase	Mathematical Expression
1.	Eight less than twelve	____________
2.	Five more than thirteen	____________
3.	Three times as large as five	____________
4.	Twice the sum of seven plus two	____________
5.	The product of four and three	____________
6.	Twelve divided by the sum of five plus three	____________
7.	One-fifth of thirty	____________
8.	Five less than the sum of eight and ten	____________
9.	Five more than the product of five and four	____________
10.	Five less than the result of dividing twenty by four	____________
11.	____________	$14 + 23$
12.	____________	7×5
13.	____________	$20 - 7$
14.	____________	$\frac{1}{3} \times 15$
15.	____________	$(10 - 3) + 5$
16.	____________	$(8 + 6) - 7$
17.	____________	$\frac{18}{(2 \times 3)}$
18.	____________	$36 \div (5 + 4)$

Worksheet 5.6

Solve these problems.

1. Sue's age is 5 years *less than* Ann's age.
a. If Sue is 35, how old is Ann?
b. If Sue is 15, how old is Ann?
c. If Sue is 42, how old is Ann?
d. If Ann is 36, how old is Sue?

2. Paul's income is $2,500 *less than* Mary's income.
a. If Paul makes $8,000, how much does Mary earn?
b. If Paul makes $20,000, how much does Mary make?
c. If Paul makes $13,500, what is Mary's salary?
d. If Mary makes $25,000, what does Paul earn?

3. Diane's income is $2,000 *less than* Ted's.
a. If Diane earns $17,000, how much does Ted earn?
b. If Diane earns $32,000, how much is Ted's income?
c. If Ted's income is $13,000, how much is Diane's?

4. Bill's income today is $3,000 more than it was two years ago.
a. If he makes $27,000 now, what did he make then?
b. If he makes $19,000 now, what did he make then?
c. If he made $15,000 two years ago, what does he make now?
d. If he made $32,000 two years ago, what does he make now?

5. Angela's age is three times *more than* Robert's age.
a. If Robert is 17, how old is Angela?
b. If Robert is 25, how old is Angela?
c. If Angela is 24, how old is Robert?
d. If Angela is 48, how old is Robert?

6. Peter's salary is exactly *half* of David's.
a. If Peter earns $800, how much does David earn?
b. If Peter earns $1,200, how much does David earn?
c. If David earns $14,000, how much does Peter earn?
d. If David earns $20,000, how much does Peter earn?

GUESS CHARTS

Guessing is a very valuable strategy for solving problems. Most people don't like to get wrong answers. Unless we're unusually lucky, we probably won't ever get the correct answer on our first try. But even an incorrect guess provides useful information that brings us much closer to the solution. Many types of algebra problems can be solved by guessing techniques without even writing an equation. In this section we will learn how to solve algebra problems by organizing the information and our guesses on a chart. In the next section we will learn how to make algebraic equations from these charts.

Here is the first part of a problem:

PROBLEM 16: *Susan has 3 more blouses than skirts.*

First, we'll record our information and our guesses in Table 5.2.

Guess 1: 14 blouses

If Susan has 14 blouses, how can we find out how many skirts she has? We would subtract 3 from 14.

Guess 2: 20 blouses

If she has 20 blouses, how many skirts does she have?

Make three more guesses for blouses, and fill in the guess chart.

Blouses	Skirts
14	11
20	______
______	______
______	______
______	______

Table 5.2

Now we're ready for the next part of the problem:

She has a total of 17 blouses and skirts. How many blouses does she have?

With this new information, how do we check to see if one of our guesses is right? The total number of blouses and skirts needs to be 17. Let's add a *total* column to our chart and check the totals.

Do any of the guesses give a total of 17? If so, then you can read the number of blouses from the chart. If not, which total is closest to 17? Is it larger or smaller than 17? Make some more guesses until your total is 17.

Blouses	Skirts	(17) Total
14	11	25
20	17	37
______	______	______
______	______	______
______	______	______

Table 5.3

Here is another, similar problem. The first part of it states:

PROBLEM 17: *Melissa is 5 years older than Nancy.*

Fill in Table 5.4. This time, let's guess Nancy's age.
Guess 1: Nancy is 8 years old. If Nancy is 8, how can you find Melissa's age?
Guess 2: Nancy is 20 years old. What is Melissa's age?
Make three more guesses of Nancy's age, and fill in the chart.

Melissa	Nancy
______	8
______	20
______	______
______	______
______	______

Table 5.4

The rest of the problem states:

The total of their ages is 51. How old is Melissa?

We need to add a *total* column and fill in our information on Table 5.5.

Do you have a total of 51? If so, read Melissa's age directly from the chart.

Do you have a total close to 51? Is it greater or less than 51? Take a few more guesses until your total is 51.

Melissa	Nancy	(51) Total
13	8	21
25	20	45
______	______	______
______	______	______
______	______	______

Table 5.5

Both problems have a similar structure. In the first, we started by guessing the number of blouses, the larger number. In the second, we started by guessing the smaller number, Nancy's age. Did you find it harder or easier to guess one rather than the other? If you can tell which number is smaller, it's usually easier to start your guesses with that number. But it doesn't really matter which column you guess first. Either will lead you in the right direction.

PROBLEM 18: *One number is 27 more than another. When you multiply both numbers, the product is 238. What are the numbers?*

Fill in the guess chart in Table 5.6. Make a first guess. If you don't know what to guess, try 10. It's an easy number to work with.

Guess 1: The first number is 10.

First Number	Second Number	Product
10	______	______
______	______	______
______	______	______
______	______	______

Table 5.6

If the first number is 10, what is the second number? Fill in 37 on your table and then the product of 37 × 10, or 370.

Was the guess of 10 too high or too low? How do you know when you have the right numbers? Write the 238 over the product column so you will remember it. Make several more guesses and fill in the products until you find the numbers. When you have 238 in the product column, read your answers directly from the chart.

Worksheet 5.7

Make guess charts to help you solve these problems. Be sure to reread the problem question before reading your answer from the chart. You may use your calculator.

1. Jack is 4 years older than Jill. The sum of their ages is 18. How old is Jack?

Jack	Jill	Sum

2. Sara is 10 years younger than her brother Eric. The sum of their ages is 52. How old is Eric?

3. It takes three times as much material to make curtains for the living room as for the bedroom. The curtains for both rooms can be made with 16 yards of material. How much is needed for the living room?

4. The difference in price between two suits is $134. Together they cost $444. How much does each suit cost?

(continued)

5. One number is four times larger than another, and their total is 85. What are the numbers?

6. The price of a movie ticket is one-third the price of a theatre ticket. The total price for one movie ticket and one theatre ticket is $18.00. How much does the movie ticket cost?

7. One number is six times larger than another, and their difference is 60. What is the larger number?

8. The length of a rectangle is 4 inches longer than its width. If the perimeter is 28 inches, what is its width?

Let's work through a few more problems.

PROBLEM 19: *Julia opens her change purse and finds that she has twice as many nickels as dimes and three times as many pennies as dimes. Altogether she has 90 coins. How many pennies does she have?*

Start by guessing the number of dimes, since there are fewer of them.
Guess 1: 10 dimes

If there are 10 dimes, then there are 20 nickels (2 × 10) and 30 pennies (3 × 10), for a total of 60 coins in all. Is 10 too high or too low? Take several more guesses until your total is 90. Then read your answer for pennies from the table.

Nickels	Dimes	Pennies	(90) Total
20	10	30	60
______	______	______	______
______	______	______	______
______	______	______	______

Table 5.7

In this problem the *number* of coins is important, but the *value* of the coins is irrelevant. In the following coin problem we must consider the value of the coins as well.

PROBLEM 20: *Jason opens the cash register and finds that he has four times as many pennies as dimes and 16 more nickels than pennies. The value of the coins is $6.92. How many nickels does he have?*

Make a table and take a guess.
Guess 1: 10 dimes

Pennies	Dimes	Nickels
______	10	______

Table 5.8

If there are 10 dimes, then there are 40 pennies (10 × 4) and 56 nickels (40 + 16). Fill in the chart. Because we still need to use the value of the coins, we must extend our table, as in Table 5.9, on the next page.

Number of Coins			Value of Coins			($6.92)
Pennies	Dimes	Nickels	Pennies	Dimes	Nickels	Total Value
40	10	56	$0.40	$1.00	$2.80	$4.20
______	______	______	______	______	______	______
______	______	______	______	______	______	______
______	______	______	______	______	______	______

Table 5.9

Are there more or less than 10 dimes in Jason's collection? Make several more guesses, fill in your chart, and read your answer when your total value is $6.92.

Worksheet 5.8

Make guess charts to help you solve these problems. Make at least two incorrect guesses for each problem. Remember, you may use your calculator.

1. Jennifer is 4 years older than her brother Stephen. Alice is twice as old as Stephen. The sum of their ages is 34. How old is each?

2. Avocados cost twice as much as artichokes. The total cost of three avocados and five artichokes is $3.74. How much does one artichoke cost?

3. Lamb chops costs $0.79 per pound more than hamburger, and steak costs $1.20 per pound more than lamb chops. The total bill for 1 pound of each meat is $9.23. What is the price of 1 pound of steak?

4. The length of a rectangular garden is 3 feet more than twice its width. The area is 90 square feet. What are the dimensions of the garden?

(continued)

5. Nancy's change purse contains three more quarters than dimes and five fewer nickels than quarters. She has exactly $2.25 in change. How many quarters does she have?

6. In one week Cheryl ran twice as many miles as Bruce, and Deborah ran 7 miles less than Cheryl. The three ran a total of 63 miles. How many miles did Cheryl run?

7. The sum of three numbers is 149. The first is 5 less than the second. The second is 5 times the third. What are the numbers?

8. If a comb and brush together cost $2.50 and the brush costs $2.00 more than the comb, how much does the comb cost?

ALGEBRAIC EQUATIONS

One advantage of using guess charts is that it is easy to write an algebraic equation using the headings. For example, let's look again at our first guess chart problem.

PROBLEM 21: *Susan has 3 more blouses than skirts. She has a total of 17 blouses and skirts. How many blouses does she have?*

Our guess table looked like Table 5.10. If we guess that Susan has 8 blouses, how do we find the number of skirts? We must subtract 3 from 8 to get 5. How do we check to see if we are right? We add 8 and 5 to get 13, and we see that our total is too small.

Blouses	Skirts	(17) Total
8	5	13

Table 5.10

Using algebra, we can express these facts in an abbreviated form. First let's choose the letter b to stand for the number of blouses. Put a b in the blouses column. Since the number of skirts is 3 less than the number of blouses, we can write $b - 3$ in the skirts column. We know that our guess is correct when the number of blouses plus the number of skirts equals 17, or, using our abbreviations, when

$$b + (b - 3) = 17$$

This is an algebraic equation for this problem. The parentheses around the $(b - 3)$ help us to distinguish the symbols that represent the blouses and the skirts.

If we start guessing the number of Susan's *skirts* first, we will get a different equation. Guess that Susan has 8 skirts.

Blouses	Skirts	(17) Total
	8	

Table 5.11

Since she has 3 more blouses than skirts, we add 3 to 8 to get 11 blouses. We check by adding both numbers together to get 19, which is too large. Let's use symbols to make an algebraic equation. If we let s represent the number of skirts, then we need $s + 3$ for the number of blouses, and we know we are correct when

$$(s + 3) + s = 17$$

We now have two equations for this problem. Solving either equation will give the answer. The solution to the first equation will give us the number of blouses; the solution to the second, the number of skirts.

Our intent in this section is to help you learn to set up equations from the guess charts. For your information, we have included algebraic solutions to these equations at the end of the chapter, but not as part of the regular text.

The next problem was an example in the earlier section on guessing.

PROBLEM 22: *One number is 27 more than another. When you multiply both numbers, their product is 238. What are the numbers?*

Let's fill in one guess on the guess chart (Table 5.12). Then write the algebraic equation. If we guess that the first number is 10, then the second number is 10 + 27, or 37, and the product is 10 × 37, or 370, which is too big.

First No.	Second No.	(238) Product
10	37	370

Table 5.12

Now let's use algebraic symbols. If f represents the first number, then $(f + 27)$ represents the second number. We know we are correct when their product is equal to 238, or, using our abbreviations, when

$$f \times (f + 27) = 238$$

In algebra it is common to replace the multiplication sign (×) with a raised dot, or to completely omit it. The expressions $f \cdot (f + 27) = 238$ and $f(f + 27) = 238$ are also correct ways of writing this equation.

Worksheet 5.9

Set up a guess chart for each problem. Fill in the results from one guess. Then label the columns algebraically. Finally, write the algebraic equation.

1. Jim is 23 years older than his son Bill. The sum of their ages is 87. How old is each?

2. Sara is 9 inches taller than her daughter Jennifer. Their total height is 117 inches. How tall is Sara?

3. Linda bought a total of 24 apples and oranges. The number of apples was 3 more than twice as many oranges. How many apples did she buy?

4. One number is 7 more than 8 times the second. The sum of the numbers is 295. What are the numbers?

(continued)

5. There are 75 quarters and dimes altogether in the cash register. The number of dimes is 5 more than the number of quarters. How many dimes are there?

6. Holly and Dolly together earned $7.36 selling paperbacks at a garage sale. Holly earned $1.50 more than Dolly. How much did each woman earn?

7. A pair of boots costs $53 more than a pair of shoes. On sale one pair of boots and one pair of shoes together cost $137. How much do the boots cost?

8. Ted's weight is 23 pounds more than twice Alice's weight. Together they weigh 299 pounds. How much does Ted weigh?

PROBLEM 23: *Henry has six times as many rock records as classical records. He has 16 more jazz records than classical records. All together he has 96 records. How many jazz records does he have?*

We will make a guess chart, fill in one guess, and then write the algebraic equation. If we guess that there are 5 classical records, then there must be 30 rock records (6 × 5) and 21 jazz records (5 + 16). This leads to a total of 56, which is too small.

Rock	Classical	Jazz	(96) Total
30	5	21	56

Table 5.13

Let c represent the number of classical records. Then $6c$ represents the number of rock records, and $c + 16$ stands for the number of jazz records. We know we are correct when the total is equal to 96, or when

$$6c + c + (c + 16) = 96$$

We could have started by using r to represent rock records, or j to represent jazz records. Can you write equations using those letters? Did you get these equations?

$$r + \frac{r}{6} + \left(\frac{r}{6} + 16\right) = 96$$

$$6(j - 16) + (j - 16) + j = 96$$

For the first equation, you must use the fact that, if the number of rock records is six times as large as the number of classical records, then the number of classical records must be one-sixth the number of rock records.

Here is the last example for this section.

PROBLEM 24: *Jason opens the cash register and finds that he has four times as many pennies as dimes and 16 more nickels than pennies. The value of his coins is $6.92. How many nickels does he have?*

Make the guess chart and take one guess. Then write the algebraic equation.

Number of Coins			Value of Coins			($6.92)
Pennies	Dimes	Nickels	Pennies	Dimes	Nickels	Total Value
40	10	56	$0.40	$1.00	$2.80	$4.20
$4d$	d	$4d + 16$				

Table 5.14

(continued)

If we let d represent the number of dimes, then $4d$ stands for the number of pennies (4 times as many pennies), and $4d + 16$ represents the number of nickels (16 more nickels). Our next step is to find the value of these coins so that we can check if our total value is $6.92. Since each penny is worth 1 cent, the value in dollars of $4d$ pennies is $(.01)4d$, or $.04d$. Since each dime is worth 10 cents, the value of d dimes is $.10d$. Since each nickel is worth 5 cents, the value of $4d + 16$ nickels is $.05(4d + 16)$. Fill in these expressions on the chart.

We can find the total by combining these values, and our equation is

$$.04d + .10d + .05\,(4d + 16) = 6.92$$

Worksheet 5.10

Set up a guess chart for each problem. Fill in the results from one guess. Then write the algebraic equation.

1. In my change purse there are twice as many dimes as quarters and four times as many nickels as quarters. There are 49 coins in all. How many dimes are there?

2. Jane is 7 years younger than Kathy, and Linda is 7 years older than Kathy. The sum of their ages is 63. How old is Jane?

3. The width of a rectangle is $\frac{1}{5}$ its length. The perimeter of the rectangle is 96 inches. What are the dimensions (length and width) of the rectangle?

4. Apples cost 8 cents per pound less than pears. Three pounds of apples and 2 pounds of pears cost $1.11. How much does each fruit cost per pound?

5. In my change purse the number of pennies is twice the number of dimes, and the number of nickels is 5 less than three times the number of dimes. The value of the coins is $2.99. How many nickels are there?

6. In exercise class Diane did 7 less than three times as many sit-ups as Nancy, and Liz did 4 more sit-ups than Diane. In all, they did 88 sit-ups. How many sit-ups did Liz do?

7. The first number is 2 less than three times the second number, and the third number is 8 more than the first. The sum of all three numbers is 67. What are the numbers?

8. The price of movie tickets is half as much for children as for adults. The cost for 4 adults and 3 children is $19.25. What is the cost for an adult ticket?

ALGEBRAIC SOLUTIONS

The algebraic solutions for the equations in Problems 21–24 are given in this section. In Problem 22, in particular, you may note that we must factor a quadratic equation in order to find the solution. This requires a fair amount of algebraic sophistication. In contrast, the guess chart solution requires only the use of addition and multiplication. Often we find that not only can we solve algebra problems using guess charts, but also the computations for these solutions are easier to carry out.

PROBLEM 21:

Starting with b to represent the number of blouses, we have:

$$b + (b - 3) = 17$$
$$b + b - 3 = 17$$
$$2b - 3 = 17$$
$$2b = 20$$
$$b = 10$$

The number of blouses: $b = 10$.
The number of skirts: $b - 3 = 10 - 3 = 7$.

When s = the number of skirts:

$$(s + 3) + s = 17$$
$$s + 3 + s = 17$$
$$2s + 3 = 17$$
$$2s = 14$$
$$s = 7$$

The number of skirts: $s = 7$.
The number of blouses: $s + 3 = 7 + 3 = 10$.

PROBLEM 22:

If we let f represent the first number:

$$f(f + 27) = 238$$
$$f^2 + 27f = 238$$
$$f^2 + 27f - 238 = 0$$
$$(f - 7)(f + 34) = 0$$
$$f = 7 \text{ or } f = {}^{-}34$$

The first number: $f = 7$ or $^{-}34$.
The second number: $f + 27 = 7 + 27 = 34$, or $f + 27 = {}^{-}34 + 27 = {}^{-}7$.

PROBLEM 23:

If c = the number of classical records:

$$6c + c + (c + 16) = 96$$
$$6c + c + c + 16 = 96$$
$$8c + 16 = 96$$
$$8c = 80$$
$$c = 10$$

The number of classical records: $c = 10$.
The number of rock records: $6c = 6 \times 10 = 60$.
The number of jazz records: $c + 16 = 10 + 16 = 26$.

If r = the number of rock records:

$$r + \frac{r}{6} + \left(\frac{r}{6} + 16\right) = 96$$
$$r + \frac{r}{6} + \frac{r}{6} + 16 = 96$$
$$r + \frac{r}{6} + \frac{r}{6} = 80$$
$$6\left(r + \frac{r}{6} + \frac{r}{6}\right) = 6 \times 80$$
$$6r + 6\left(\frac{r}{6}\right) + 6\left(\frac{r}{6}\right) = 6 \times 80$$
$$6r + r + r = 480$$
$$8r = 480$$
$$r = 60$$

The number of rock records: $r = 60$.
The number of classical records: $r/6 = 60/6 = 10$.
The number of jazz records:

$$\frac{r}{6} + 16 = \frac{60}{6} + 16 = 10 + 16 = 26$$

If j = the number of jazz records:

$$6(j - 16) + (j - 16) + j = 96$$
$$6 \times j - 6 \times 16 + j - 16 + j = 96$$
$$6j + j + j - 96 - 16 = 96$$
$$8j = 208$$
$$j = 26$$

The number of jazz records: $j = 26$.
The number of classical records: $j - 16 = 26 - 16 = 10$.
The number of rock records:

$$6(j - 16) = 6(26 - 16) = 6 \times 10 = 60$$

PROBLEM 24:

Let d = the number of dimes:

$$
\begin{aligned}
.04d + .10d + .05(4d + 16) &= 6.92 \\
.04d + .10d + .20d + .80 &= 6.92 \\
.34d + .80 &= 6.92 \\
.34d &= 6.12 \\
d &= 18
\end{aligned}
$$

The number of dimes: $d = 18$.
The number of pennies: $4d = 4 \times 18 = 72$.
The number of nickels:

$$4d + 16 = 4 \times 18 + 16 = 72 + 16 = 88$$

CHAPTER Six

Probability and Statistics

Today information is often presented to us in statistical terms or in tables or graphs. We need to understand the concepts of probability and statistics in order to read and analyze this information and to protect ourselves from misleading conclusions. H. G. Wells once wrote: "Statistical thinking will one day be as necessary for efficient citizenship as the ability to read and write." This chapter presents an introduction to the fields of *probability* and *inferential statistics*. You will need dice, graph paper, and a calculator for the activities.

Statistics is the study of how to organize and analyze collections of data. A *summary statistic*, such as a mean or a median, is used to describe or simplify data. A *test statistic* is used together with probability theory to make predictions and decisions, such as:

Who will win the election?
Is the new medicine better than the old?
How much chocolate milk should be ordered for lunch?
Will it rain tomorrow?

PROBABILITY

Probability is the chance that something (an event) will—or will not—happen. We talk of the probability that it will rain or the probability of having a winning raffle ticket.

When we toss a *fair* coin, we say that two possible outcomes, heads or tails, are *equally likely* to occur. Since a head is one of two ways that a coin can turn up, we say that the probability of heads is one out of two, or ½. What is the probability of tossing a tail? ____________

Mathematically, we say:

$$\text{the probability of an event} = \frac{\text{the number of ways the event can happen}}{\text{the total number of possible outcomes}}$$

Common abbreviated forms are:

$$Pr(\text{tossing a head}) = \frac{1}{2}$$

$$Pr(\text{head}) = \frac{1}{2}$$

$$Pr(H) = \frac{1}{2}$$

Sometimes these expressions are written with just a capital P, as in $P(\text{head})$.

Think about the regular six-sided dice we use to play games. One of them is called a *die*. (You will need two for later activities in this chapter.)

List the possible number of dots that can show when a die is rolled:

____

If the die is fair, we say that each of the outcomes is *equally likely*.

In this case, what is the probability of rolling a 1? __________

A 2? __________ A 3? __________ A 4? __________

A 5? __________ A 6? __________

What is the probability of rolling an even number? (Hint: first list all of the possible even numbers.)

$Pr(\text{even})$ = __________

What is the probability of rolling a number less than 3? __________

Worksheet 6.1

For each problem, list all possible outcomes; then find the probabilities. You may assume fair situations.

1. There are ten balls in a box, six red and four black. The possible outcomes when you draw one ball out of the box might be listed as: red 1, red 2, . . . , red 6, black 1, . . . , black 4, thus distinguishing among balls of the same color.

a. What is the probability of drawing a black ball?

b. What is the probability of drawing a red ball?

2. There are 25 cards, numbered 1 through 25, in a box. In this problem, cards are drawn *at random*; that is, they are thoroughly mixed and then picked out of the box by someone who does not look while picking.

a. List the possible outcomes if you draw one card from the box:

b. Which numbers from this list are divisible by 5?

c. What is the probability of drawing a number that is divisible by 5?

d. Which numbers in the list are greater than 20?

e. What is the probability of drawing a number greater than 20?

f. What is the probability of *not* drawing a number greater than 20?

g. Which numbers in the list are divisible by 3?

h. What are the even numbers in the list?

i. What is the probability of drawing a number that is *both* even *and* divisible by 3?

What is the probability of rolling a 9 on a regular die? There are *no* ways to roll a 9; therefore, the probability is 0. The smallest probability we can have is 0.

What is the probability of rolling a number smaller than 8 on a regular die? ____________ All six possible outcomes fulfill this event; therefore, the probability is 6/6, or 1. In fact, the largest probability we can have is 1.

What happens when we add the probabilities of all the possible outcomes of rolling one fair die? This question can be represented mathematically by the following equation:

$$Pr(1) + Pr(2) + Pr(3) + Pr(4) + Pr(5) + Pr(6)$$
$$= \_\_\_\_ + \_\_\_\_ + \_\_\_\_ + \_\_\_\_ + \_\_\_\_ + \_\_\_\_ = \_\_\_\_\_\_\_\_$$

Did you get a sum of 1.0? ____________

What is the sum of the probabilities of all possible results of tossing a fair penny?

$$Pr(\text{head}) + Pr(\text{tail}) = \_\_\_\_\_\_\_\_\_\_\_\_ + \_\_\_\_\_\_\_\_\_\_\_\_$$
$$= \_\_\_\_\_\_\_\_\_\_\_\_$$

We have just illustrated two basic facts about probability: (1) The probability of an event can range from 0, the event cannot possibly occur, to 1, it is certain to occur; (2) The sum of the probabilities of *all* possible outcomes in a situation is equal to 1.

Consider the event of rolling an odd number with a regular die. List the possible ways an odd number can occur: ____________ What is the probability of rolling an odd number? ____________

Now think about *not* rolling an odd number. List the ways this can happen: ____________ What is the probability of *not* rolling an odd number? ____________

Add these two probabilities together:

$Pr(\text{odd}) + Pr(\textit{not}\ \text{odd}) =$ ____________

This last fact illustrates a basic rule in probability theory:

$$Pr(\text{a particular event happens})$$
$$+\ Pr(\text{a particular event does } \textit{not} \text{ happen}) = 1$$

Suppose we know that the probability that it will rain is 0.40. What is the probability that it will *not* rain? ____________ The answer is 0.60. To find this, we subtract: $1.00 - 0.40 = 0.60$.

Worksheet 6.2

Solve these problems.

1a. If you buy 1 raffle ticket and 100 were sold, what is your chance of winning the prize?

b. What is the probability that you will *not* win?

c. If 1,000 tickets were sold, what is your probability of winning?

d. What is the probability that you will *not* win in this situation?

e. If a second prize is given after the first prize name is drawn, what is your chance of winning this prize when 100 tickets were sold, assuming you did not win the first one?

f. When 1,000 tickets were sold?

2. Suppose you get up very early one morning. With your eyes half closed, you reach into a drawer and pull out a blue sock.

a. If there are three blue, two red, four brown, and two black socks left in the drawer, what is the probability that the second sock you pull out (without looking) will be blue?

b. What is the probability that you will *not* pull out a blue sock on your second try?

(continued)

3. The friend who is to meet you is also reaching into a drawer that contains two blue socks, one white sock, and one red sock. Your friend pulls out two socks at a time.

a. List the possible outcomes. Distinguish between the blue socks by using the symbols $B1$ and $B2$.

b. What is the probability of pulling out one red and one white sock?

c. What is the probability of pulling out one red and one blue sock?

d. Of pulling out one white and one blue sock?

e. Of pulling out two blue socks?

f. Have you found the probabilities for all of the possibilities? (Add the probabilities you have found, to check.)

g. What is the probability of *not* getting two blue socks?

4. There are ten Famous Women cards in a complete set. One card comes in each box of Wonder Cereal. Sue already has four of the ten cards.

a. Assuming that the cards are *uniformly* (evenly) distributed in the boxes, what is the probability that the next box she buys will have a card she needs?

b. When she has collected nine different cards, what is the probability that the next box will have the last card she needs?

c. What is the probability that it will *not*?

COUNTING PROBLEMS

Consider the question: what is the probability of tossing a coin two times in a row and getting two heads?

We list the possible results using H for heads and T for tails: HH, HT, TH, TT. Looking at the list, can you determine the probability of tossing two heads? ______________. There is one way out of four possibilities, therefore the probability is 1/4. What is the probability of one head and one tail in either order? ______________ Of two tails? ______________

Making the list of possible outcomes for this problem was not difficult. However, as the number of tosses increases, it will become more and more difficult. Looking for a pattern to use when you make your list will help.

Suppose you want to find the probabilities when you toss a coin three times. Make a list of the possible outcomes, starting with three heads (HHH), then two heads and 1 tail, next one head and two tails, and finally no heads—that is, three tails (TTT). Use a pattern to list all of the outcomes. Explain your pattern to a partner.

HHH

TTT

What is the probability of all heads? ______________ Of two heads and one tail in any order? ______________ Of one head and two tails in any order? ______________ Of no heads and three tails? ______________

Another helpful piece of information in these problems is to know the total number of outcomes that you need to list. One way to look at this in the coin-tossing problem is to ask: How many different outcomes are possible on each toss? The answer is two: heads or tails. Thus, the total number of possibilities in two tosses is 2×2, or 4. For three tosses, we have $2 \times 2 \times 2$, or 8 possibilities. How many possibilities are there for four tosses?

_______ × _______ × _______ × _______ = ______________

This method of multiplication, sometimes referred to as the *counting* or *multiplication principle*, works in other situations as well.

For example, when Helen drives to the university, she has three routes to choose from to reach the bridge and five routes from the bridge to the university. How many possible routes are there from her house to

Figure 6.1

the university? The answer is 3×5, or 15. To check, make a list of the outcomes, using the labels in Figure 6.1.

Here is another example for you to solve. If Ann has brought three blouses and two skirts on her trip, how many different outfits can she wear?

Worksheet 6.3

Use the properties of probability, the *multiplication principle*, and organized lists to help you solve these problems.

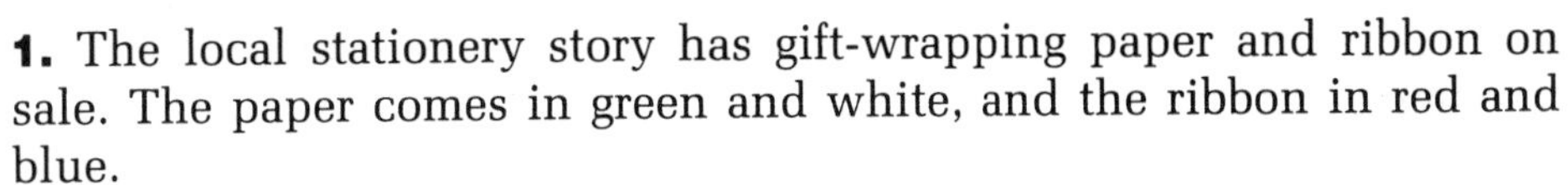

1. The local stationery story has gift-wrapping paper and ribbon on sale. The paper comes in green and white, and the ribbon in red and blue.

a. If you buy one package of each, how many different color combinations of packages can you wrap?

b. If a friend picks out a package *at random* from these, what is the probability that she will get a package with white paper and blue ribbon?

c. With white paper and red ribbon?

d. With green paper?

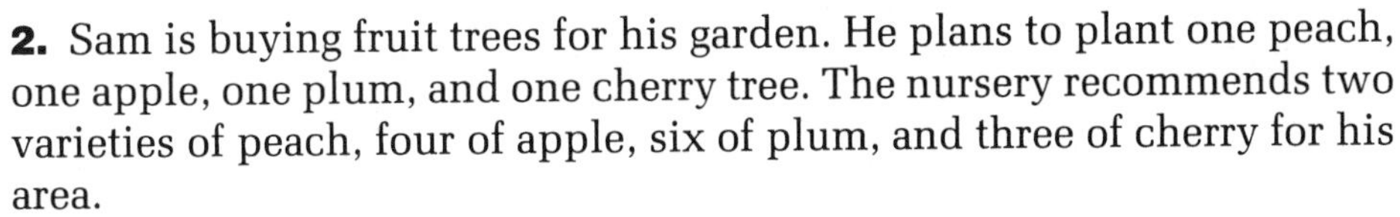

2. Sam is buying fruit trees for his garden. He plans to plant one peach, one apple, one plum, and one cherry tree. The nursery recommends two varieties of peach, four of apple, six of plum, and three of cherry for his area.

a. How many possible different groups of trees could he plant?

b. If he has already decided on the cherry, how many choices are left for the other trees?

3. In California, many license plates have three numbers followed by three letters: __ __ __ __ __ __ .

a. How many different license plates can be made up in this format? Remember, there are ten possible numbers for each slot and 26 possible letters.

b. What is the probability that a car chosen at random will have license 982FTM?

4. California ran out of license plates recently. To make new plates, they reversed the numbers and letters and added a single number in front of the pattern.

a. How many license plates are possible now?

b. What is the probability of getting 2MPQ163? __________

(continued)

5. HAPPY HAMBURGERS has the following menu:

Salads	Hamburgers	Buns	Drinks
Carrot	Basic Burger	Wheat	Milk
Green	Bacon Burger	French	Soda
Coleslaw	Soy Vegi	Sesame	Tea
	Spinach Vegi	Onion	Coffee
		Rye	

a. How many different meals are possible? (Each meal consists of salad, hamburger, bun, and drink.)

b. How many of these are vegetarian, assuming that milk may be included?

c. If you order at random, what is the probability of getting a vegetarian meal?

d. What is the probability of getting a nonvegetarian meal?

6. The Joneses are planning a two-child family. They might have two boys, two girls, or one girl and one boy.

a. How many possibilities are there?

b. List all of the possible outcomes. Assume that having a girl first and then a boy is different from having a boy and then a girl.

c. Assuming that the chance of having a girl is equal to the chance of having a boy, 1/2, what is the probability that they will have one girl and one boy in either order?

7. The Smiths are planning a four-child family.

a. How many arrangements of boys and girls are possible for this family?

b. List the possible arrangements. (Hint: start with all girls and no boys, then three girls and one boy, two girls and two boys, one girl and three boys, and finally all boys.)

c. What is the probability of two boys and two girls?

MORE COUNTING PROBLEMS

Here is another type of problem. Ann, Bob, and Carol are about to move into the three new offices in a row at the end of the hall. The offices are to be assigned *at random*—that is, by placing the names in the proverbial hat, mixing them thoroughly, and drawing them out without looking. What is the probability that their offices will be assigned in alphabetical order? First, we need to know how many ways they can be assigned to these offices. Using *A* to stand for Ann, *B* for Bob, and *C* for Carol, let's list the possibilities:

ABC, *ACB*, *BAC*, *BCA*, *CAB*, *CBA*.

What is the probability of an alphabetical assignment? ________

Can you see a pattern in how the list was made for this problem?

In this problem, making a list for only three names was fairly easy. It might not be too hard even if we added one more name, Dan. But if we must also assign offices to Emily, Frank, and Gertrude as well, things will begin to get complicated.

There is another way to approach this problem. These lines represent the offices: ______ ______ ______ ______ ______ ______ ______ If we pick out one of the seven people *at random* for the first office, there are seven possible results. Once that office is assigned, there are only six possibilities for the second office, then five for the third office, and so on. Thus, we have

$7 \times 6 \times 5 \times 4 \times 3 \times 2 \times 1$

or 5,040 possible assignments! Too many to list.

The expression $7 \times 6 \times 5 \times 4 \times 3 \times 2 \times 1$ has an abbreviation: 7! This is *not* read "seven with an exclamation point," but "*seven factorial.*" The expression tells us how many arrangements or *permutations* can be made with seven objects taken seven at a time.

Try these problems. What is the probability of an alphabetical office assignment for five people? (Hint: first find the total number of possible assignments and then the number of ways the assignment can be made alphabetically.)

Six horses are running in a race. How many ways can the first, second, and third places be taken? For the first place there are six possibilities, then five for the second and four for the third. Thus, we have $6 \times 5 \times 4$, or 120 possibilities. Notice that the answer is not 6! because we are only interested in the first three places. What is the probability that you will pick the exact winners? ________

Sometimes counting problems like these have special conditions that require our attention. Suppose we change the horse-race problem. We are positive that Jumping Jack will be first. How many arrangements are possible for the first three places, given this condition? Since there is only one possibility for first, we are left with five possibilities for second and then four for third. The answer is $1 \times 5 \times 4$, or 20 arrangements.

In the office problem, suppose Ann has been promised the first office and Ed the second. Under these circumstances, how many possible arrangements are there for assigning the seven people to offices? The first two offices are already determined, leaving five possibilities for the third office, four for the fourth, and so on. We have $1 \times 1 \times 5 \times 4 \times 3 \times 2 \times 1$, or 120.

What is the probability that Gertrude will get the third office? First, in how many ways can the assignments be made so that Ann has the first, Ed has the second, and Gertrude has the third office? There is only one way to assign each of the first three offices in this case, then four ways for the fourth, three for the fifth, and so on, giving us $1 \times 1 \times 1 \times 4 \times 3 \times 2 \times 1$, or 24 ways. Therefore, the probability of Gertrude getting the third office is 24/120, or 1/5.

Worksheet 6.4

1. Native Bolivian women often wear as many as five skirts at a time.

a. In how many ways can a woman layer all five skirts?

b. If she wears only three skirts, in how many arrangements can she wear them?

c. If she wears her oldest skirt on top, how will this affect the arrangements in problem 1a?

d. In problem 1b?

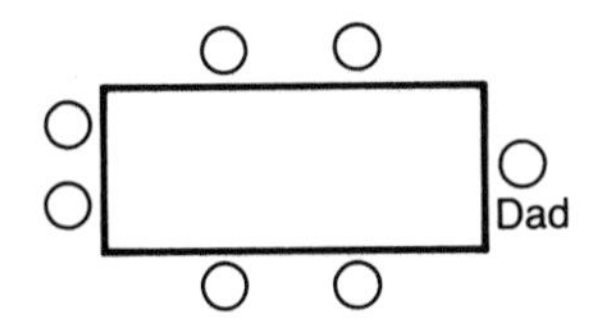

2. There are seven people in the Brown family. The father always sits at the head of the table.

a. In how many ways can the others be seated around the table?

b. What is the probability that Sally will sit directly to the right of her father?

3. Consider the letters of our alphabet.

a. How many different five-letter arrangements are possible when repeated letters are allowed?

b. What is the probability that we will get a five-letter "word" with no repeated letters?

c. What is the probability of getting a "word" with one or more repeated letters? (Hint: use the answer from problem 3b and a basic probability fact.)

4. In the game Pico-Fermi-Bagels, the players try to guess a three-digit number that has no repeated digits. Assuming that numbers beginning with 0, such as 023, are acceptable:

a. How many possible numbers are there to guess from?

b. What is the probability of guessing correctly on the first try?

PROBABILITY EXPERIMENTS

Think about rolling two fair dice and adding the two numbers. What is the largest possible result? ______ What is the smallest possible result? ______ List all of the possible results: ______

______

Suppose you are about to roll your dice 36 times. What kind of pattern or distribution of the possible sums would you expect? ______ Do you think each sum will occur about the same number of times—or will some of them occur more frequently? ______ Which sums might occur more frequently? ______ Why? ______

______

Roll your dice 36 times, and record the sums on the graph in Figure 6.2. Mark an *X* in the appropriate column each time a particular sum occurs. Start at the bottom of the graph. The *X* over the 6 tells us that a 6 has already been rolled. If you were to roll a 7 next, you would mark an *X* over the 7 (next to the one over the 6).

Describe your results. ______

______

Are you surprised? ______

				X	X					
2	3	4	5	6	7	8	9	10	11	12

Figure 6.2

Combine your data on a graph with four other people—or roll 144 more times to make a total of 180 rolls.

How would you describe the combined results? ________________ ________________________________ Is the shape of this graph different from your own for 36 rolls? __________ Are you surprised at the combined results? __________ Do you think your dice are fair? _______

How can we compare our results with what should happen theoretically when we roll two dice and find the sum? To begin with, what is the probability of rolling a sum of, say, 5 with two dice? To find out, we must find the number of ways to roll a 5 and divide by the total number of possible outcomes when rolling two dice.

We can obtain a 5 from the following combinations: 1 + 4, 4 + 1, 3 + 2, and 2 + 3—that is, in four ways. When we roll two dice, six results are possible on the first die and six on the second, for a total of 6 × 6, or 36 possibilities. Thus, the probability of rolling a 5 is 4/36, or 1/9.

We can roll a sum of 4 with the following combinations: 1 + 3, 3 + 1, and 2 + 2. Looking at this list, students often ask the following question: Why do we list both 1 + 3 and 3 + 1, but only a single 2 + 2? Many students in college statistics courses are stumped by this question. One way to clear this up is to use a table to record all of the possible sums when rolling two dice. The table will also help us find the rest of the theoretical probabilities for all of the outcomes.

Blue Die

Red Die	1	2	3	4	5	6
1			4			
2		4				
3	4					
4						
5						
6						

Figure 6.3

Suppose we have one red and one blue die. In the table in Figure 6.3, the numbers in the column under the red die represent the possible results when we roll that die. The numbers in the top row of the table are possible results from the blue die.

If we roll a red 1 and a blue 3, we have a sum of 4 (recorded under the blue 3); a red 3 and a blue 1 also give a sum of 4 (recorded under the blue 1). Thus, a red 3 and a blue 1 are distinct from a red 1 and a blue 3. However, if we roll two 2s (a red 2 and a blue 2), we obtain only the 4 recorded under the blue 2.

Finish filling in the table. Count the number of times each sum occurs in the table, and record the probability of each sum.

Pr(roll 2) = *Pr*(roll 8) =
Pr(roll 3) = *Pr*(roll 9) =
Pr(roll 4) = *Pr*(roll 10) =
Pr(roll 5) = *Pr*(roll 11) =
Pr(roll 6) = *Pr*(roll 12) =
Pr(roll 7) =

According to these theoretical probabilities, which three numbers are most likely to occur when you roll two dice and add? ________

How does the distribution of theoretical probabilities compare to your "experiment" of 180 rolls? To find out how many 5s should theoretically occur in 180 rolls, we multiply 4/36, the probability of rolling a 5, by 180. This number is called the *theoretical frequency* or *expected number of outcomes* for 5. How does this number compare with the actual number of 5s you rolled?

Record your actual results and the expected results in Table 6.1.

Sum	Actual	Expected
2	______	______
3	______	______
4	______	______
5	______	______
6	______	______
7	______	______
8	______	______
9	______	______
10	______	______
11	______	______
12	______	______

Table 6.1

Do your results seem to be extremely different from what you would expect theoretically?

When we answer this question, we need to keep in mind a very important fact. Probability theory can provide us with theoretical frequencies. However, when we do an experiment, such as rolling a pair of dice 180 times, we will not necessarily get results that match those expected values *exactly*. In fact, there is only a *very small* chance that this will occur. However, we should get results that are relatively close to the theoretical frequencies; and, as the number of times we roll the dice increases, we should come closer and closer to these results if we are working with fair dice. This idea is referred to as the *law of large numbers*.

Statisticians have developed *tests* that compare theoretical predictions with experimental results and help us decide whether the discrepancies are due to chance or to an error in our assumptions. These procedures are part of a body of knowledge referred to as *inferential statistics* because we use these procedures to make inferences from data. Here our assumption or hypothesis is that we have fair dice. We will do a second experiment with this assumption and then use a statistical test to decide whether to accept or reject the hypothesis that our dice are fair.

Consider the following experiment: roll two dice and subtract the smaller number from the larger. For example, if you roll a 6 and a 2, the difference is 4. List the possible results: ____________ . Which outcome or outcomes do you think will occur most often? ____________ .

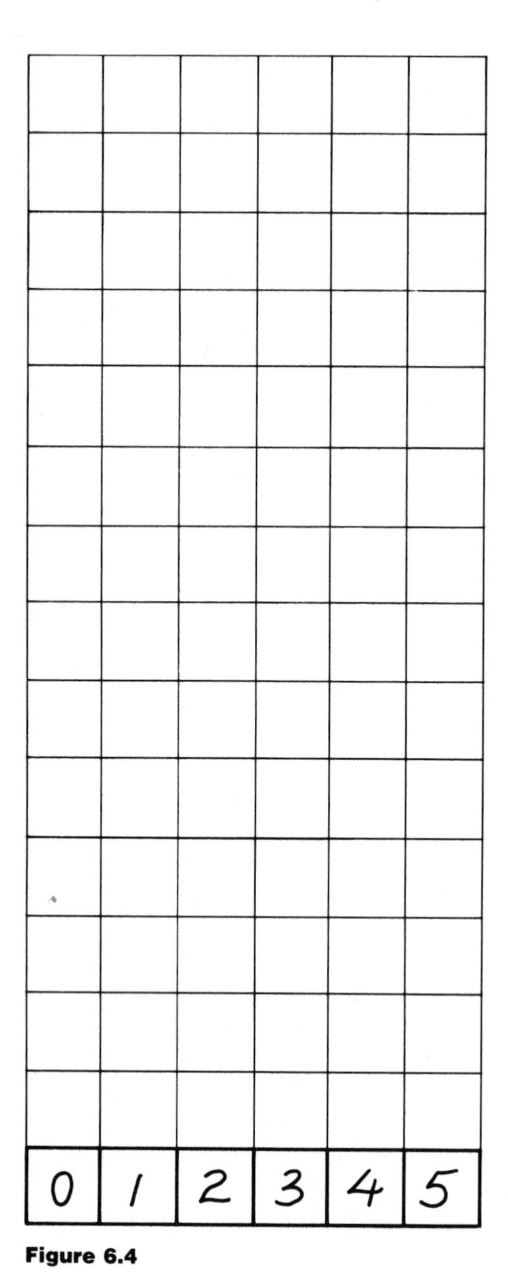

Figure 6.4

Roll your dice 36 times, subtract each time, and record your results on the graph in Figure 6.4, starting from the bottom. Are you surprised at your results? ____________

Combine your results with those of four other students—or roll 144 more times. Do the combined results seem different from your original results? ____________

Worksheet 6.5

1. Complete the table, and record the theoretical probabilities for rolling two dice and subtracting.

Blue Die (columns), Red Die (rows)

	1	2	3	4	5	6
1	0					
2		0				
3			0			
4				0		
5					0	
6						0

$Pr(0) = \frac{6}{36}$ $\qquad$ $Pr(3) =$ ______

$Pr(1) =$ ______ $\qquad$ $Pr(4) =$ ______

$Pr(2) =$ ______ $\qquad$ $Pr(5) =$ ______

2. Calculate the theoretical frequency for each outcome for an experiment with 180 rolls. Record these theoretical frequencies and the combined results of your last experiment.

Difference	Experimental Frequency	Theoretical Frequency
0	______	______
1	______	______
2	______	______
3	______	______
4	______	______
5	______	______

3. How do your experimental frequencies compare with the theoretical frequencies?

4. Do you think that your dice are fair?

THE CHI-SQUARE TEST

The chances are very unlikely that even the combined results from either of our dice experiments will exactly match what theory tells us to expect in 180 rolls. We might ask just how different from the theoretical frequencies our results can be and still be acceptable. There is a field of study in inferential statistics called *testing hypotheses* that addresses this question. We will use the *Chi-Square Test* (sometimes written χ^2 Test, using the Greek letter *chi*) to decide if the results from our experiments are "too far off." If the dice are loaded or not fair, then the results might be "too far off."

We need some way to summarize the difference between our results and what we expect theoretically. It would be convenient if we could find an expression that will give us a single number to represent this summary. Then we could easily compare that number, called a *test statistic*, with statistics from similar experiments and decide if we should accept or reject the hypothesis that our dice are fair. Statisticians have found such an expression or function—the *chi-square statistic*.

The data in Table 6.2 consist of the sums of 180 rolls of two dice. The "Observed" column contains a set of experimental frequencies, and the "Expected" column contains the theoretical frequencies.

Sum	Observed (O)	Expected (E)	($O - E$)	$(O - E)^2$	$\frac{(O - E)^2}{E}$
2	0	5	−5	25	5
3	11	10	______	______	______
4	18	15	______	______	______
5	16	20	______	______	______
6	25	25	______	______	______
7	36	30	______	______	______
8	31	25	______	______	______
9	21	20	______	______	______
10	10	15	______	______	______
11	10	10	______	______	______
12	2	5	______	______	______
				Total	______

Table 6.2

To find the value of the chi-square statistic for this experiment, we first find the difference between the observed and expected frequencies. The first calculation is recorded for you; fill in the rest. Note that we are subtracting the expected frequency from our observed frequency ($O - E$). This will give a negative number for the sum of 2: $0 - 5 = -5$. We will also obtain negative answers for the sums of 5, 10, and 12.

We now have eleven numbers, some with negative signs. If we just add the ($O - E$) column, we will get zero (or very close to zero), which does us no good at all. To eliminate the negative signs, we square each of these numbers. (Remember that a negative times a negative is positive.) Complete the $(O - E)^2$ column.

Next, divide each $(O - E)$ term by its E. This gives a measure of the error, which tells us, in effect, whether or not the observed result (O) is too far from the expected result (E).

We now have eleven positive numbers. We add these to obtain a single number, which is our value for the chi-square statistic for this experiment. If this number is "too large," we will be suspicious of our dice and reject the hypothesis that they are fair.

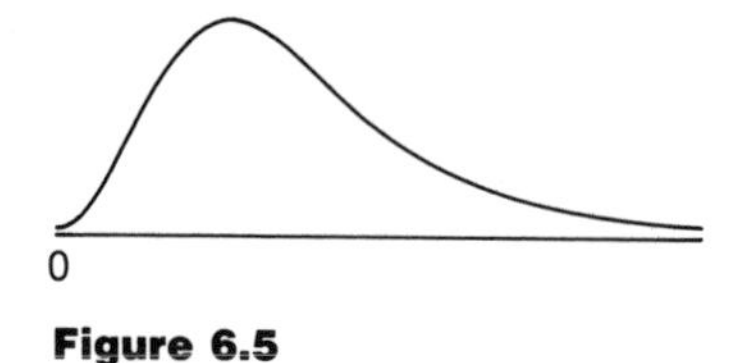

Figure 6.5

The value of the chi-square statistic can be calculated for any set of observations from this experiment. If we plotted all possible chi-square values and smoothed out the graph, we would obtain a curve like the one in Figure 6.5. This curve gives us an idea of the distribution of all of the possible chi-square values for this experiment. The total area under this curve is equal to 1, just as, when we add the probabilities of all possible outcomes of an experiment, we get 1. We still need to determine if our chi-square value is "too large" to believe the hypothesis that our dice are fair. To do this, we need to use the chi-square table in Table 6.3.

Note the heading of the left-hand column in Table 6.3, "*Degrees of freedom*." The exact shape of the chi-square curve is determined by the number of possible outcomes in the experiment *minus* one. This experiment has eleven possible outcomes (2, 3, 4, 5, 6, 7, 8, 9, 10, 11, and 12); therefore, there are ten degrees of freedom.

Degrees of freedom	99%	95%	90%	70%	50%	30%	10%	5%	1%
1	0.00016	0.0039	0.016	0.15	0.46	1.07	2.71	3.84	6.64
2	0.020	0.10	0.21	0.71	1.39	2.41	4.60	5.99	9.21
3	0.12	0.35	0.58	1.42	2.37	3.67	6.25	7.82	11.34
4	0.30	0.71	1.06	2.20	3.36	4.88	7.78	9.49	13.28
*5	0.55	1.14	1.61	3.00	4.35	6.06	9.24	11.07	15.09
6	0.87	1.64	2.20	3.83	5.35	7.23	10.65	12.59	16.81
7	1.24	2.17	2.83	4.67	6.35	8.38	12.02	14.07	18.48
8	1.65	2.73	3.49	5.53	7.34	9.52	13.36	15.51	20.09
9	2.09	3.33	4.17	6.39	8.34	10.66	14.68	16.92	21.67
*10	2.56	3.94	4.86	7.27	9.34	11.78	15.99	18.31	23.21
11	3.05	4.58	5.58	8.15	10.34	12.90	17.28	19.68	24.73
12	3.57	5.23	6.30	9.03	11.34	14.01	18.55	21.03	26.22
13	4.11	5.89	7.04	9.93	12.34	15.12	19.81	22.36	27.69
14	4.66	6.57	7.79	10.82	13.34	16.22	21.06	23.69	29.14
15	5.23	7.26	8.55	11.72	14.34	17.32	22.31	25.00	30.58
16	5.81	7.96	9.31	12.62	15.34	18.42	23.54	26.30	32.00
17	6.41	8.67	10.09	13.53	16.34	19.51	24.77	27.59	33.41
18	7.00	9.39	10.87	14.44	17.34	20.60	25.99	28.87	34.81
19	7.63	10.12	11.65	15.35	18.34	21.69	27.20	30.14	36.19
20	8.26	10.85	12.44	16.27	19.34	22.78	28.41	31.41	37.57

Source: Adapted from p. 112 of Sir R. A. Fisher, *Statistical Methods for Research Workers* (Edinburgh, Scotland: Oliver and Boyd, 1958).

Table 6.3 A Chi-Square Table

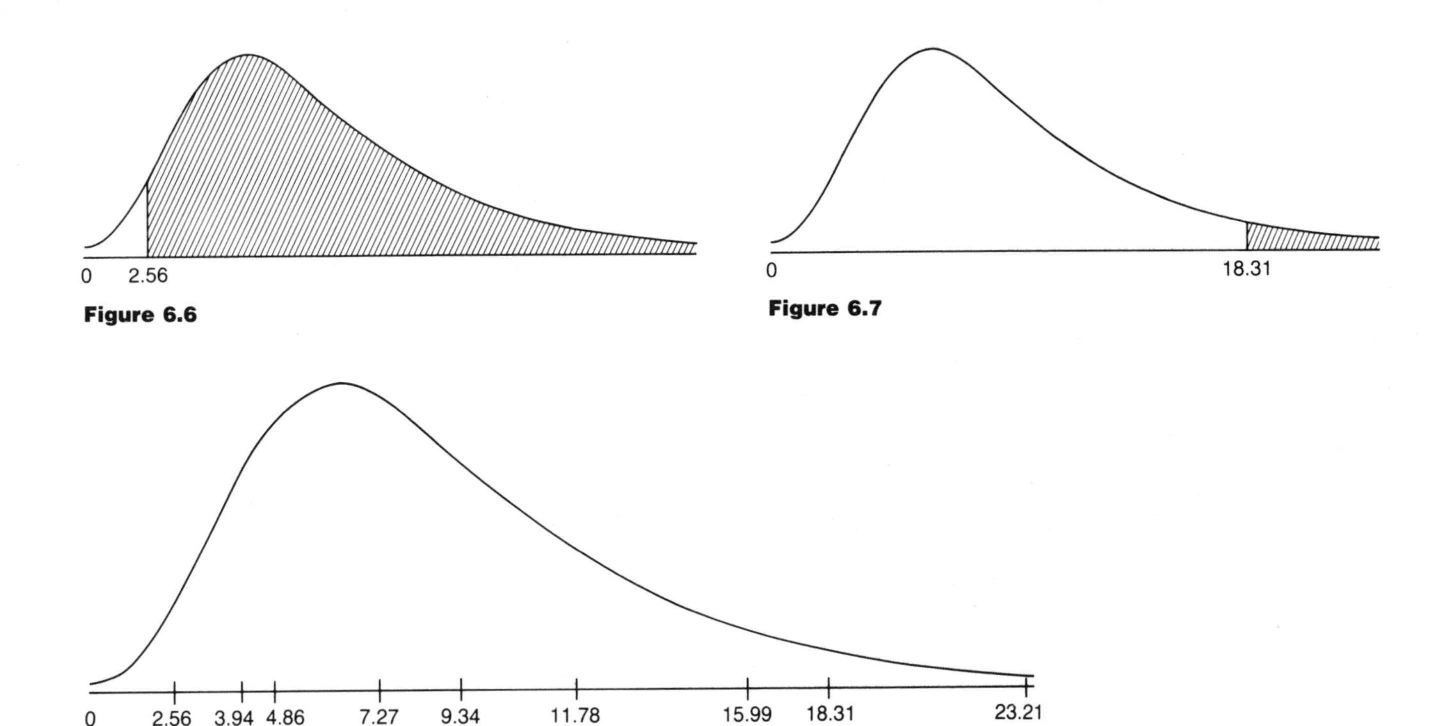

Figure 6.6

Figure 6.7

Figure 6.8

Now look across the row for ten degrees of freedom. The figure 99% in the top row above the 2.56 in the table tells us that 99% of the area under the chi-square curve is to the right of 2.56, as illustrated in Figure 6.6. This tells us that 99% of the time we can expect to get a chi-square value of 2.56 or larger for ten degrees of freedom. The figure 5% above the 18.31 tells us that only 5% of the time would we expect a chi-square value of 18.31 or larger for ten degrees of freedom. Only 5% of the area under the curve in Figure 6.7 is to the right of 18.31.

The numbers 2.56 and 18.31 are referred to as *cut-off points* at the 99% and 5% levels, respectively. Figure 6.8 illustrates the relative positions of the other *cut-off points* for ten degrees of freedom.

In general, statisticians become suspicious of their original hypothesis or assumption when they obtain a chi-square value that occurs 5% or less of the time. They will usually reject their original hypothesis if their chi-square value is greater than or equal to the *cut-off point* of 18.31 at the 5% level. However, some who are more worried about mistakenly rejecting the original assumption will use the *cut-off point* of 23.21 at the 1% level.

Where does the chi-square value for this experiment fit? Is your chi-square value greater than or equal to 18.31? ____________ Would you reject the original assumption at the 5% level? ____________ At the 1% level? ____________

Worksheet 6.6

1. Calculate the chi-square value for your first dice experiment. Use your combined data of 180 rolls from the example on page 235.

Sum of Dice Experiment

Sum	Observed (O) Frequency	Expected (E) Frequency	$(O - E)$	$(O - E)^2$	$\frac{(O - E)^2}{E}$
2	______	______	______	______	______
3	______	______	______	______	______
4	______	______	______	______	______
5	______	______	______	______	______
6	______	______	______	______	______
7	______	______	______	______	______
8	______	______	______	______	______
9	______	______	______	______	______
10	______	______	______	______	______
11	______	______	______	______	______
12	______	______	______	______	______

Total: ____________

2. How many degrees of freedom does this experiment have?

3. Do you reject the assumption of fair dice at the 5% level?

4. At the 1% level?

Worksheet 6.7

1. Calculate the chi-square value for your second dice experiment. Use your combined data for 180 rolls from Worksheet 6.5.

Difference of Dice Experiment

Difference	Observed (O) Frequency	Expected (E) Frequency	$(O - E)$	$(O - E)^2$	$\frac{(O-E)^2}{E}$
0	______	______	______	______	______
1	______	______	______	______	______
2	______	______	______	______	______
3	______	______	______	______	______
4	______	______	______	______	______
5	______	______	______	______	______

Total: __________

2. How many degrees of freedom does this experiment have?

3. What is the 5% cut-off point for five degrees of freedom?

4. Do you reject the assumption of fair dice at the 5% level?

5. What is the 1% cut-off point?

6. Do you reject the assumption at the 1% level?

Don't be disappointed if you didn't get to reject the assumption of fair dice. Most dice are fair. However, if you want to load your dice, put several layers of masking tape over the 1s. Then repeat one of the experiments to see if your test results are different.

Another interesting activity is to deliberately make up a set of data for rolling two dice that are obviously far from the theoretical values. Try this for the sums for 180 rolls. Perform a chi-square test on your made-up data.

Some more practical uses of the chi-square test are to determine if levels of pollution are unacceptable and to determine the effectiveness of new medicines in medical research.

In this section we have used the chi-square test to decide whether to reject or accept a hypothesis. A basic statistics course will introduce you to many other tests of hypotheses as well as to other methods of making decisions in the area of *inferential statistics*. It will also include methods from *descriptive statistics* for organizing, describing, and analyzing collections of data.

CHAPTER Seven

Logic and Spatial Problems

Logical thinking is the foundation of mathematical thought. Although the other chapters in this book all require logical reasoning, this chapter focuses on solving traditional logic problems and using logic to play strategy games and to solve spatial puzzles. These topics are often considered to be recreational in nature. We hope that by the time you finish this chapter you will agree with this description. The Bibliography contains references for books on these topics.

COOPERATIVE LOGIC

We began the mathematics activities in this book with a cooperative logic problem. We will begin this chapter with three more of these problems. If you have not done the cooperative logic problem on Worksheet 1.1 in the introduction, you may wish to do that first.

To prepare the cooperative logic envelopes, make a copy or copies of each of the four problems. Cut each page apart on the indicated lines. Put the pieces in an envelope, and label the envelope appropriately.

You will need groups of three to six people sitting around a table. Each group takes an envelope containing clues for a logic problem. Distribute the six clue cards to your group members. (Some people will receive two cards if there are less than six members in your group.) Your group's task is to solve a logic problem cooperatively by pooling the information from the clue cards. You may read out loud to the group any information on your own clue card(s), but you may not show your card(s) to anyone. Everyone in the group must agree with the solution. When you have done one problem, try another.

If there are extra slips of paper in the envelope that are not clue cards, put them in the middle of the table. These are to be moved around to help you solve the problem. If there are no extra slips, you may make your own, draw pictures, or take notes; but don't write on the clue cards.

If you are working at home, find two or three friends to work with you, or go through the clues one at a time on your own.

The format for these problems is adapted from the *Green Box*, Humboldt County Schools, Office of Environmental Education, Eureka, California. For further problems, see the *SPACES* book prepared by the EQUALS project under the direction of Sherry Fraser, now available from the Dale Seymour Publishing Company.

PROBLEM 1: BABY QUILT

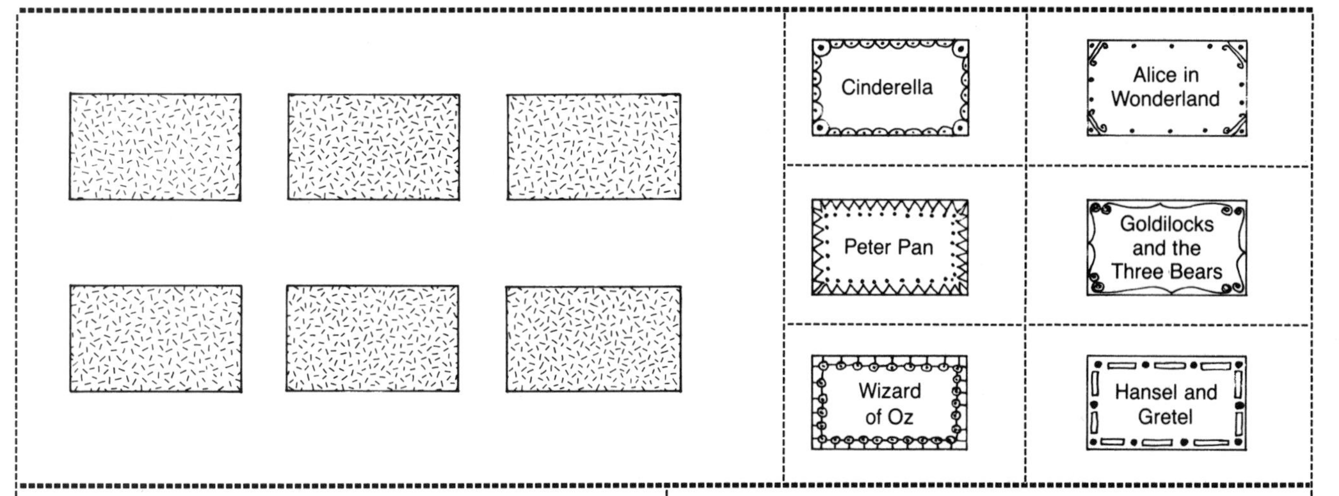

CLUE CARD

These clues will help solve your problem. You may read them out loud, but don't show your card to anyone.

Problem: Where is each storybook scene on the baby quilt?

*Six friends each made a square for a baby quilt.
*Cinderella is to the left of Peter Pan.

CLUE CARD

These clues will help solve your problem. You may read them out loud, but don't show your card to anyone.

Problem: Where is each storybook scene on the baby quilt?

*Hansel and Gretel are below Cinderella.
*The quilt was hung on a wall over the baby's bed.

CLUE CARD

These clues will help solve your problem. You may read them out loud, but don't show your card to anyone.

Problem: Where is each storybook scene on the baby quilt?

*Each square on the quilt depicts a children's storybook scene.
*Alice in Wonderland is above the Wizard of Oz.

CLUE CARD

These clues will help solve your problem. You may read them out loud, but don't show your card to anyone.

Problem: Where is each storybook scene on the baby quilt?

*Peter Pan is above Goldilocks and the Three Bears
*The Wizard of Oz is next to Hansel and Gretel.

CLUE CARD

These clues will help solve your problem. You may read them out loud, but don't show your card to anyone.

Problem: Where is each storybook scene on the baby quilt?

*Cinderella is to the left of Alice in Wonderland.
*The Wizard of Oz is next to Goldilocks and the Three Bears.

CLUE CARD

These clues will help solve your problem. You may read them out loud, but don't show your card to anyone.

Problem: Where is each storybook scene on the baby quilt?

*Alice in Wonderland is next to Peter Pan.
*The border of the quilt is a blue print.

PROBLEM 2: WHO TEACHES WHAT?

CLUE CARD

These clues will help solve your problem. You may read them out loud, but don't show your card to anyone.

*Henrietta, Elena, and Martha are the only teachers of calculus, trigonometry, and geometry at Union High School, but not necessarily in that order.

*Martha's office is next to the geometry teacher's office.

CLUE CARD

These clues will help solve your problem. You may read them out loud, but don't show your card to anyone.

Problem: What are the names of the only calculus, trigonometry, and geometry teachers at Union High School?

*The calculus teacher is Martha's sister.

*The trigonometry and geometry teachers both own computers.

*Elena likes poetry.

CLUE CARD

These clues will help solve your problem. You may read them out loud, but don't show your card to anyone.

*Henrietta and the calculus teacher go to math conferences together.

*Elena and the geometry teacher graduated from the same college, but ten years apart.

CLUE CARD

These clues will help solve your problem. You may read them out loud, but don't show your card to anyone.

*The trigonometry teacher taught Elena celestial navigation.

*Martha, Elena, and Henrietta all love puzzles.

CLUE CARD

These clues will help solve your problem. You may read them out loud, but don't show your card to anyone.

*Each woman teaches only one of the math subjects.

*All three majored in math at college.

CLUE CARD

These clues will help solve your problem. You may read them out loud, but don't show your card to anyone.

*Henrietta and Martha were childhood friends.

*The calculus teacher lent the trigonometry teacher a book of poetry.

PROBLEM 3: POTLUCK PARTY

CLUE CARD

These clues will help solve your problem. You may read them out loud, but don't show your card to anyone.

*Sue, Bill, Donna, and George each prepared one dish for the potluck party.
*George hates desserts.
*No two people brought the same dish.

CLUE CARD

These clues will help solve your problem. You may read them out loud, but don't show your card to anyone.

*Bill's dish contained fresh greens from his garden.
*Sue was planning to make a pie but didn't have the ingredients.
*All four like the dishes they brought to the party.

CLUE CARD

These clues will help solve your problem. You may read them out loud, but don't show your card to anyone.

*The dishes at the potluck were spaghetti, apple pie, salad, and chicken casserole.
*The spaghetti had a tomato sauce.
*The salad contained cucumber, lettuce, spinach, and olives.

CLUE CARD

These clues will help solve your problem. You may read them out loud, but don't show your card to anyone.

*Sue and Donna don't use olives in their cooking.
*Sue doesn't like tomatoes.
*Each person brought only one type of food to the party.

CLUE CARD

These clues will help solve your problem. You may read them out loud, but don't show your card to anyone.

*Sue knows how to prepare three of the dishes.
*George is glad he didn't make chicken casserole, because someone else did.
*Donna doesn't like what George brought.

CLUE CARD

These clues will help solve your problem. You may read them out loud, but don't show your card to anyone.

Problem: Who prepared each dish for the potluck party?

*Donna doesn't use tomatoes in her cooking because she is allergic to them.
*Sue is an excellent cook.
*George never makes salads.

SOLVING LOGIC PROBLEMS USING CHARTS

The cooperative logic problems are similar to logic puzzles that appear in magazines and recreational math books. Organizing the information from such problems into a chart or table often makes them easier to solve. Let's see how this works with Problem 2, "Who Teaches What?".

The problem asks who teaches calculus, who teaches trigonometry, and who teaches geometry. The first clue card tells us that Henrietta, Elena, and Martha teach these subjects. We will use Table 7.1 to record the information. We learn next that Martha's office is next to the geometry teacher's; therefore, Martha cannot be the geometry teacher. To record this fact, write "No" in the box where geometry and Martha intersect.

	Calculus	Trigonometry	Geometry
Henrietta			
Elena			
Martha			no

Table 7.1

Next, we learn that Henrietta and the calculus teacher go to math conferences together. This means that Henrietta is not the calculus teacher. Record a "No" in the appropriate box.

We also know that Elena and the geometry teacher graduated from the same college; therefore, Elena is not the geometry teacher. When we write the "No" this time, we can see that Henrietta is the only one left to teach geometry. Write a "Yes" in the appropriate box to record this fact.

At this stage your chart should look like Table 7.2. We can extend our knowledge at this point without reading any further clues. Since each person teaches only one subject, we can write a "No" to indicate that Henrietta does not teach trigonometry.

	Calculus	Trigonometry	Geometry
Henrietta	no		yes
Elena			no
Martha			no

Table 7.2

"The calculus teacher is Martha's sister" tells us that Martha is not the calculus teacher. When we fill in the "No", that leaves trigonometry for Martha to teach. And when we put in the "No" to show that Elena

	Calculus	Trigonometry	Geometry
Henrietta	no	no	yes
Elena	yes	no	no
Martha	no	yes	no

Table 7.3

does not teach trigonometry, we see that she must teach calculus, as the final form of the chart shows in Table 7.3.

There are more clues. Some, such as "Martha, Elena, and Henrietta all love puzzles," may be of interest but do not contribute to the solution. But we should check to see if the other relevant clues agree with our conclusions. "The trigonometry teacher taught Elena celestial navigation" tells us that Elena does not teach trigonometry, which agrees. Check the rest of the information on the clue cards with a partner. Decide which clues contribute to the solution and which provide only extraneous information.

Use charts or slips of paper to solve the logic problems on the next worksheet. The order in which you use the clues will not affect the outcome.

Worksheet 7.1

1. Three people are deciding who gets which dessert. They have cheesecake, pecan pie, and chocolate mousse. Mark likes pecan pie and chocolate mousse. Nancy is allergic to nuts. Roger has a hard time deciding but finally chooses pecan pie. Which dessert does each person eat?

	Mark	Nancy	Roger
Cheesecake			
Chocolate mousse			
Pecan Pie			

2. Anna, Tom, Colleen, Luke, and Diana are at a birthday party. Tom, though not the oldest, is older than Colleen. Anna and Luke are younger than Tom. Colleen, not the youngest, is younger than Anna. The baby of the group is just old enough to vote. Diana is more than three times as old as Luke.

Put these men and women in order by age, with the youngest first. Write each name on a slip of paper. Moving the names around will help you solve the problem.

3. Adena bought five flavors of yogurt to have for lunch at work each day. The flavors are blueberry, boysenberry, strawberry, pineapple, and apricot. On Monday she didn't eat the boysenberry yogurt. On Thursday she ate the pineapple. On Tuesday she didn't have the apricot. She didn't have the apricot on Friday, either. The day before she ate the pineapple, she ate the boysenberry. Strawberry is her favorite flavor, so she saved that for the last day of the week. Which flavor did Adena eat on each day?

	Monday	Tuesday	Wednesday	Thursday	Friday
Blueberry					
Boysenberry					
Strawberry					
Pineapple					
Apricot					

(continued)

4. The chamber music group has four members. They play the cello, violin, flute, and piano. No one plays an instrument that begins with the same letter as his or her first name. Conrad never learned to play the piano. Penelope and the violinist share an apartment. Francis plays the cello, which he inherited from his aunt. Which instrument does each person play?

	Conrad	Valerie	Francis	Penelope
Cello				
Violin				
Flute				
Piano				

5. Decameter, centimeter, kilometer, hectometer, meter, millimeter, and decimeter are metric units of length. Use the following clues to arrange the units from largest to smallest.

- A hectometer is about 10 yards longer than a football field.
- A meter is a bit longer than a yardstick.
- We might buy a decameter of fabric to make drapes for the bay window in the living room.
- The speed limit on California highways is about 90 kilometers per hour.
- The width of an eyelash, paper clip, or point of a pen can be measured in millimeters.
- Ten decimeters make a meter.
- A little more than 2 centimeters make an inch.

1. ____________ 2. ____________ 3. ____________ 4. ____________

5. ____________ 6. ____________ 7. ____________

6. Two young women, Alice and Beverly, and two young men, Charles and Donald, each won a trip to spend a month in Europe. Each person spent his or her vacation in a different country. The countries visited were Spain, Italy, France, and England. Donald did not go to Spain or Italy. Beverly did not go to France or Italy. Alice did not go to Spain or France. Charles did not go to Spain or Italy. Donald studied French especially for this trip. Which person went to which country?

STRATEGY GAMES

Strategy games provide interesting logic problems that use inductive reasoning. These games challenge the players to develop an optimal method of play or a winning strategy. We will give the rules for two games in this section. To develop a strategy for each game, you will need to play it frequently over a period of time to draw conclusions from your experiences. Share your conclusions with a partner, and work together to develop a winning method of play.

We have included only two strategy games here, but there are many others, such as Mastermind, Kalah, and Three-Dimensional Tic-Tac-Toe. Most game stores carry a variety of strategy games.

Nim

In this version of the game, a specified number of counters (beans, pennies, toothpicks, or the like) are placed in a row. Two players take turns picking up counters. The person who picks up the *last* counter wins.

To start with, put out ten counters. When it is your turn, you may take *one* or *two* counters. The person who takes the last one (or two) counters wins. Play this game several times with a partner. See what information you can determine about winning and losing. After you have played for a while, read the discussion about the strategy for this game. Feel free to stop and try out any new ideas as you go along.

Did you discover any "trouble points" as a Nim player? Most players decide that it is impossible to win this game when only three counters are left and it is their turn. If you take one counter, your opponent will win by taking two, and vice versa.

One good approach to working on Nim strategies is to start with just a few counters and work backwards to the original number. Suppose we start with one counter. As we go along, put out the appropriate number of counters and act out what would happen in the game. If it is your turn with one counter left, you can take it and win. With two counters left, you can also win.

Record your findings in Table 7.4 on the next page. The left column indicates the number of counters. The right column indicates whether you will win or lose if it is your turn. The first two results are recorded.

Number of counters	Win or lose
1	win
2	win
3	
4	
5	
6	
7	
8	
9	
10	

Table 7.4

We have already decided that you lose with three counters. Record this in the table. Now what about four counters? Put four out. If it is your turn, what will you do? (Assume that you have a smart opponent who knows the strategy.) If you take one counter, you leave the opponent in a losing position with three. So you win with four counters. For five, how many counters do you need to take to leave the opponent with three? Two, and you will win again. Record these results in Table 7.4.

O OOO

Figure 7.2

OO OOO

Figure 7.3

Now put out six counters. If it is your turn and you take one, what would a smart opponent do? If you take two, what would the opponent do? There is no way to win if it is your turn with six counters.

OOO OOO

Figure 7.4

Look at the arrangements of seven and eight counters. For seven, what would you do? Take one, leaving the opponent with six. For eight? Take two and leave the opponent with six again. Record these results in the table.

O OOO OOO

Figure 7.5

OO OOO OOO

Figure 7.6

What happens with nine counters? If you take one, what will your opponent do? If you take two, what will your opponent do? Can you win with nine? No.

OOO OOO OOO

Figure 7.7

What about ten? If you take one counter, that leaves the opponent with nine in a losing position. Record these results in Table 7.4, and look at the pattern of wins and losses.

O OOO OOO OOO

Figure 7.8

What conclusions can we make? For this particular Nim game—starting with ten counters and picking up one or two on a turn—it is best to go first and take one counter. Then continue playing so that you leave your opponent with nine, six, and three (multiples of 3) counters. Try some games using this strategy with unsuspecting opponents. Then see if you can help them discover the strategy for themselves.

Here are some variations of Nim that you might try:

Add more counters: first try 18, 21, and 24.
Change the rules so each player can take 1, 2, or 3 counters at a time.
Play that the one who takes the last counter *loses*.

Try to find strategies for these variations. For other types of Nim games, see *The Scientific American Book of Mathematical Puzzles and Diversions* by Martin Gardner.

Pico-Fermi-Bagels

If you have seen the commercial game Mastermind, you will have some familiarity with the game called Pico-Fermi-Bagels. In this game one player thinks of a number, which other players try to figure out using the fewest possible guesses.

This is how the game works. One player thinks of a two-digit number with no repeating digits; numbers like 77, 55, or 66 cannot be chosen. The other players guess a number, and the response (which will be explained) provides clues for the next guess. Remember, the object is to guess the number in as few turns as possible.

These are the three responses and an example of what each means.

Pico: one (and only one) of your digits is correct, but it's in the wrong place. Example: If the number is 46 and you guess 63, the response would be *pico*. This means that one of the digits is correct but in the wrong place and that the other digit is not in the number. Of course, you wouldn't know whether the 6 or the 3 is the correct digit.

Fermi: one of your digits is correct and in the right place. Example: If 46 is the number and you guess 86, the response would be *fermi*. This means one of the digits is correct and in the right place and that the other digit is not in the number. Again, you wouldn't necessarily know whether the 8 or the 6 is the correct digit.

Bagels: None of your digits are the same as the digits in the number. Example: If the number is 46 and you guess 82, the response would be *bagels*.

Here is a sample game.

Guess	Response
82	*Pico*
47	*Bagels*
84	*Pico*

From these three guesses, you should have some information about one of the digits. Since we know that 4 is not one of the digits (second clue), we know that it must be the 8 in the third clue that is in the wrong place. So the number so far is ? 8; that is, we are looking for the number in the tens place.

Guess	Response
18	*Fermi*
53	*Pico*

Now you should be able to figure out what the number is. Since *Pico* means the digit is in the wrong place, it can't be the 5 (which is already in the 10s place). So the next guess is

Guess	Response
38	*Fermi Fermi*

(Both numbers are correct, and each is in the correct place.)

Try this game with a partner. Take turns choosing the number, giving the clues, and guessing the number. For more challenge, try a game with three- or four-digit numbers.

Worksheet 7.2

Solve these Pico-Fermi-Bagels puzzles. P (*Pico*) means one digit is correct and in the wrong place; F (*Fermi*) means one digit is correct and in the right place; B (*Bagels*) means none of the digits is correct.

1. 25 B
39 F
76 P
98 B
____ FF

2. 34 B
58 F
27 B
61 P
71 P
____ FF

3. 35 B
76 B
98 P
12 P
89 F
41 B
____ FF

4. 80 B
74 B
32 F
53 B
61 P
____ FF

5. 521 P
750 PF
102 B
394 F
648 B
973 PP
735 PPP
______ FFF

6. 493 F
639 P
764 B
250 PP
815 P
534 PF
821 F
698 B
______ FFF

7. 406 B
901 PP
345 B
980 PF
809 PF
673 B
902 P
______ FFF

8. 325 B
246 F
690 F
789 B
______ FFF

9. 4760 FFPP
6074 FPPP
7064 FFPP
7046 FPPP
4076 FFPP
6740 PPPP
________ FFFF

SOME WELL-KNOWN LOGIC PROBLEMS

Here are some different kinds of logical reasoning problems. Some clues will be given to help you start thinking about them. Variations of these problems are found over and over again in many books and publications. Many people consider solving problems of this type to be a recreational math activity.

PROBLEM 4: *Three sisters named Barbara, Betty, and Becky are running in their first Bonnie Bell 10K (10 kilometer) race. Barbara, the fastest runner of the three, always tells the truth. Betty sometimes tells the truth, whereas Becky, the slowest runner, never does. Use the clues in the picture to find out who is who. (A good way to start is to first figure out which one is Barbara.)*

Figure 7.9

Spend a few moments thinking about this problem. If you want some help, continue reading.

We're trying to first figure out which person is Barbara. Remember, Barbara *always* tells the truth. Let's assume the runner on the left is Barbara. Since Barbara always tells the truth, she wouldn't say, "The one in the middle is Barbara." Thus, there is a *contradiction*, and we conclude that the woman on the left is not Barbara.

Now look at the person in the middle. Can that person be Barbara? Could Barbara truthfully say, "I'm Becky." We have another contradiction. By process of elimination we see that Barbara must be the woman on the right. Finish the problem on your own.

PROBLEM 5: *There are two cans in Figure 7.10. One holds exactly 2 gallons, and the other holds exactly 5 gallons. The cans are not marked, and you may not make any marks on the cans. You have an* *unlimited supply of water and may pour water freely from one can to another, or you may empty the can onto the ground (or into the sink). Using just the 5-gallon can and the 2-gallon can, explain how you can show each of the following amounts of water: 1 gallon; 2 gallons; 3 gallons; 4 gallons; 5 gallons; 6 gallons; 7 gallons.*

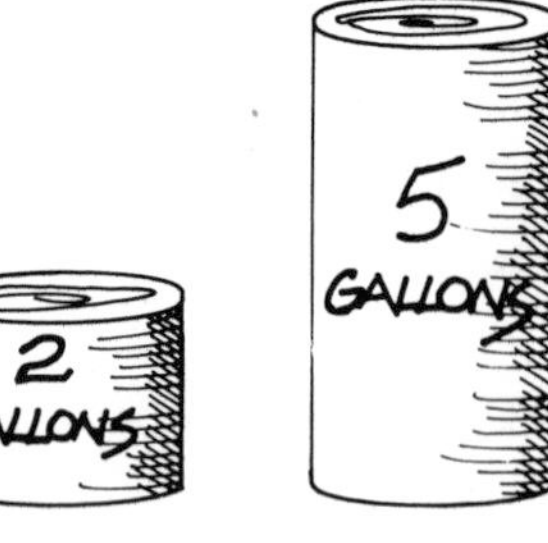

Figure 7.10

The hardest part of this kind of problem is getting started and understanding the rules. Since the cans are not marked, we can't make observations like "This is half full." We can be much more precise than that, as you will soon see.

It's easy to show 2 gallons—just fill up the 2-gallon can. In the same way we can show 5 gallons. And we can fill up both cans and show 7 gallons. If we fill up the 5-gallon can and pour it into the 2-gallon can, we have 3 gallons left in the 5-gallon can.

We still have to figure out how to show 1 gallon, 4 gallons, and 6 gallons. Try to figure it out on your own. If you want some help, read on.

Fill up the 2-gallon can and pour it into the 5-gallon can; fill up the 2-gallon can again and pour it into the 5-gallon can—you now have 4 gallons. If you fill up the 2-gallon can once more, you have a total of 6 gallons (4 in the 5-gallon can and 2 in the 2-gallon can).

We still have to figure out how to get 1 gallon. Try to get it on your own. If you get stuck, read the following two solutions.

First fill up the 5-gallon can, then pour it into the 2-gallon can, leaving 3 gallons in the 5-gallon can. Dump out the 2-gallon can and fill it once more from the 5-gallon can. One gallon will be left in the 5-gallon can.

Or we can solve the problem this way. Fill up the 2-gallon can, then pour it into the 5-gallon can. Do it again, and you will have 4 gallons in the 5-gallon can. Fill up the 2-gallon can once more. This time only 1 gallon will fit into the 5-gallon can, leaving 1 gallon in the 2-gallon can.

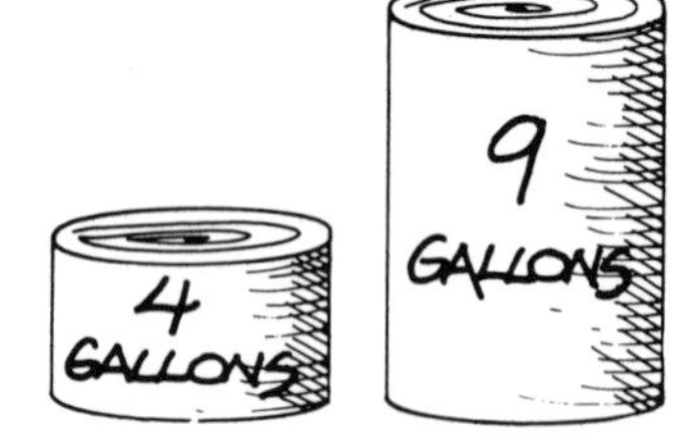

Figure 7.11

Now that you have the idea, try to show how to obtain 1 to 13 gallons using a 4-gallon can and a 9-gallon can.

PROBLEM 6: *In one box there are two blue socks; in another box there are two green socks; and in a third box there is one blue sock and one green sock. The boxes are incorrectly labeled BB, GG, and BG. By looking at only one sock from one of the boxes, you are to tell what's in each box. How can you do this?*

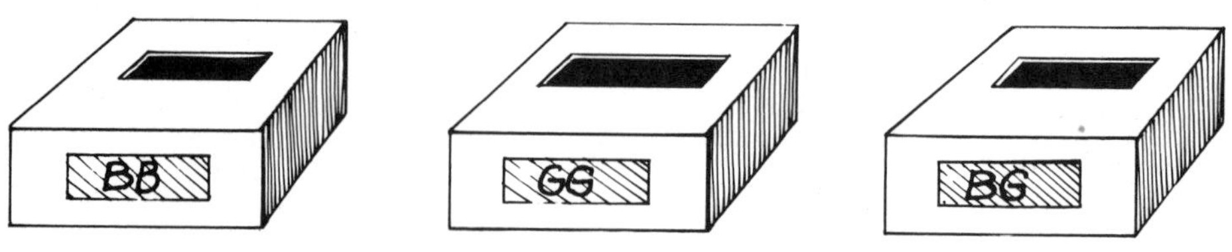

Figure 7.12

Think about the problem. We have only one chance to look at a sock in any box. Once we see the color of that sock, we should be able to figure out what color socks are in all the boxes. Just looking at *any* sock won't solve the problem. The real question is to figure out which box will give us enough information to know for certain what color socks are in all three boxes.

If you want more help, read on. Let's try one guess and see what happens. Suppose we reach into the box labeled BB. What color sock could we pull out? Remember, the boxes are labeled *incorrectly*. The correct label for the box labeled BB is, therefore, either GG or BG, but *not* BB. If we reach into the box labeled BB then, we will pull out either a blue sock or a green sock. What information would we have if we pulled out a blue sock? We would know for certain that the box holds one blue sock and one green sock. Why? But if we pulled out a green sock, we wouldn't know for sure if the label was GG or BG. Therefore, pulling a sock from the box labeled BB will not always solve our problem.

Continue in this way, imagining that you pull a sock from the box labeled GG. What are the possibilities? What information do you get? When you've chosen the correct box, you can, no matter which sock you pull out of it, determine what color socks are in all three boxes.

PROBLEM 7: *You have eight coins that look exactly alike except that one of them is counterfeit and weighs less than the others. Can you find the counterfeit coin by using only two weighings on a pan balance?*

The thought of attacking this problem with eight coins seems overwhelming. As in the earlier problems in this section, we must understand what the problem means. We can simplify this problem by changing it to include fewer coins. In this way we can get the feel of the problem and will be able to approach the eight-coin problem with more confidence.

Suppose there are three coins, one of which is lighter. If we put one coin in each pan (coin A and coin B), two things can happen. The two pans will balance, in which case coin C is counterfeit. Or they will not balance, and we will know that the lighter coin is counterfeit. For three coins we only need a single weighing to find the lighter, counterfeit coin.

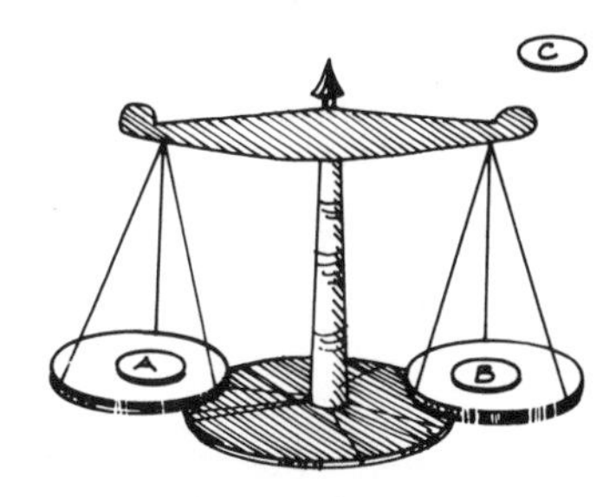

Figure 7.13

Suppose there are four coins, one of which is lighter. Put two coins (A and B) into the pans and leave coins C and D outside. If A and B balance, we find the counterfeit coin by weighing C and D. That takes two weighings. If A and B do not balance, we know the counterfeit coin in a single weighing. We can find the coin for certain in two weighings.

Now try a similar method with five, six, seven, and eight coins. You should be able to find the lighter, counterfeit coin out of eight coins with only two weighings.

Figure 7.14

SPATIAL PUZZLES

The puzzles in this section will improve your ability to visualize geometric shapes and their relationships. Each puzzle is made up of two- or three-dimensional pieces that we can move around to form new shapes and designs. The first three, Tangrams, Toothpick Puzzles, and Tetrominoes, can be easily made at home. The last three, Perceptual Puzzle Blocks™, the Soma Cube, and Wheeler's Design Tiles™, are commercial materials for which we give sample puzzles. References for them are listed in the Bibliography.

The skills that these puzzles help develop—especially the ability to visualize objects moving in space—are a very important part of mathematical and scientific reasoning. Many adults, especially women, have not had many experiences that develop this skill of spatial visualization. Some of you will be surprised at your skill at solving these puzzles. Others of you will be surprised at how quickly you improve with practice.

Tangram Puzzle

The Tangram is an ancient Chinese puzzle consisting of seven geometric shapes that form a square. Cut out the pieces from the model, and try to fit them into the different outlines. Can you put the seven pieces back together to form the original square?

You can also make up your own puzzles by creating a shape and tracing around it. Ask your partner to fill in the pieces.

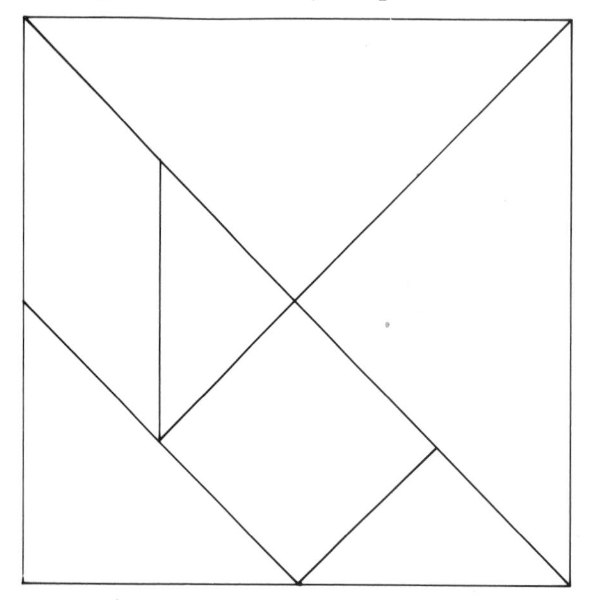

Figure 7.15

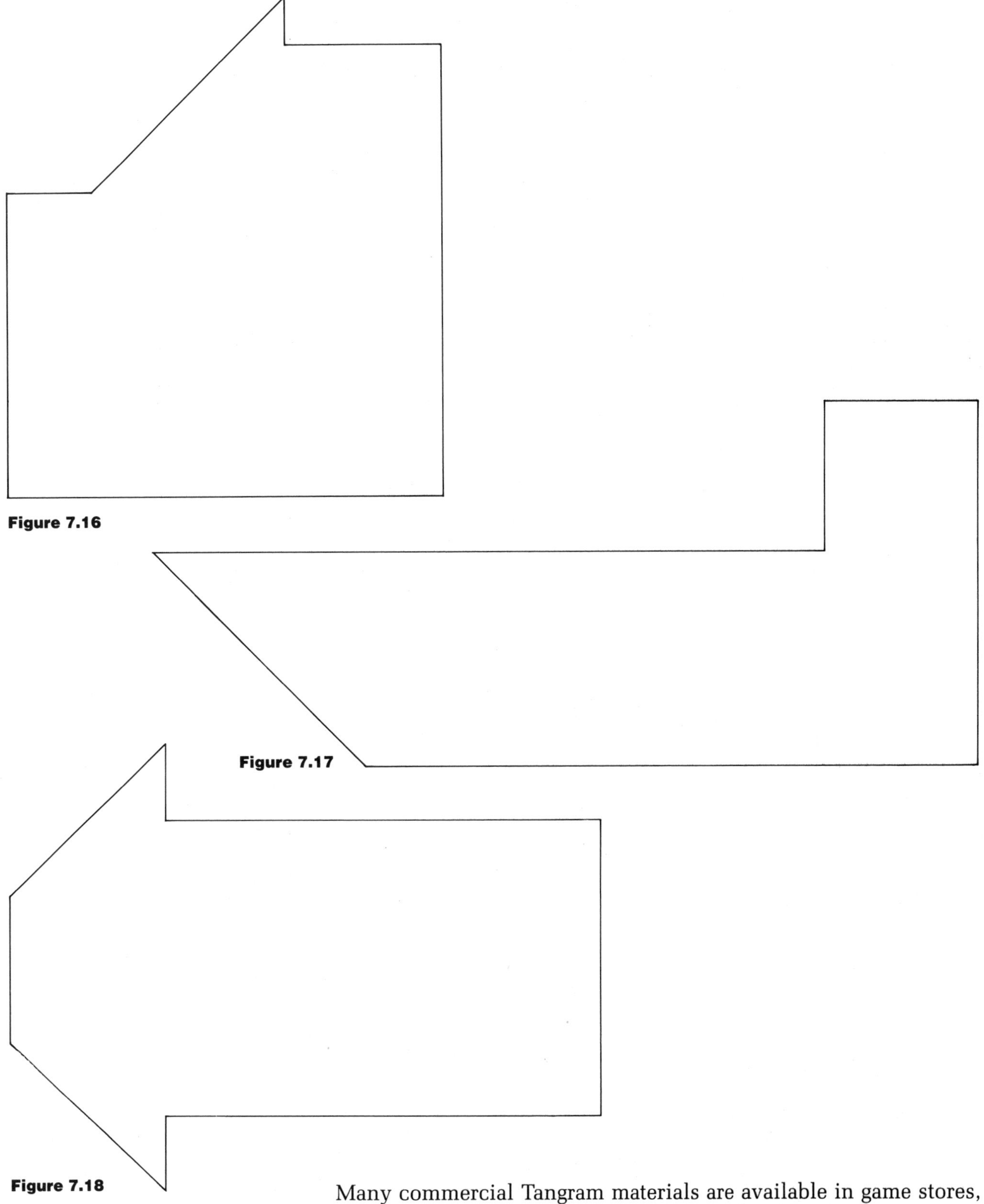
Figure 7.16

Figure 7.17

Figure 7.18

Many commercial Tangram materials are available in game stores, including plastic or wooden pieces, task cards, and books.

Cut out the Tangram pieces from Figure 7.15. Use them to cover the three shapes in Figures 7.16, 7.17, and 7.18.

Toothpick Puzzles

Many spatial puzzles use toothpicks (or matches or pencils). The following are samples of different types of problems to whet your appetite. The book *Tricks, Games and Puzzles with Matches* by Maxey Brooke contains 101 of these puzzles.

First copy the design of each puzzle with toothpicks so you can move the pieces around to help you solve the problems.

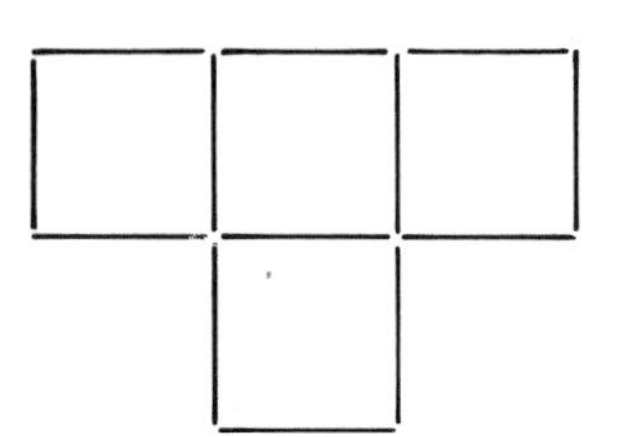

Figure 7.19

Remove one toothpick and leave three squares.

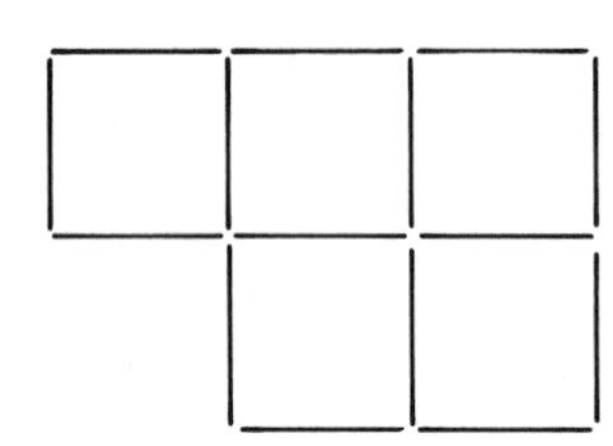

Figure 7.20

Remove three toothpicks and leave three squares.

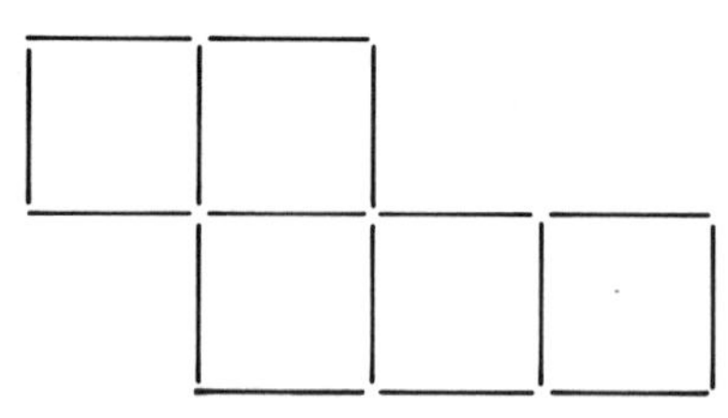

Figure 7.21

Move two toothpicks to new positions so that you form four squares (instead of five). Each toothpick must be the side of a whole square, and all four squares must be the same size.

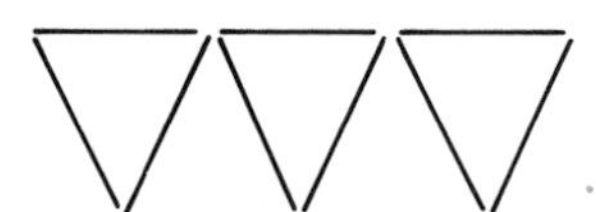

Figure 7.22

Move three toothpicks so you have five triangles.

Figure 7.23

These toothpicks form Roman numerals. Move one toothpick so that the equation is correct.

Tetromino Puzzles

Many different covering puzzles can be made from squares that are attached together. A variety of shapes can be made from three or more squares connected so that a whole side of one square touches a whole side of another square.

For these puzzles we will use *tetrominoes*, made up of four squares. Here are the five tetrominoes.

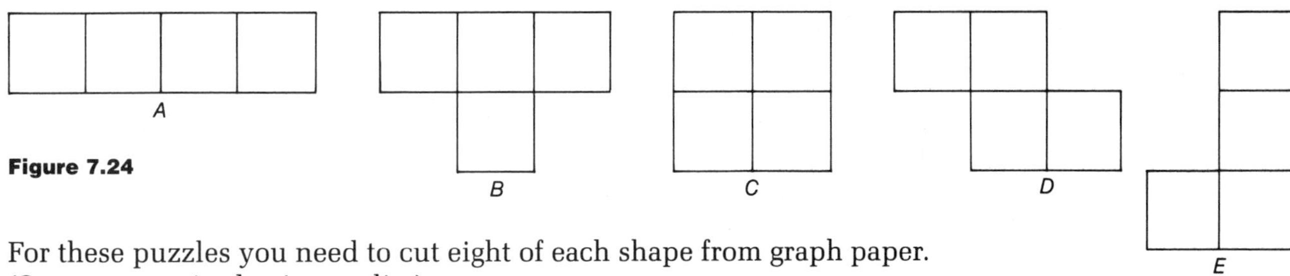

Figure 7.24

For these puzzles you need to cut eight of each shape from graph paper. (See page 281 in the Appendix.)

Can you cover the five-by-four rectangle in Figure 7.25 using five shape *A*s? Try to do it with all *B*s, all *C*s, all *D*s, or all *E*s.

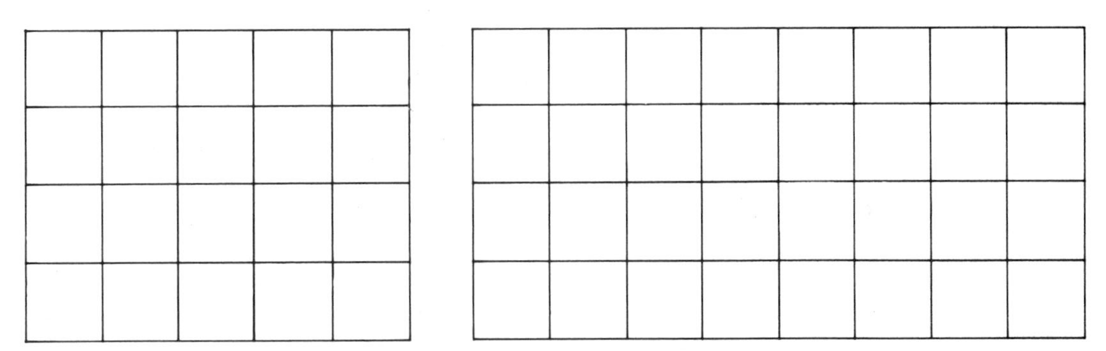

Figure 7.25 **Figure 7.26**

Which shapes will cover the eight-by-four rectangle in Figure 7.26?

You might like to investigate pentominoes (5 squares). First see if you can draw all 12 shapes on graph paper. Cut out four of each pentomino. Can you find different ways to cover the 4-by-5 rectangle in Figure 7.25. Can you cover it with four of the same shape? Can you cover it with four different shapes? Try to make different-sized rectangles using these shapes. For a real challenge, try to make a rectangle using 1 of each of the 12 pentominoes.

The next spatial activities are samples of commercial materials.

Perceptual Puzzle Blocks™ Activity Cards

These materials are designed by Dale and Margo Seymour and distributed by Creative Publications. They provide experiences with two- and three-dimensional objects. The nine shapes of the blocks represent the possible configurations of one, two, three, and four squares on grid paper. Five of the blocks are sketched in Figure 7.27.

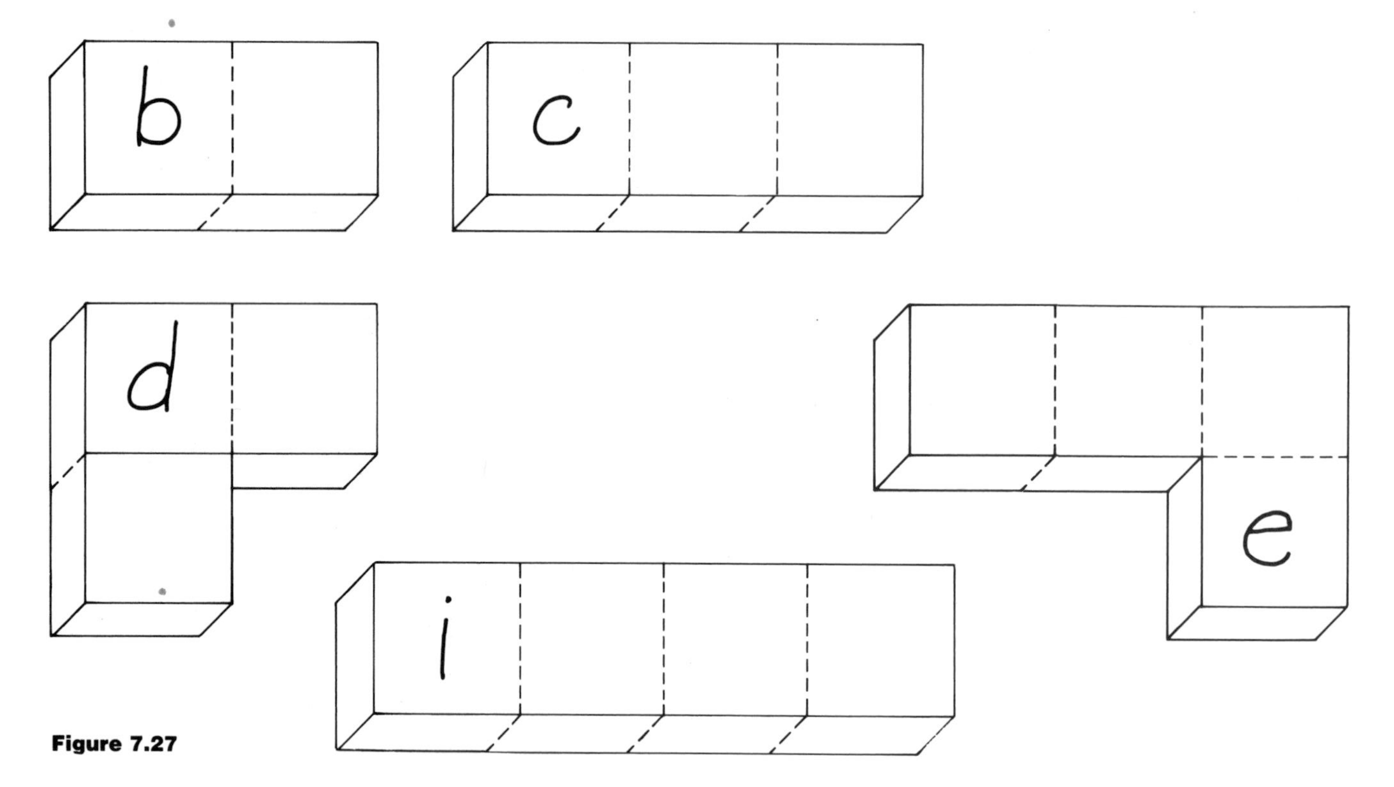

Figure 7.27

These blocks are used to cover given areas exactly or to build three-dimensional solids. The first puzzles help to develop the spatial skills of the beginner, whereas the later ones are a challenge to the expert. Figures 7.28 and 7.29 give examples of two covering activities. To do them, cut out the faces of the blocks in Figure 7.27 from 2-centimeter graph paper. (See page 282 in the Appendix.)

A three-dimensional problem might ask you to use blocks *b*, *c*, *d*, *e*, and *i* to construct a two-by-two-by-three rectangular solid.

Figure 7.28 Use blocks *b*, *c*, *d*, and *i* to cover this area.

Figure 7.29 Use blocks *b*, *c*, *d*, *e*, and *i* to cover this area.

Wheeler's Design Tiles™

These tiles are designed by Dan Wheeler and Dale Seymour and distributed by Creative Publications. They consist of a large set of hexagons colored in wholes, halves, and thirds with red, yellow, and blue. They are used to construct two-dimensional designs that give the illusion of three-dimensional objects.

The designs in Figure 7.31 can be made with the hexagons from Figure 7.30. If you wish to try to reproduce these designs, use the hexagonal paper on page 286 in the Appendix to make a set of hexagons.

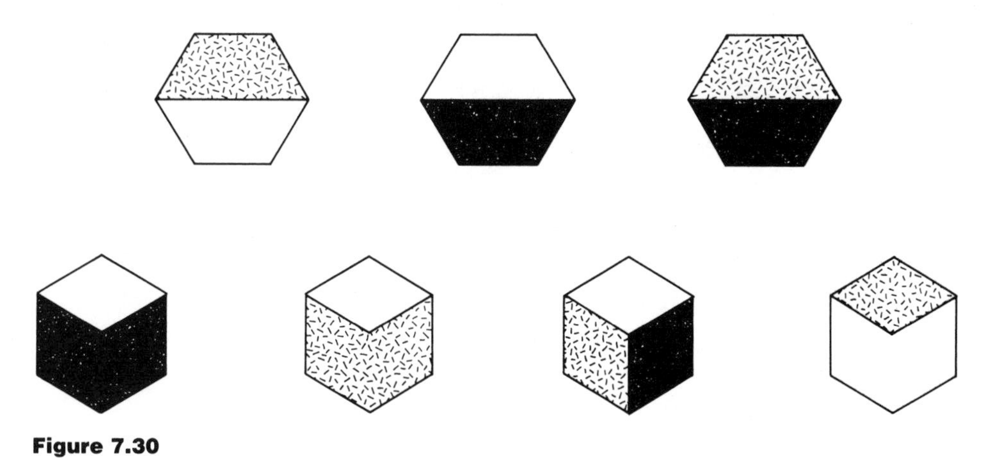

Figure 7.30

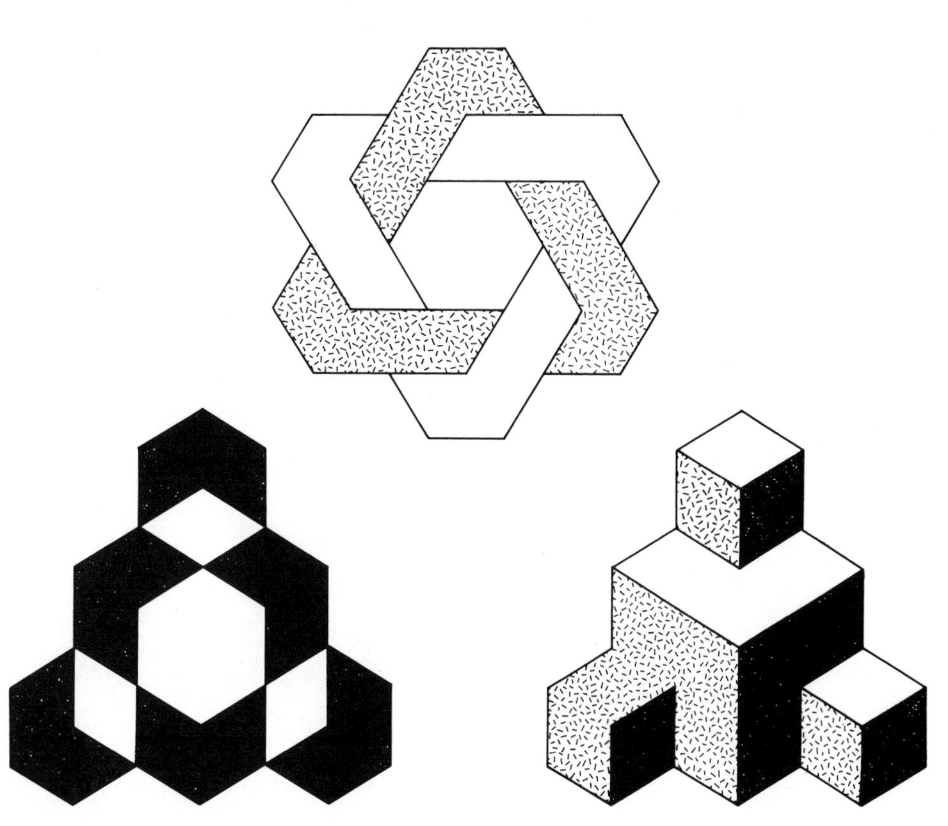

Figure 7.31

Soma Cube

The Soma Cube, which is made up of the seven three-dimensional shapes drawn in Figure 7.32, is a popular item at game stores.

Putting these shapes together to form the original three-by-three-by-three cube can be a real challenge. To make this task easier, you might label the squares on each face with a different type of sticker *before* you take the cube apart for the first time. Even with these clues, the project is not an easy one.

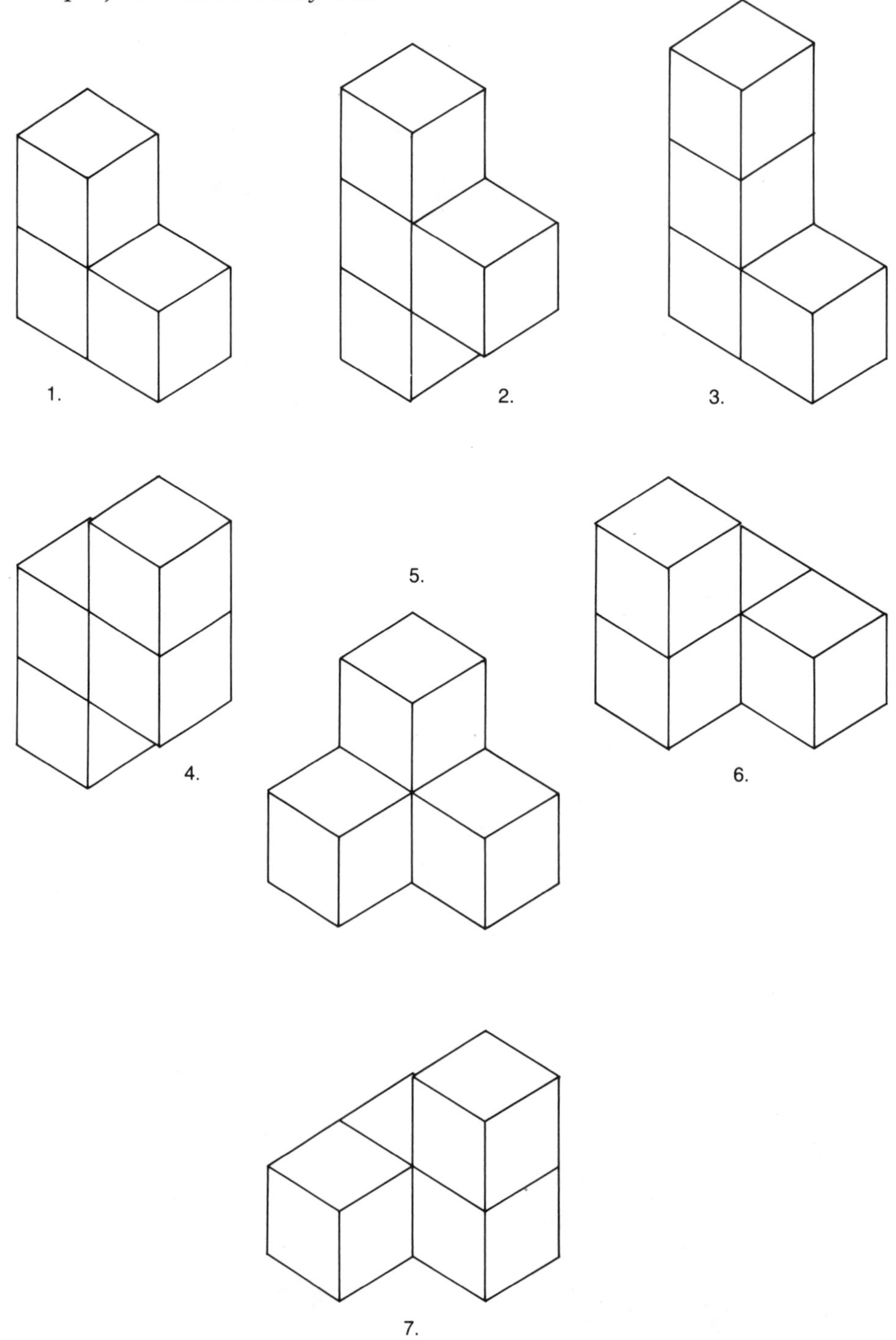

Figure 7.32

To give you a flavor of this puzzle, three "simple" examples are given in Figure 7.33

The Soma Cube comes with a booklet of much more difficult puzzles. If you would like a further challenge, see the *Soma Cube* book listed in the Bibliography.

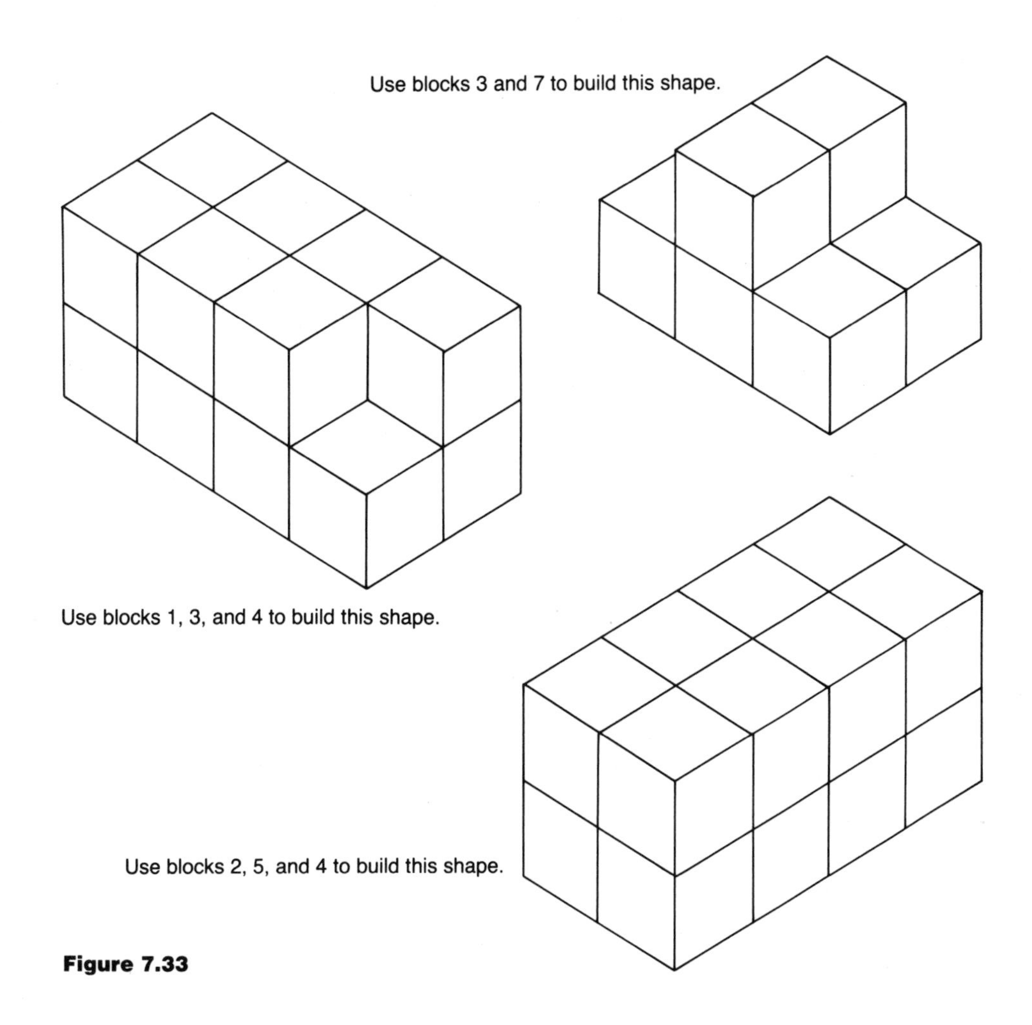

Figure 7.33

CHAPTER Eight
What Next?

Some of you may have already decided on the next step in your mathematics education. Some may even be currently enrolled in another math course. Others may wonder, "Where do I go from here?" For these last, three avenues are open. You can look for a class to take, find a tutor to work with you on specific topics, or work on your own.

Where can you find the appropriate math course? Math classes are available in continuing education and adult education programs, at community colleges, universities, and four-year colleges, and on the job. They vary in style from formal lectures to self-paced courses in which you work at your own rate, with little or no contact with the instructor. Some students flourish under a self-paced program, relying on their own self-discipline to keep them moving along. Others find that they need the pressure of outside deadlines and the structure of a more formal course. You may need to experiment a bit to figure out which system is better for you.

Shop around for your course and instructor. Get a recommendation from someone who has taken the class. There is no point in putting yourself into an uncomfortable situation that is all too similar to the one that caused you to drop out of math in the first place. If you don't understand the instructor or can't obtain the help you need, feel free to drop that course and look for another. You deserve to have a class and instructor that suit your learning style.

No matter which avenue you choose, you need to decide the level of math at which you want to start. For some people the answer will be easy: start where you dropped out, with a general math or beginning algebra course. Others may wonder just how much background knowledge they need in order to start with, say, geometry. Or perhaps you want to consider a specialized course that prepares you for college entrance, graduate record, or other professional exams. Many schools offer a math placement exam for their regular courses or a special placement exam in their self-paced courses. The results of these tests can provide you with advice on where to start. But what if you feel too uncomfortable to try such a test, or none is available, or you are still not sure even after the test?

Look for a course that seems reasonable for your background. Don't plan to overextend yourself. Set yourself up for success by selecting a course that is partially a review. Most students fare far better if their first math course in several years is on the easy side. They find that later, when they are used to studying, they can handle more difficult challenges.

If you decide to work with a tutor or through a textbook on your own, the advice still holds: shop around and start easy. No matter which route you choose, you will find it helpful to have someone to work with. Studying with someone, discussing problems, and reviewing the material together will help to clarify your thinking. Whatever you do, remember to use the approaches that are emphasized in this book. They will help you tackle new material with confidence.

Appendix

Coordinate Tic-Tac-Toe Record Sheet

Play tic-tac-toe with a partner. Keep a record of the points that have been called.

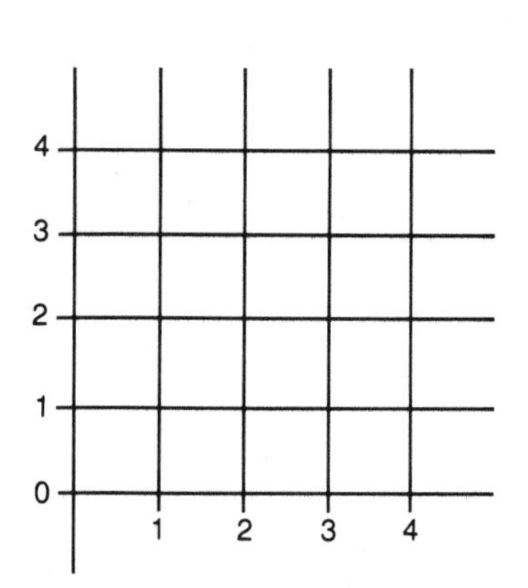

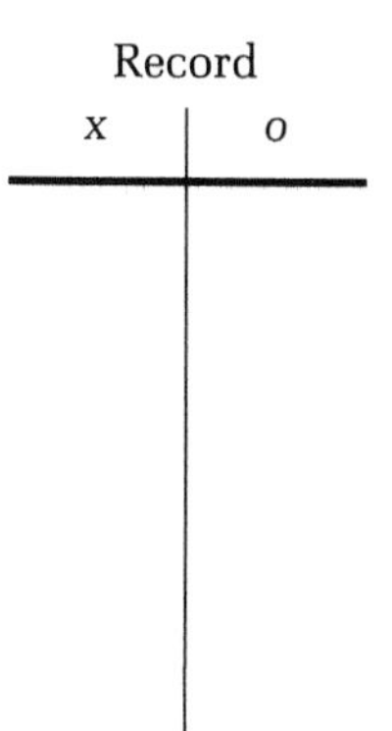

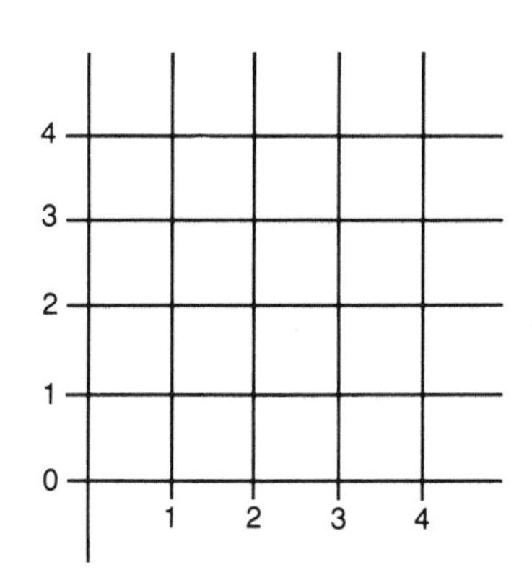

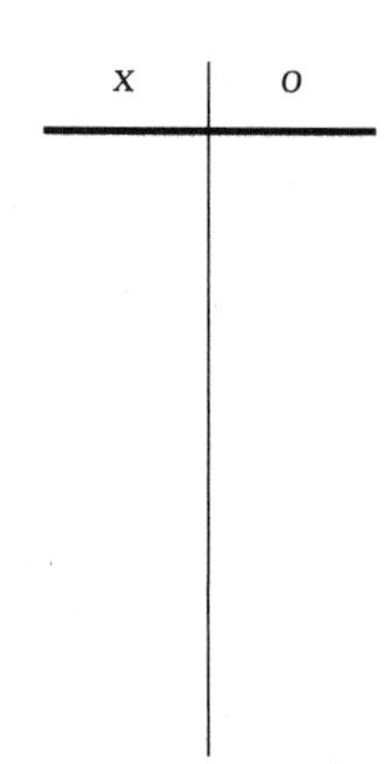

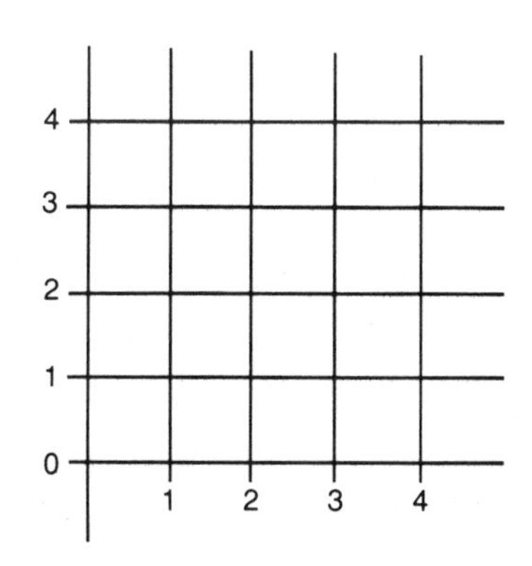

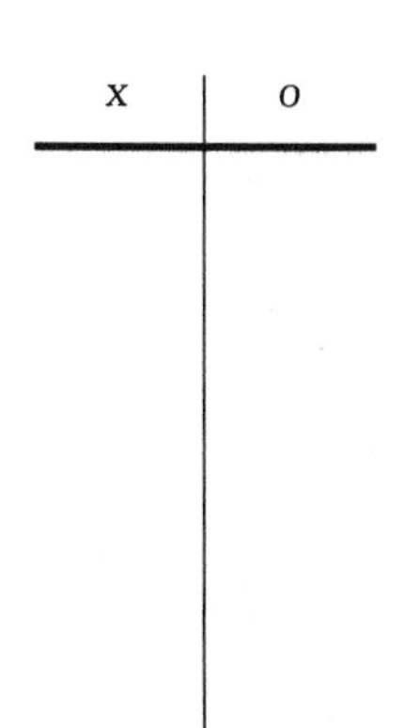

Coordinate Tic-Tac-Toe
Master for Overhead Transparency

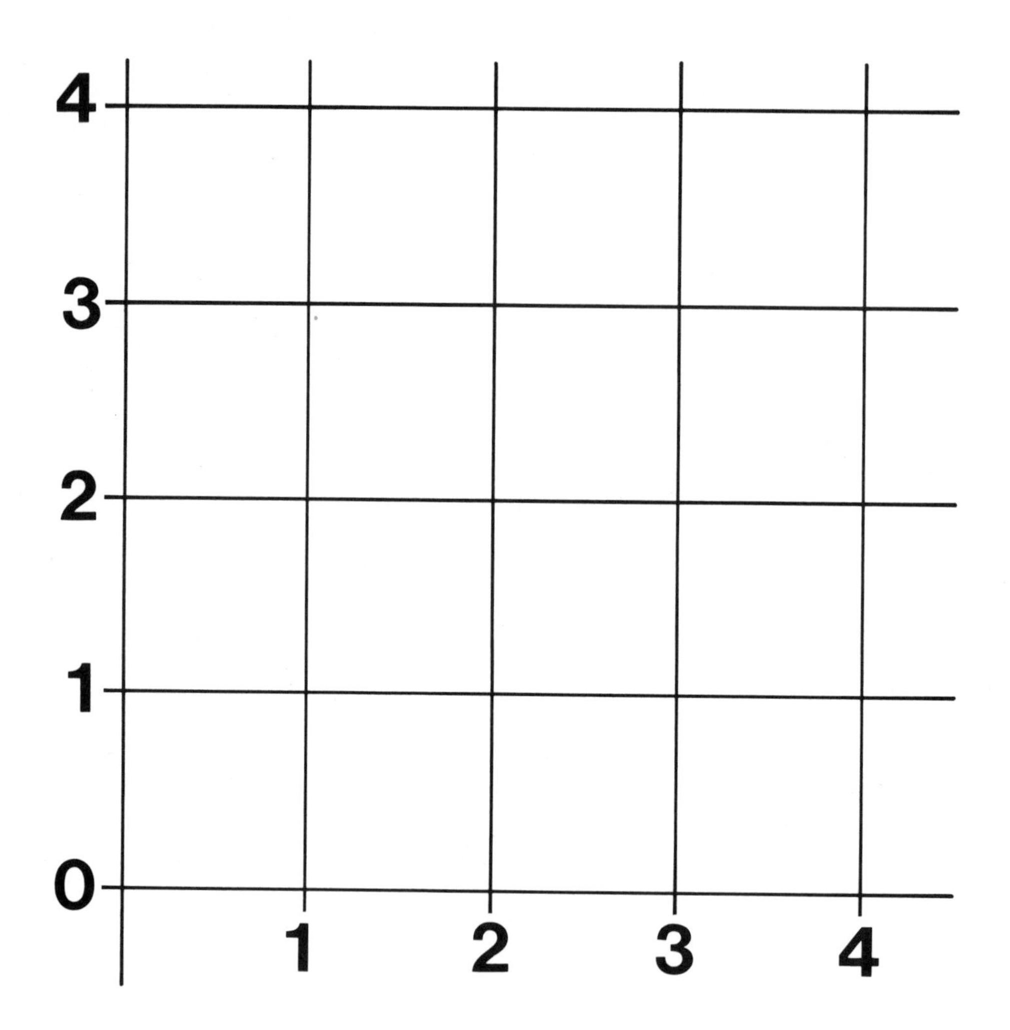

Coordinate Tic-Tac-Toe Record Sheet for Four Quadrants

Play tic-tac-toe using both positive and negative numbers to name the points. By limiting the size of the grids, as we have done, you will have more practice in working in all four quadrants.

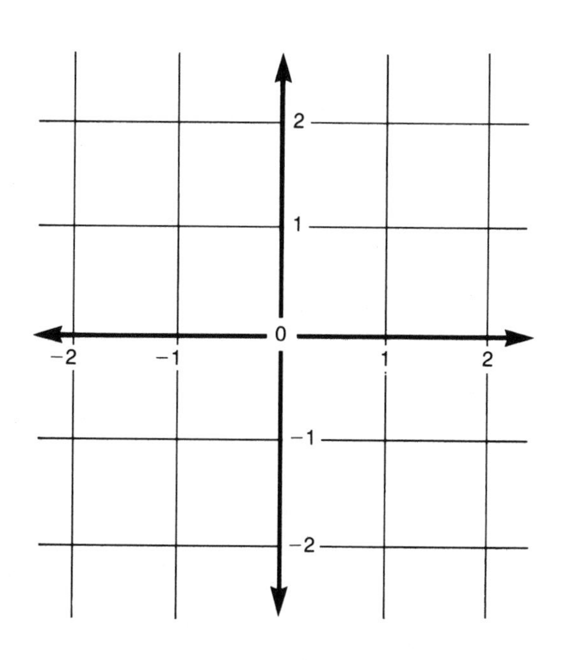

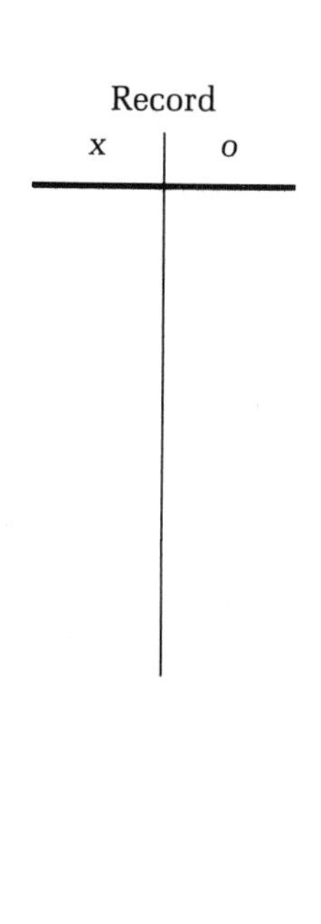

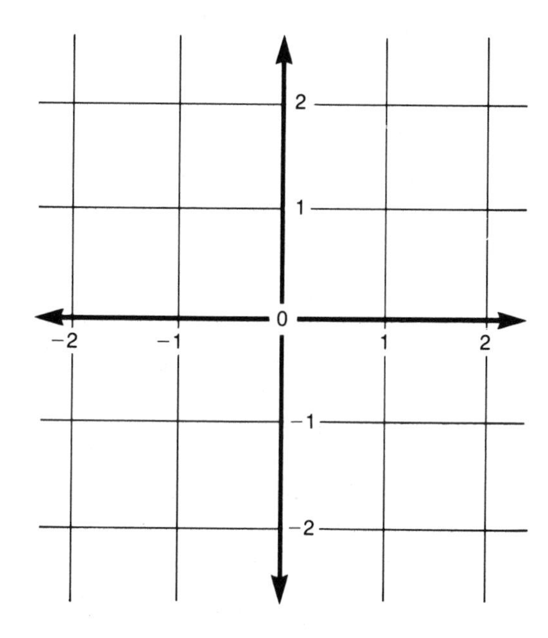

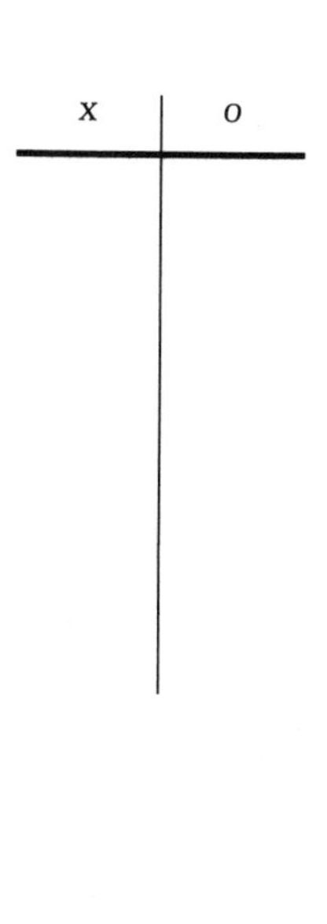

Coordinate Tic-Tac-Toe
Master for Overhead Transparency
for Four Quadrants

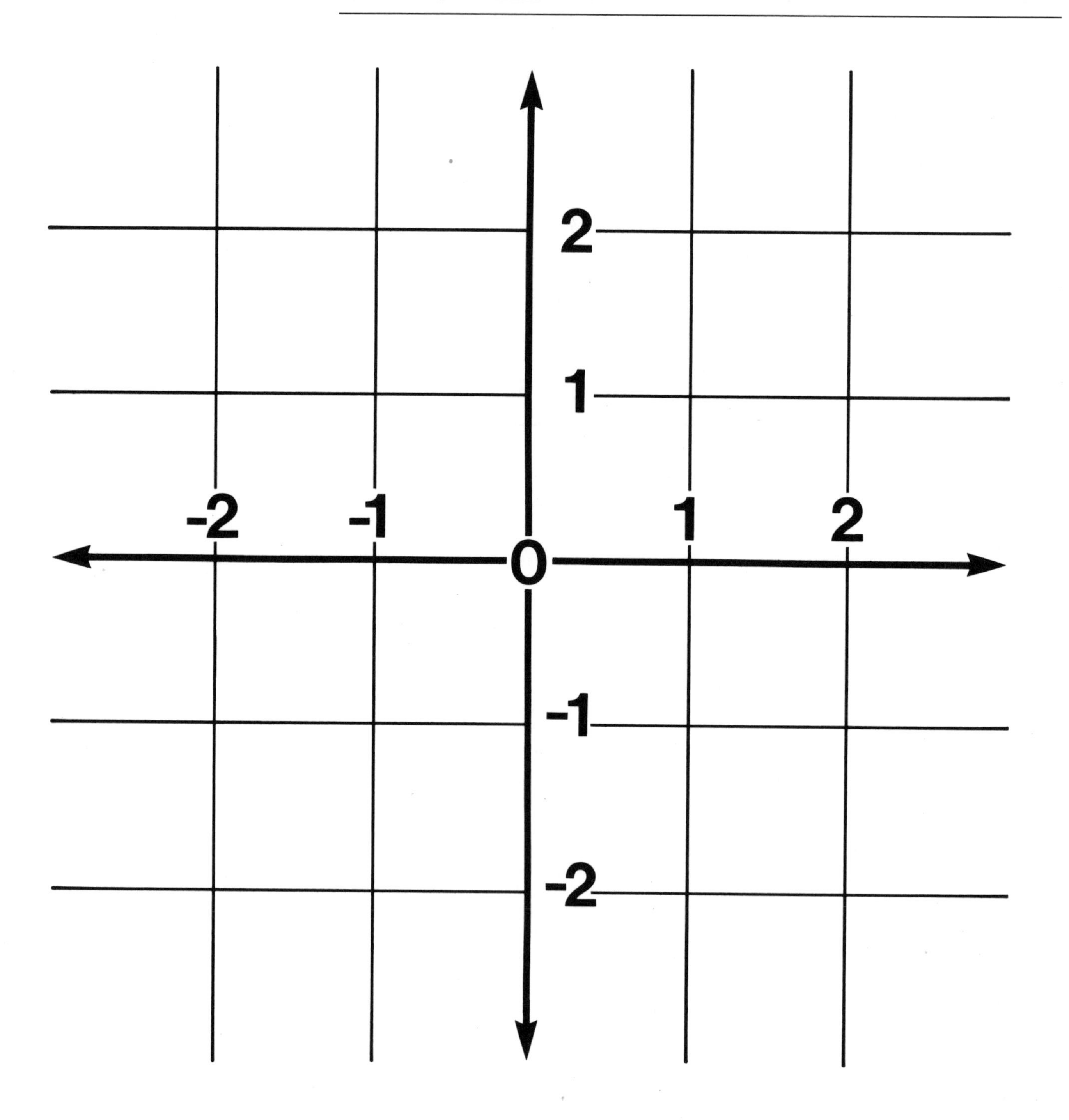

Graph Paper

Draw and number the axes for your problems. Be sure to write the numbers *on* the lines.

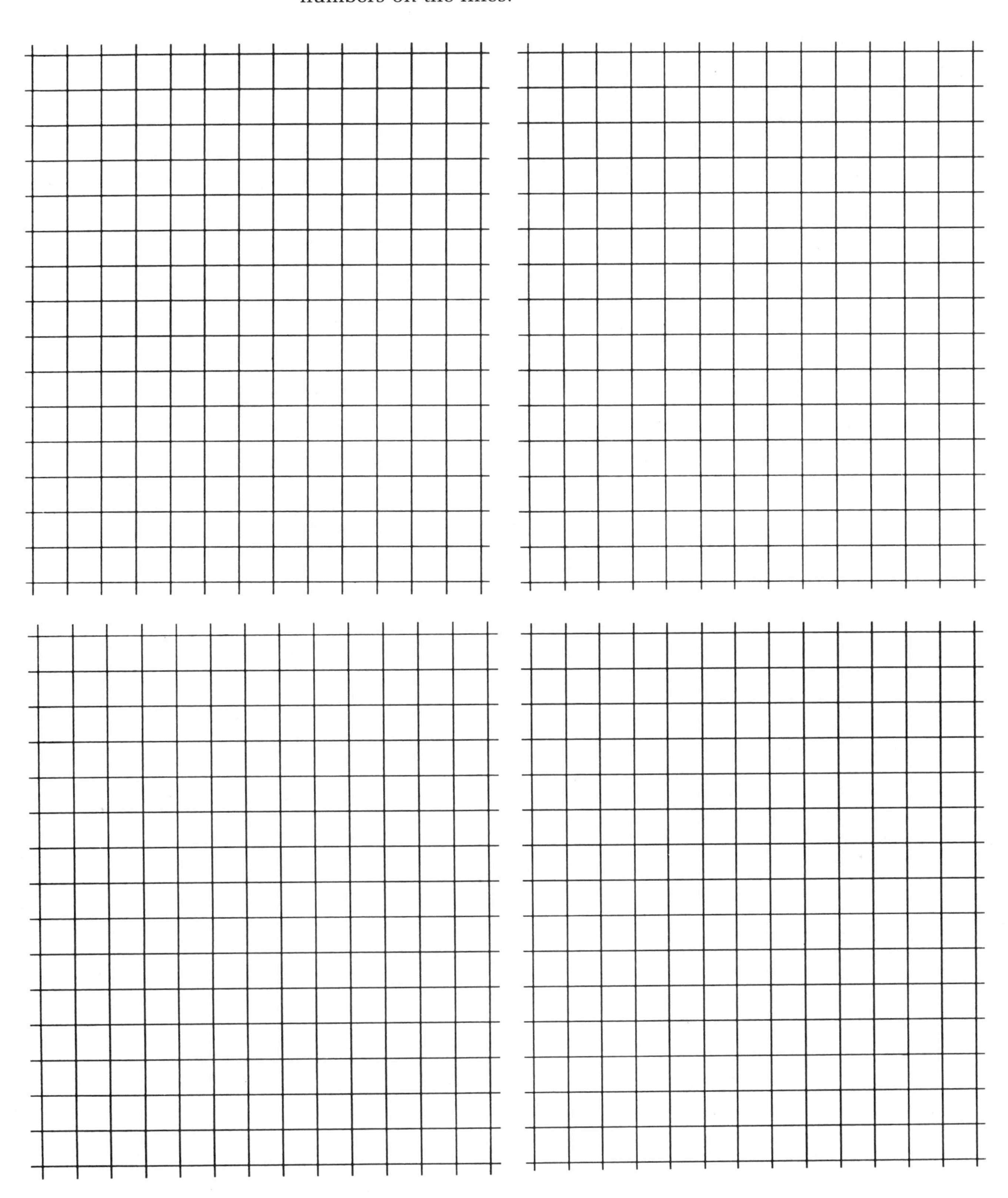

Two-Centimeter Graph Paper

Quarter-Inch Graph Paper

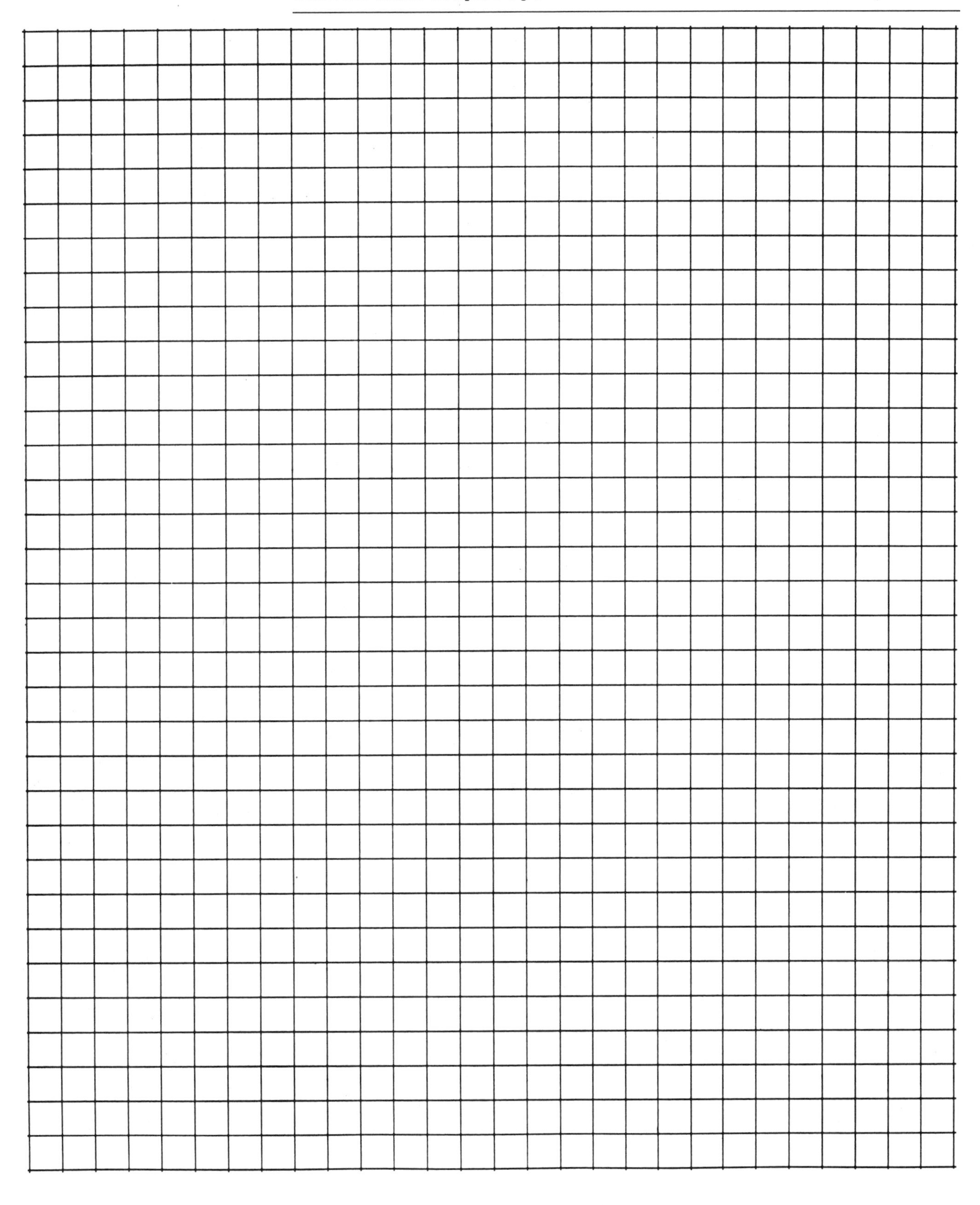

Dot Paper

Half-Inch Graph Paper

Hexagon Paper

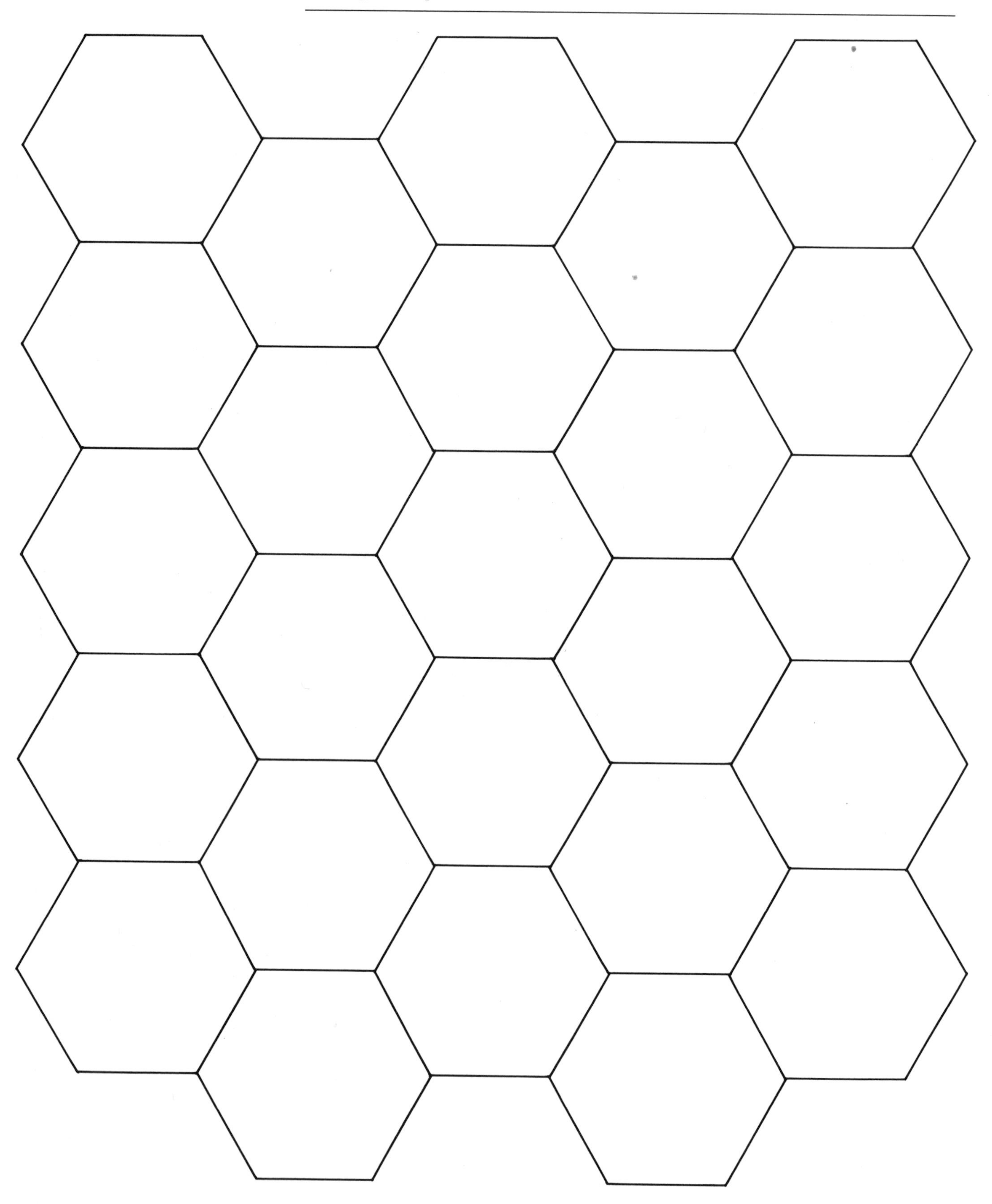

Bibliography

Afflack, Ruth. *Beyond Equals: To Encourage the Participation of Women in Mathematics.* Math/Science Network, Math/Science Resource Center, Mills College, Oakland, California 94613, 1982.

Burns, Marilyn. *The I Hate Mathematics! Book.* Little, Brown, Boston, 1975.

Burns, Marilyn. *The Book of Think.* Little, Brown, Boston, 1976.

Burns, Marilyn. *Math for Smarty Pants.* Little, Brown, Boston, 1982.

Brooke, Maxey. *Coin Games and Puzzles.* Dover, New York, 1963.

Brooke, Maxey. *Tricks, Games and Puzzles with Matches.* Dover, New York, 1973.

Carmen, Robert and Marilyn. *Basic Mathematical Skills: A Guided Approach,* 2nd ed. Wiley, New York, 1981.

Downie, Diane; Slesnick, Twila; and Stenmark, Jean K. *Math for Girls and Other Problem Solvers.* Regents of the University of California, EQUALS, Lawrence Hall of Science, Berkeley, California 94720, 1981.

Farhi, Sivy. *Soma Cubes.* Pentacubes, Box 308, Auckland, New Zealand, 1978.

Fraser, Sherry, et al. *SPACES: Solving Problems of Access to Careers in Engineering and Sciences.* Dale Seymour Publications, P.O. Box 10888, Palo Alto, California 94303, 1982.

Freedman, David; Pisani, Robert; and Purves, Roger. *Statistics.* Norton, New York, 1978.

Gardner, Martin. *The Scientific Book of Mathematical Puzzles and Diversions.* Simon & Schuster, New York, 1959.

Hayslett, Jr., H. T. *Statistics Made Simple.* Doubleday, New York, 1968.

Huff, Darrell, and Geis, Irving. *How to Lie with Statistics.* Norton, New York, 1954.

Huff, Darrell, and Geis, Irving. *How to Take a Chance.* Norton, New York, 1959.

Humboldt County Office of Environmental Education. *Green Box.* Humboldt County Office of Education, Eureka, California, 1975.

Jacobs, Harold. *Mathematics a Human Endeavor.* Freeman, San Francisco, 1970.

Jacobs, Harold. *Geometry.* Freeman, San Francisco, 1974.

Jacobs, Harold. *Elementary Algebra.* Freeman, San Francisco, 1979.

Kogelman, Stanley, and Warren, Joseph. *Mind over Math.* McGraw-Hill, New York, 1978.

Larson, Loren. *Algebra and Trigonometry Refresher.* Freeman, San Francisco, 1979.

Laycock, Mary, and Schadler, Reuben. *Algebra in the Concrete.* Activity Resources, Box 4875, Hayward, California 94545, 1973.

Lazarus, Mitchell. "MATHOPHOBIA: Some Personal Speculations." *National Elementary Principal,* vol. 53, no. 2 (Jan.–Feb. 1974), pp. 16–22.

McFadden, Scott. *Success with Solving Algebra Word Problems*. Action Math Associates, 1358 Dalton Drive, Eugene, Oregon 97404, 1977.

Moore, David S. *Statistics: Concepts and Controversies*. Freeman, San Francisco, 1979.

Perl, Teri. *Math Equals*. Addison-Wesley, Menlo Park, California, 1978.

Read, Ronald. *Tangrams—330 Puzzles*. Dover, New York, 1965.

Seymour, Dale, and Shedd, Margaret. *Finite 'Differences*. Creative Publications, P.O. Box 10328, Palo Alto, California 94303, 1973.

Seymour, Dale and Margo. *Perception Puzzle Blocks™ Activity Cards*. Creative Publications, P.O. Box 10328, Palo Alto, California 94303, 1981.

Shoecraft, Paul. *The Arithmetic Primer: Blueprint for Success in Basic Mathematics*. Addison-Wesley, Menlo Park, California, 1979.

Skolnick, Joan; Langbort, Carol; and Day, Lucille. *How to Encourage Girls in Math and Science: Strategies for Parents and Educators*. Prentice-Hall, Englewood Cliffs, New Jersey, 1982.

Struik, Dirk. *A Concise History of Mathematics*. Dover, New York, 1967.

Swann, Howard, and Johnson, John. *Prof. E. McSquared's Fantastic Original & Highly Edifying Calculus Primer*. Kaufmann, Los Altos, California, 1977.

Tobias, Sheila. *Overcoming Math Anxiety*. Houghton-Mifflin, 1978.

Tobias, Sheila. "Stress in the Math Classroom." *Learning Magazine* (Jan. 1981), p. 34.

Wheeler, Dan, and Seymour, Dale. *Wheeler's Design Tiles™*. Creative Publications, P.O. Box 10328, Palo Alto, California 94303, 1979.

CHAPTER 1: INTRODUCTION

Worksheet 1.1

First the *Mary Sue;* second the *Sunbeam*; third the *Infinity*; fourth the *Lightning.*

CHAPTER 2: COORDINATE GRAPHING AND FUNCTIONS

Naming Coordinates

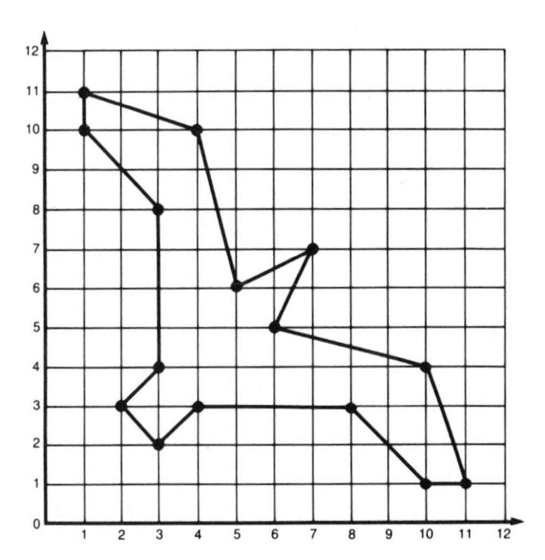

Figure 2.3

Graphing Patterns

Table 2.1: (4, 13); (5, 16); (6, 19); (7, 22); for 10 squares, 31; for 20 squares, 61.

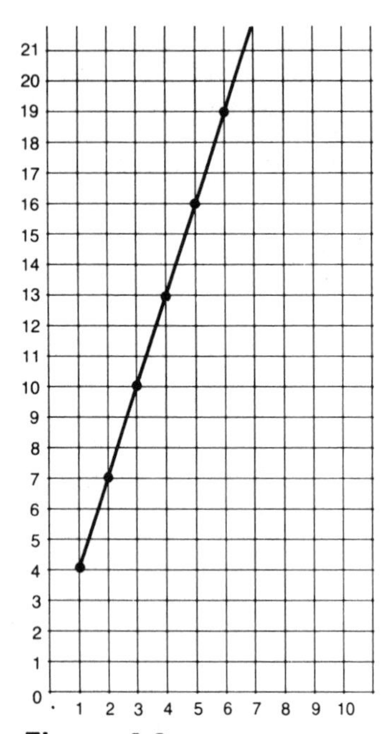

Figure 2.6

Functions and Their Graphs

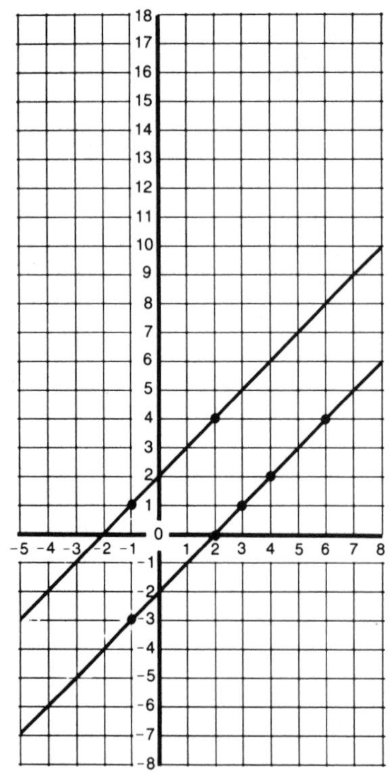

Figure 2.8

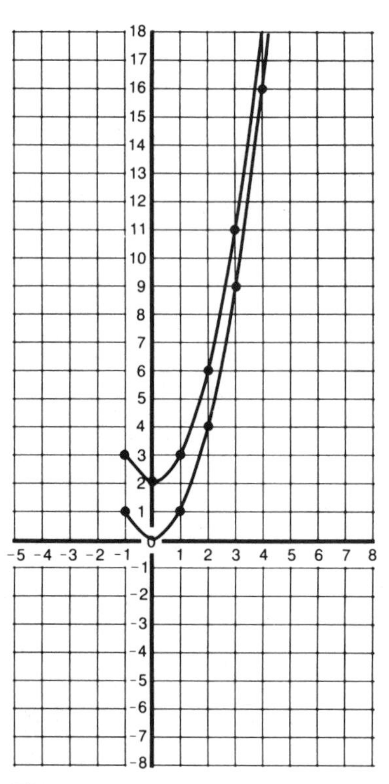

Figure 2.9

Applications

Table 2.10: (50°, 10°); (80°, $26\frac{2}{3}$°); (98.6°, 37°); (104°, 40°); (158°, 70°); (212°, 100°).

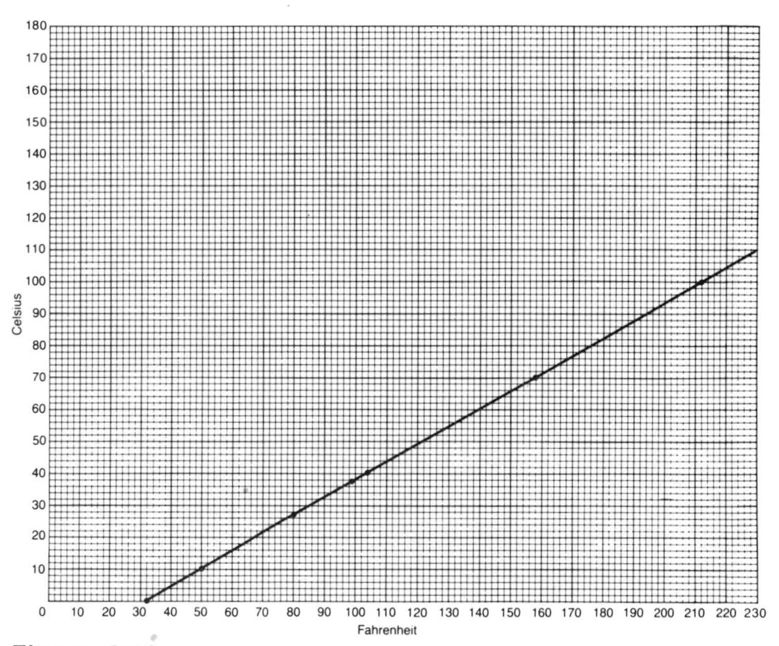

Figure 2.10

Table 2.11: (1:00, 6 miles); (2:00, 12); (3:00, 18); (4:00, 24); (5:00, 30).

Table 2.12: (2:30, 9 miles); (3:30, 18); (4:30, 27); (5:30, 36); (6:30, 45).

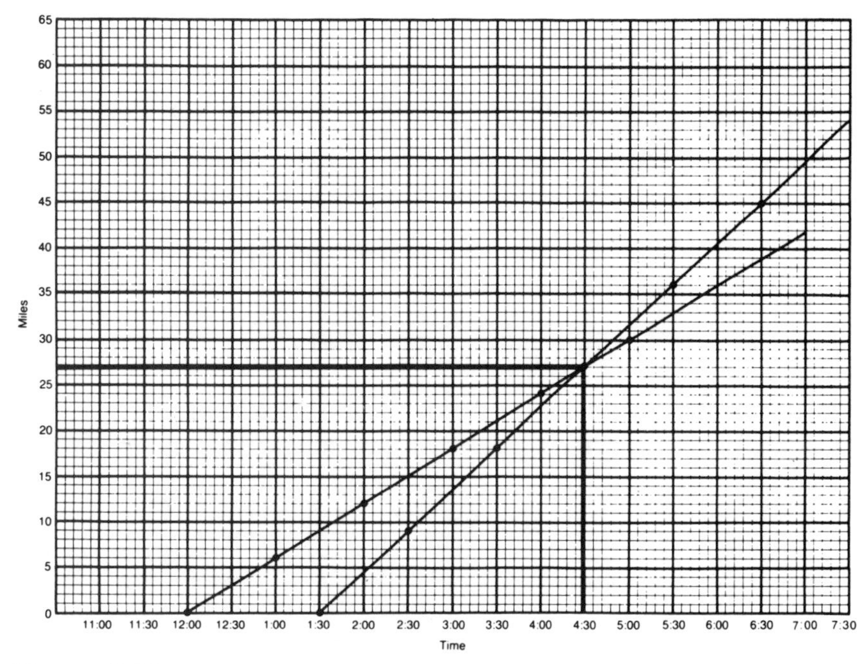

Figure 2.11

Sara caught up with Sue at 4:30 when they had both traveled 27 miles.

Table 2.13: (4, 3); (5, 2); point of intersection: (2, 5).

Table 2.14: (3, 6); (6, 9); point of intersection: (2, 5).

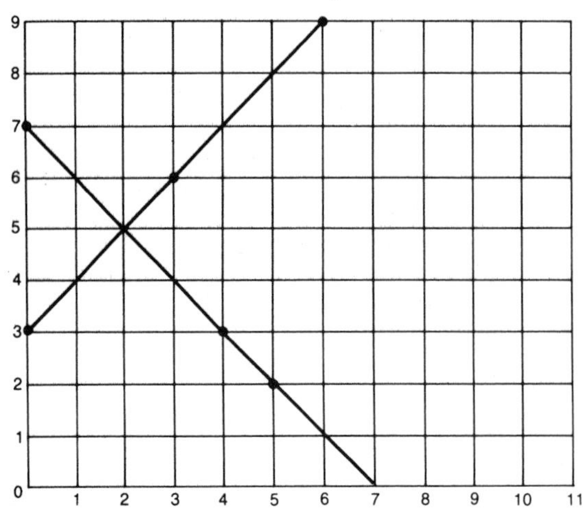

Figure 2.12

Worksheet 2.1

1. Good luck. **3.** What is today's date? **4.** When did you last take a math course? **5.** Under which sign were you born?

Worksheet 2.2

1. In which city were you born? **2.** What kind of work do you do? **3.** Name the last movie you've seen. **4.** What is the title of the last book you've read?

Worksheet 2.3

1.

2.

3.

4.

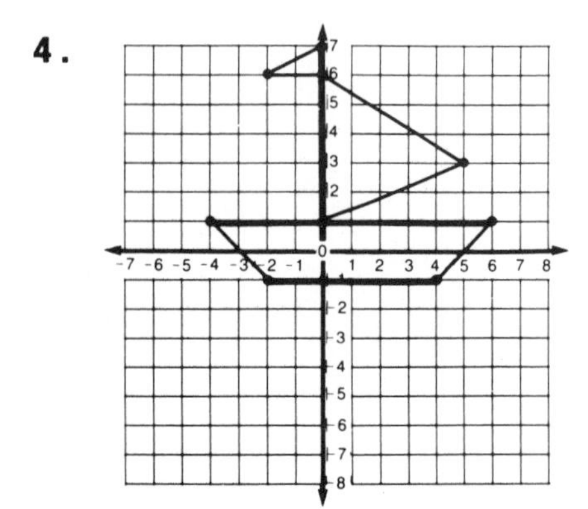

Worksheet 2.4

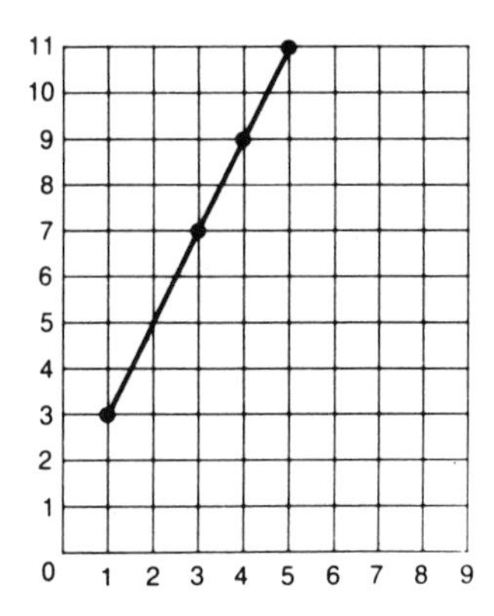

1. (3, 7); (4, 9); (5, 11).

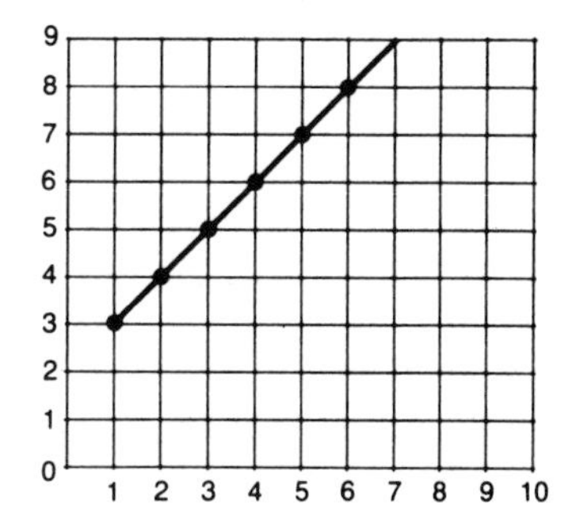

2. (4, 6); (5, 7); (6, 8).

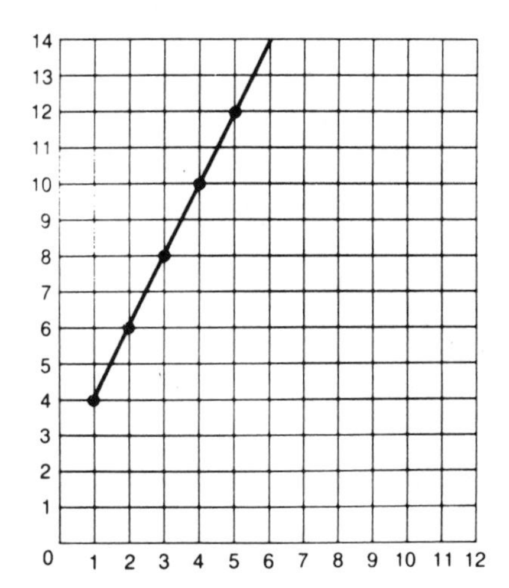

3. (4, 10); (5, 12).

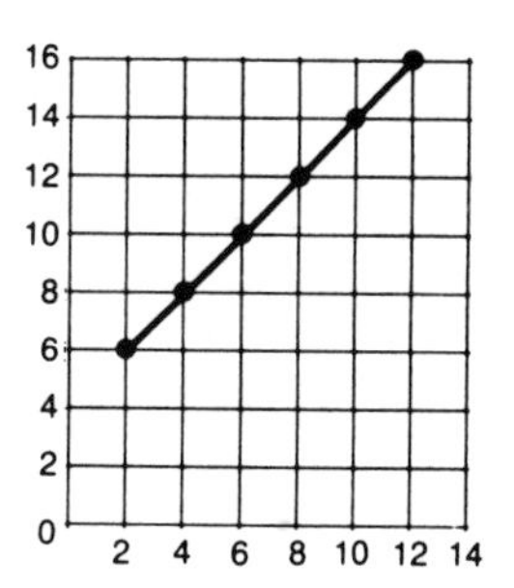

4. (8, 12); (10, 14); (12, 16).

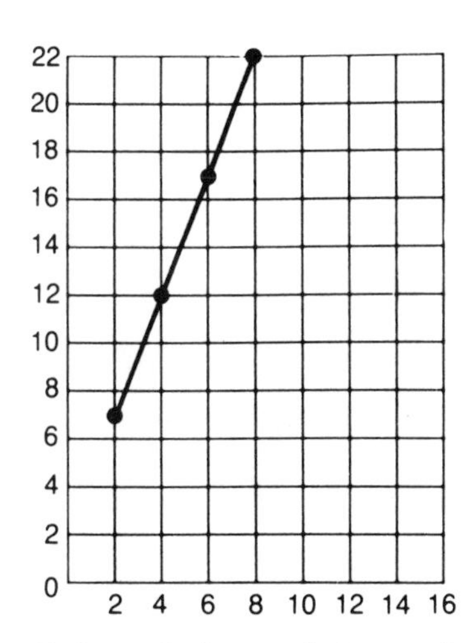

5. (8, 22); (10, 27); (12, 32).

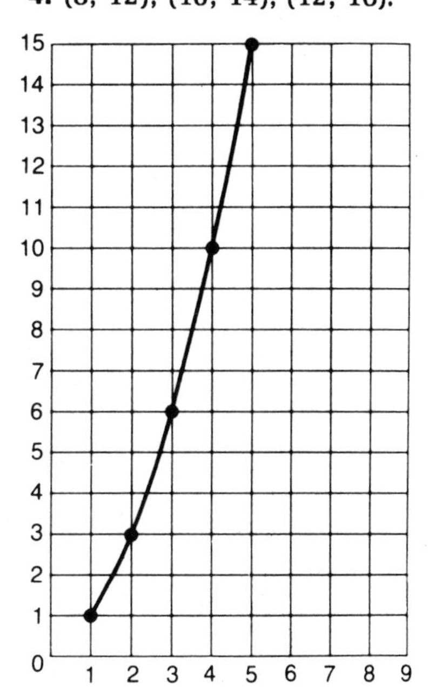

6. (4, 10); (5, 15); (6, 21).

Worksheet 2.5

1. (pancake, e); (salad, d); rule: last letter of input word. **2.** Rule: letter following second vowel. **3.** (neighborhood, p); (ritual, b); rule: letter following last vowel. **4.** (falling, f); for output c input any word ending in d; rule: letter before last letter. **5.** (often, u); (cute, u); rule: letter after third letter. **6.** (cauliflower, w); for output r input any fruit or vegetable that is red; for output g input any fruit or vegetable that is green; rule: first letter of the color of the fruit or vegetable input.

Worksheet 2.6

1. For output 3 input any three-letter word; rule: number of letters in input word. **2.** (ring, 1); (bat, 0); for output 0 input any word with no r's; rule: number of r's in input word. **3.** (hello, 8); for output 3 input any word beginning with c; rule: number of the first letter in alphabet. **4.** (wagon, 2); for output 2 input any word with 2 vowels; rule: number of vowels in input word. **5.** (enter, 2); rule: number of e's in input word. **6.** (trout, 1); (cat, 2); rule: if input a fish, output is 1; if input an animal, output is 2; if input a bird, output is 3.

Worksheet 2.7

1. (34, 25); (10, 1); (87, 78); (13, 4); $(A, A - 9)$; rule: input number minus 9.

2. (30, 10); (117, 39); (57, 19); (36, 12); $[A, \frac{A}{3}]$ if A is a multiple of 3; rule: $\frac{\text{input}}{3}$, if input is a multiple of 3, otherwise input is *.

3. (13, 19); (5, 11); (22, 28); (100, 106); (20, 26); $(A, A + 6)$; rule: input plus 6.

4. (5, 20); (9, 36); (16, 64); (8, 32); (1, 4); $(A, 4 \times A)$; rule: 4 times input.

5. (10, 90); (43, 57); (100, 0); (19, 81); (80, 20); rule: 100 minus input.

6. (4, 16); (12, 144); (8, 64); (6, 36); $(A, A \times A)$; rule: input times input.

Worksheet 2.8

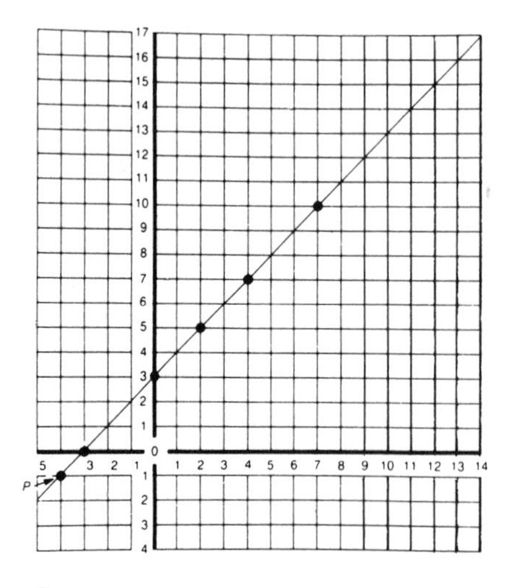

1.

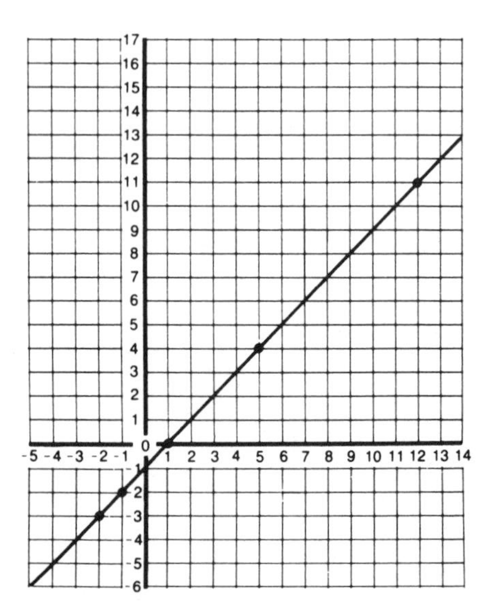

2. (9, 8); (4, 3); (⁻1, ⁻2); (2, 1); $(A, A - 1)$; rule: input minus 1.

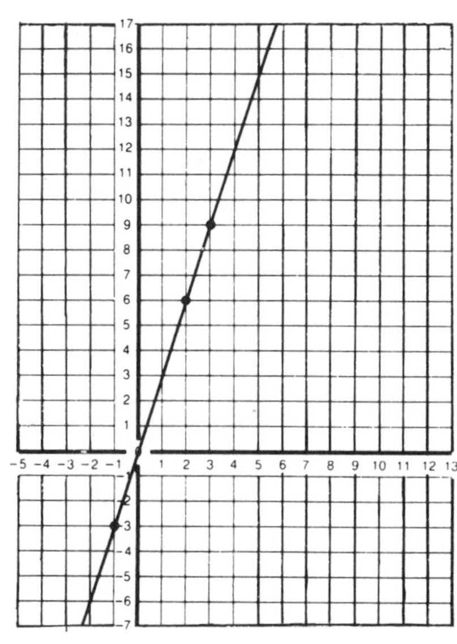

3. (1, 3); (4, 12); ($^-2$, $^-6$); rule: 3 times input.

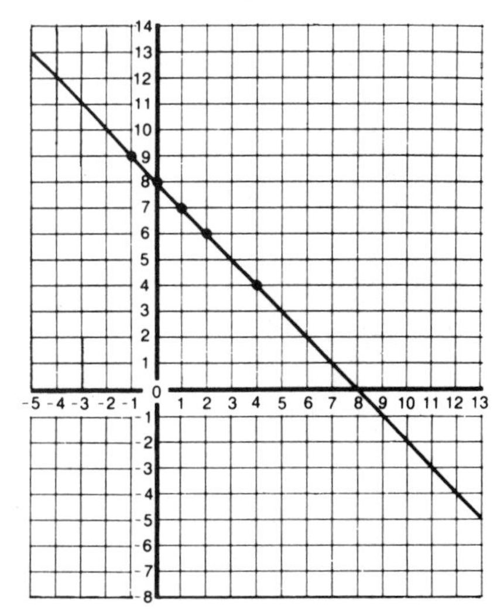

4. (3, 5); (A, $8 - A$); rule: 8 minus input.

Worksheet 2.9

1. (7, 11); (A, $2A - 3$); rule: 2 times input minus 3.
2. (0, 2); (A, $2A + 2$); rule: 2 times input plus 2.
3. (8, 20); ($^-1$, $^-7$); (A, $3A - 4$); rule: 3 times input minus 4.
4. (1, 7); (10, 52); (3, 17); (20, 102); (0, 2); (5, 27); (A, $5A + 2$); rule: 5 times input plus 2.
5. (80, 37); (20, 7); (136, 65); (A, $\frac{A}{2} - 3$); rule: half of input minus 3.
6. (10, 99); (0, $^-1$); (8, 79); (1, 9); (6, 59); (7, 69); (A, $10A - 1$); rule: 10 times input minus 1.

Worksheet 2.10

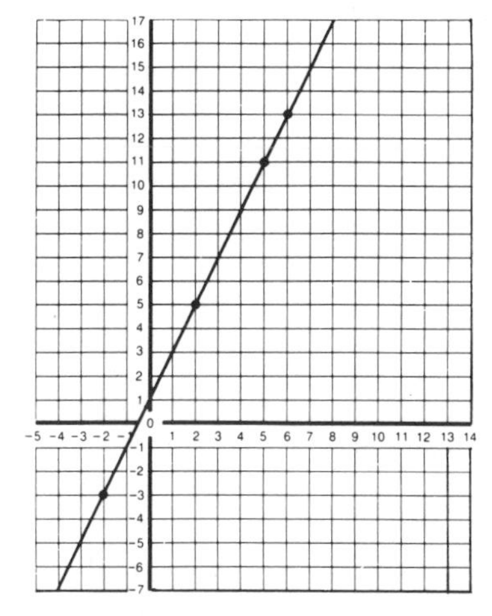

1. (4, 9); ($^-1$, $^-1$); (3, 7); (A, $2A + 1$); rule: 2 times input plus 1.

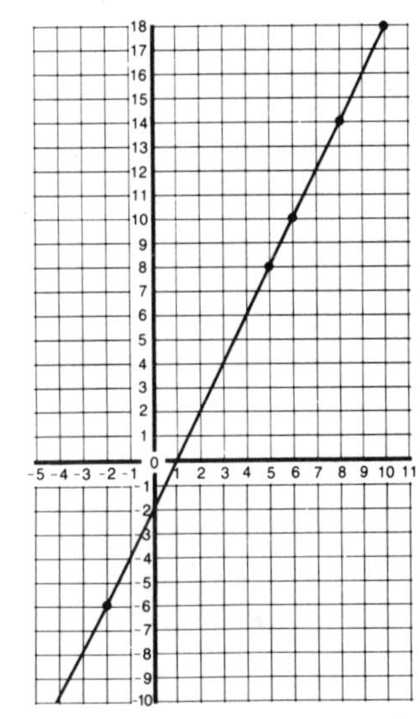

2. (1, 0); (0, $^-2$); (A, $2A - 2$); rule: 2 times input minus 2.

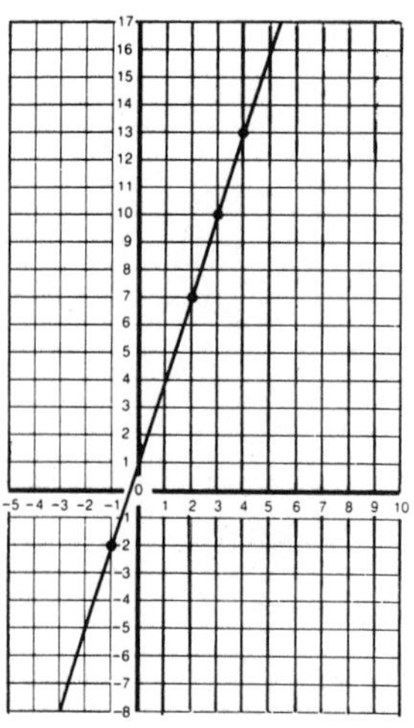

3. (1, 4); (5, 16); (10, 31); $(A, 3A + 1)$; rule: 3 times input plus 1.

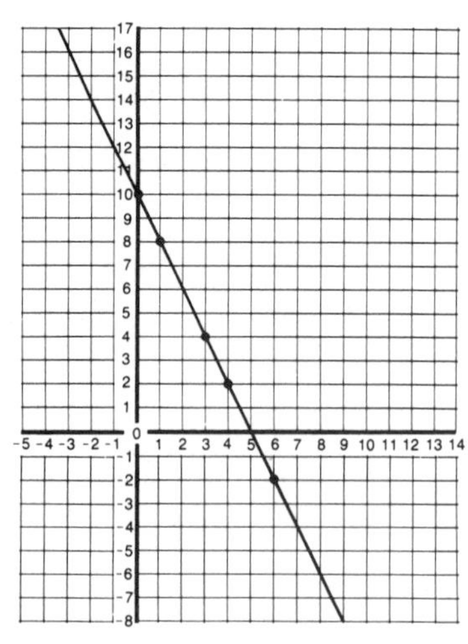

4. (3, 4); $(A, 10 - 2A)$; rule: 10 minus 2 times input.

Worksheet 2.11

1. (⁻2, ⁻3); (1, 3); (7, 15); (10, 21).

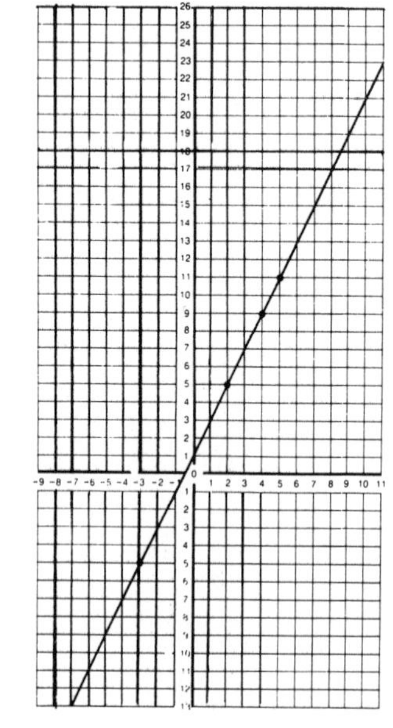

2. (3, 9); (⁻3, 9); (5, 25).

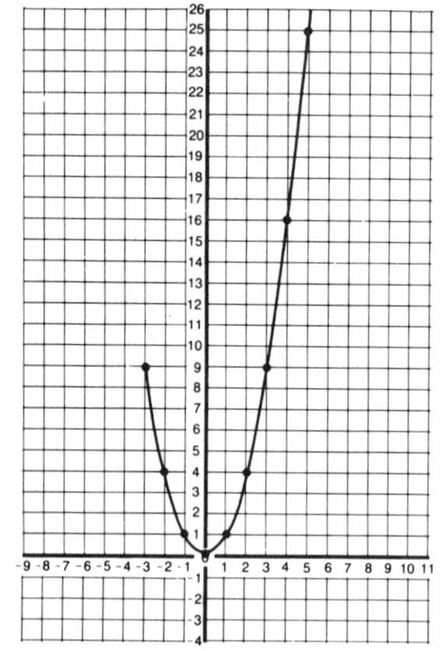

3. (⁻4, ⁻2); (10, 5); $(5, 2\frac{1}{2})$.

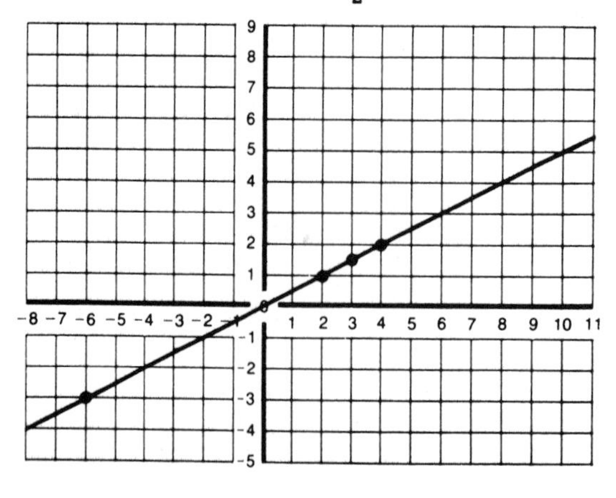

4. (5, 20).

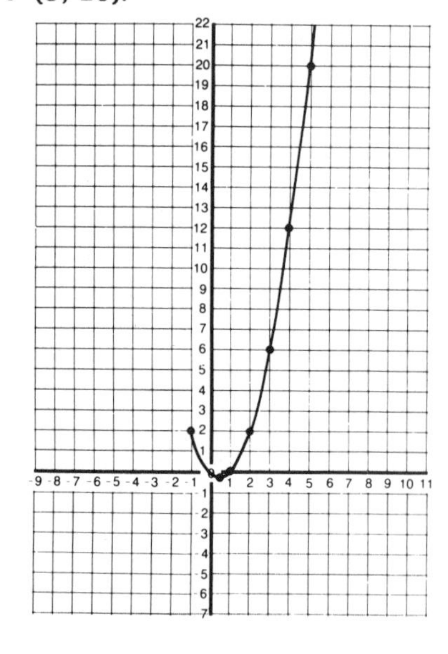

Worksheet 2.12

1. Some inputs and outputs are: (-3, 0); (-2, 1); (0, 3); (2, 5); rule: input plus 3.
2. Some inputs and outputs are: (-2, -6); (-1, -3); (0, 0); (1, 3); (2, 6); rule: 3 times input.
3. Some inputs and outputs are: (-2, -8); (0, -2); (2, 4); (4, 10); (6, 16); rule: 3 times input minus 2.
4. Some inputs and outputs are: (-2, -9); (0, -5); (2, -1); (3, 1); (5, 5); rule: 2 times input minus 5.

Worksheet 2.13

1. (9, 18); (10, 20). **2.** (9, 17); (10, 19). **3.** (9, 20); (10, 22).

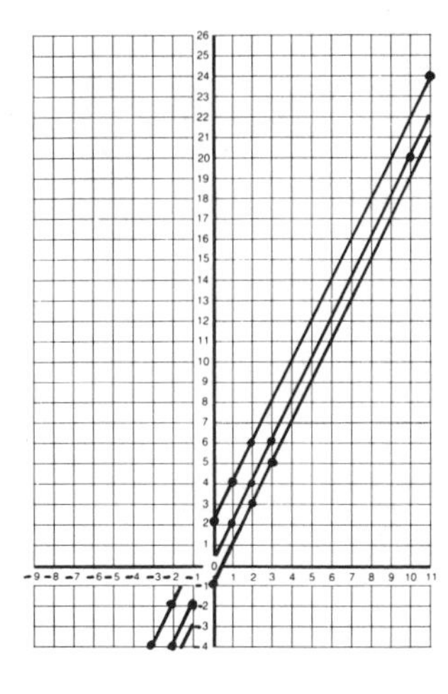

Worksheet 2.14

1. (0, 3); (3, 6). **2.** (0, 1); (3, 7). **3.** (0, -2); (3, 13).

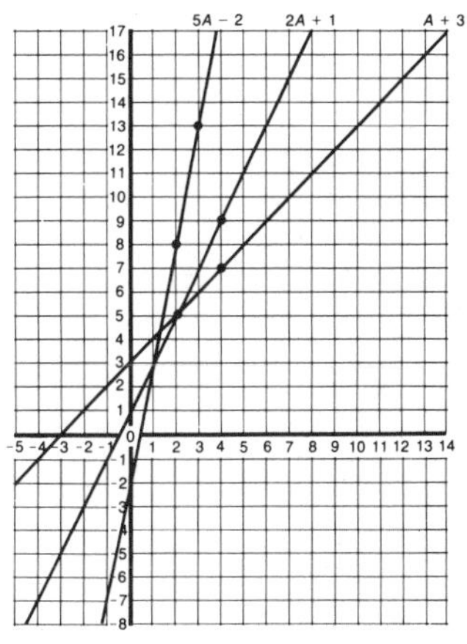

Worksheet 2.15

1. 42 liters. **2.** 23 liters. **3.** 7.6 liters. **4.** 19 liters. **5.** 5 gallons. **6.** 6.8 gallons. **7.** 7.8 gallons. **8.** 11 gallons. **9.** 9 gallons. **10.** 42 liters. **11.** $1.29.

Worksheet 2.16

These answers are the exact answers solved by using the following formulas:

$$C^\circ = \frac{5}{9}(F^\circ - 32) \quad \text{and} \quad F^\circ = \frac{9}{5}C^\circ + 32$$

The answers you get using the graph should be close to these but won't necessarily be exact.

1a. 23.9°. **1b.** 32.2°. **1c.** 40°. **1d.** 65.6°.
2a. 59°. **2b.** 86°. **2c.** 149°. **2d.** 230°.

Worksheet 2.17

1. Richard passed Joe at 4:12 when they had both run 4.8 miles. (Notice that the hours are marked in tenths [6 minutes] and the miles are marked in fifths.)

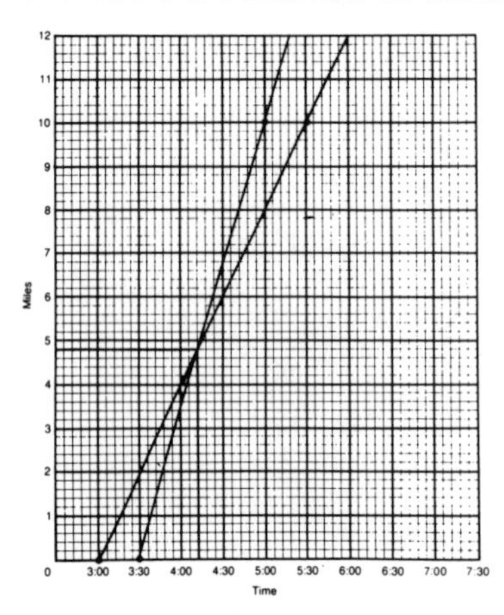

2.

	Scott		*Nancy*
Time	Miles	Time	Miles
8:00	0	10:30	0
11:00	150	2:30	300
6:00	500	5:30	525

They could plan to meet for dinner on the road at 3:30 when they had traveled 375 miles.

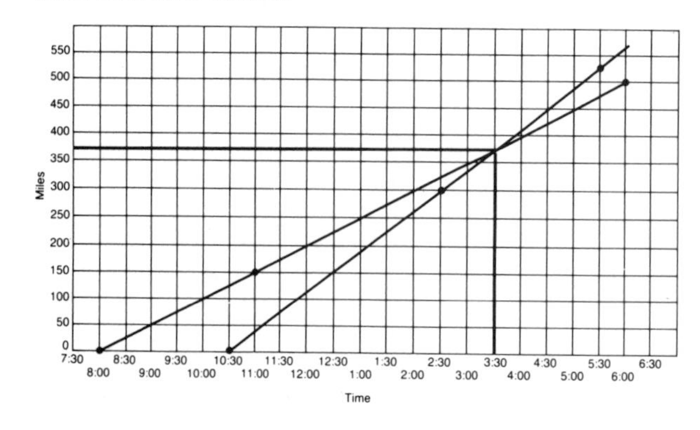

Worksheet 2.18

1. $2A - 3$: (3, 3); (5, 7); (0, -3); (-1, -5); $A - 2$: (2, 0); (4, 2); (6, 4); (0, -2). Point of intersection: (1, -1).

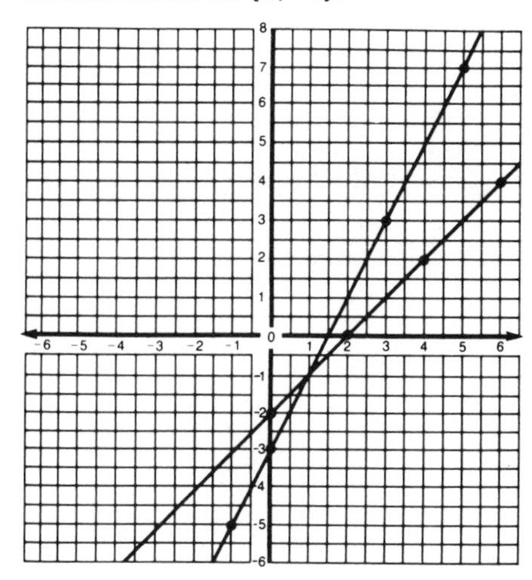

2. $2A - 1$: (4, 7); (3, 5); (0, -1); (-2, -5); $\frac{A}{2} + 2$: (4, 4); $(1, 2\frac{1}{2})$; (0, 2); (-4, 0); (-6, -1). Point of intersection: (2, 3).

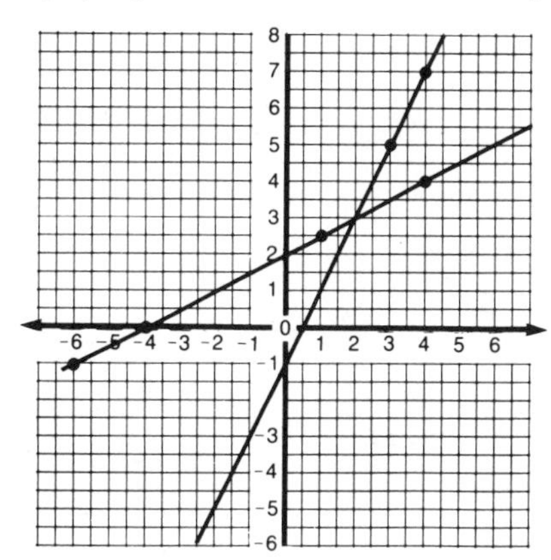

3. $5 - A$: (0, 5); (5, 0); (2, 3); (4, 1); (-1, 6); (-3, 8); $A + 2$: (3, 5); (6, 8); (5, 7); (0, 2); (-2, 0); (-3, -1). Point of intersection: $(1\frac{1}{2}, 3\frac{1}{2})$.

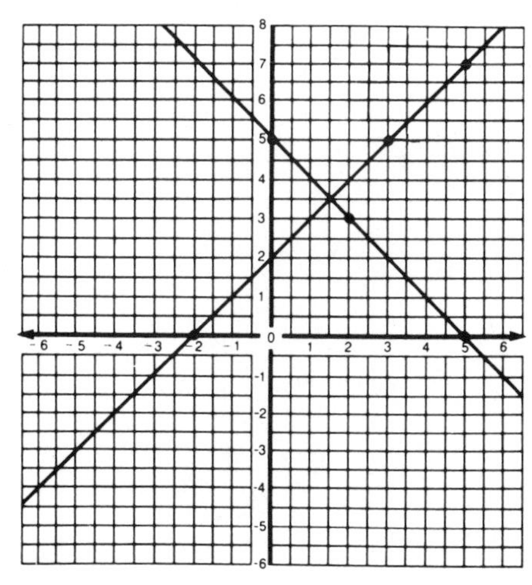

The answers may vary from those given here because of the use of different models of calculators.

Worksheet 3.1

1. 260. **2.** 64.53. **3.** 35. **4.** 67.5. **5.** 147. **6.** 35.2. **7.** 57.8. **8.** 24.9. **9.** 73.2. **10.** Move the decimal point one place to the left; finding 10% is the same as dividing by 10, or multiplying by $\frac{1}{10}$.

Worksheet 3.2

Estimated answers will vary. Following are the calculator answers for discounts of 10%, 20%, and 30%:

1.	$3.53	$7.05	$10.58
2.	$4.68	$9.36	$14.04
3.	$8.36	$16.72	$25.08
4.	$20.46	$40.91	$61.37
5.	$29.99	$59.99	$89.99
6.	$14.95	$29.90	$44.85
7.	$23.70	$47.40	$71.10
8.	$356.26	$712.51	$1068.77
9.	$423.60	$847.19	$1270.79
10.	$547.85	$1095.69	$1643.54

Worksheet 3.3

Estimated answers will vary. Following are the exact answers found with a calculator:

1. $29.78. **2.** $4.11. **3.** $195.00. **4.** $1100.75. **5.** $51.56. **6.** $31.57; $4.36; $206.70; $1166.80; $54.65. **7.** $2738.75. **8.** $3.50 x 3 = $10.50; $8.40; yes. **9.** $2.80 x 3 = $8.40; $6.72; no, the ad reads *3/$8.40.* **10.** Style 181—The regular price of three pairs of All Nude Sandalfoot is $2.80 x 3 = $8.40; with a 20% discount they should cost $6.72, not $8.40, as in the ad; S tyle 183—The regular price of three pairs of Control Top Sandalfoot is $9.60, which is the same as the advertised sale price; with the 20% discount they should cost $7.68.

Worksheet 3.4

Answers may vary.

2. between 8 and 9; 8.9442719; 79.999999.
3. between 11 and 12; 11.180339; 124.99999.
4. between 19 and 20; 19.748417; 389.99997.
5. between 30 and 40; 31.622776; 999.99996.

Worksheet 3.5

2. 8514.5338[; 851,453,380,000.
3. 202.53882[; 20,253,882,000.
4. 624484.10[; 62,448,410,000,000.
5. 676.79978[; 67,679,978,000.
6. 887000.12[; 88,700,012,000,000.
7. 314.52800[; 31,452,800,000.
8. 175.30000[; 17,530,000,000.
9. 197.96000[; 19,796,000,000.
10. 345,000,000. **11.** 7,624,500. **12.** 4,723,500.
13. 357 x 10^3. **14.** 659 x 10^6. **15.** 458 x 10^6.

Worksheet 3.6

Predictions will vary. The answers for the display on a calculator are as follows:

1. 6. ; 6. . ; 10. . ; 8. . ; 6. . ; 9. . ; 9. . ; 0. . ; 15. . ; 15. ; 0.
2. 7. ; 7. . ; 0. . ; 7. . ; 5. . ; 5. . ; 2. . ; 0. . ; 2. . ; 2. ; 0.

Worksheet 3.7

1. 366. **2.** 1222. **3.** 959. **4.** 228. **5.** 1392. **6.** 6590.

CHAPTER 4: GEOMETRY AND MEASUREMENT

Perimeter

Figure 4.14: Estimation of the area. *Method 1*: 32 whole squares, 12 partial squares, total = 44. *Method 2*: area of large square = 64, area outside circle = 16, estimated area = 48.

Worksheet 4.1

For area 6: 1 x 6; 2 x 3; *for area 9:* 1 x 9; 3 x 3; *for area 10:* 1 x 10; 2 x 5; *for area 11:* 1 x 11; 9 is the only square.

Worksheet 4.2

For area 2: 1 x 2; *area 3:* 1 x 3; *area 4:* 1 x 4; 2 x 2; *area 5:* 1 x 5; *area 6:* 1 x 6; 2 x 3; *area 7:* 1 x 7; *area 8:* 1 x 8; 2 x 4; *area 9:* 1 x 9; 3 x 3; *area 10:* 1 x 10; 2 x 5; *area 11:* 1 x 11; *area 12:* 1 x 12; 2 x 6; 3 x 4; *area 13:* 1 x 13; *area 14:* 1 x 14; 2 x 7; *area 15:* 1 x 15; 3 x 5; *area 16:* 1 x 16; 2 x 8; 4 x 4; *area 17:* 1 x 17; *area 18:* 1 x 18; 2 x 9; 3 x 6; *area 19:* 1 x 19; *area 20:* 1 x 20; 2 x 10; 4 x 5; *area 21:* 1 x 21; 3 x 7; *area 22:* 1 x 22; 2 x 11; *area 23:* 1 x 23; *area 24:* 1 x 24; 2 x 12; 3 x 8; 4 x 6; *area 25:* 1 x 25; 5 x 5; *area 26:* 1 x 26; 2 x 13; *area 27:* 1 x 27; 3 x 9; *area 28:* 1 x 28; 2 x 14; 4 x 7; *area 29:* 1 x 29; *area 30:* 1 x 30; 2 x 15; 3 x 10; 5 x 6; *area 31:* 1 x 31; *area 32:* 1 x 32; 2 x 16; 4 x 8; *area 33:* 1 x 33; 3 x 11; *area 34:* 1 x 34; 2 x 17; *area 35:* 1 x 35; 5 x 7; *area 36:* 1 x 36; 2 x 18; 3 x 12; 4 x 9; 6 x 6; *area 37:* 1 x 37; *area 38:* 1 x 38; 2 x 19; *area 39:* 1 x 39; 3 x 13; *area 40:* 1 x 40; 2 x 20; 4 x 10; 5 x 8; *area 41:* 1 x 41; *area 42:* 1 x 42; 2 x 21; 3 x 14; 6 x 7; *area 43:* 1 x 43; *area 44:* 1 x 44; 2 x 22; 4 x 11; *area 45:* 1 x 45; 3 x 15; 5 x 9; *area 46:* 1 x 46; 2 x 23; *area 47:* 1 x 47; *area 48:* 1 x 48; 2 x 24; 3 x 16; 4 x 12; 6 x 8; *area 49:* 1 x 49; 7 x 7.

Worksheet 4.3

1. 18, 12, 216 square units. **2.** 100, 3, 300. **3.** 9, 3, 27. **4.** 25, 2, 50. **5.** 45, 15, 675. **6.** 7, 7, 49. **7.** 8, 8, 64.

Worksheet 4.4

Area	*Dimensions*		*Perimeter*
	Length	Width	
4	1	4	10
4	2	2	8
8	1	8	18
8	2	4	12
16	1	16	34
16	2	8	20
16	4	4	16
24	1	24	50
24	2	12	28
24	3	8	22
24	4	6	20

Worksheet 4.5

$\sqrt{2} \approx 1.4$; $\sqrt{5} \approx 2.2$; $\sqrt{12} \approx 3.5$; $\sqrt{30} \approx 5.5$; $\sqrt{72} \approx 8.5$.

Worksheet 4.6

1. perimeter 60 units; area 110 square units.
2. 54 units; 128 square units.
3. 34 units; 44 square units.
4. 44 units; 74 square units.
5. 36 units; 38 square units.

Worksheet 4.7

1. area 14 square inches; perimeter 18 inches.
2. length 5 feet; perimeter 18 feet.
3. width 3 miles; area 24 square miles.
4. length 6 yards; width 6 yards.
5. area L x W square feet; perimeter 2 x (L + W) feet.
6. length 20 miles; area 200 square miles.

Worksheet 4.8

Perimeter	Length	Width	Area
14	6	1	6
14	5	2	10
14	4	3	12
12	5	1	5
12	4	2	8
12	3	3	9
18	8	1	8
18	7	2	14
18	6	3	18
18	5	4	20
24	11	1	11
24	10	2	20
24	9	3	27
24	8	4	32
24	7	5	35
24	6	6	36

Worksheet 4.9

All answers are estimates.

1. *Method 1:* 15 square units; *Method 2:* 18 square units.
2. *Method 1:* 36; *Method 2:* 38.
3. *Method 1:* 78; *Method 2:* 80.
4. *Method 1:* 87; *Method 2:* 90.
5. *Method 1:* 42; *Method 2:* 42.
6. *Method 1:* 2; *Method 2:* 2.

Worksheet 4.10

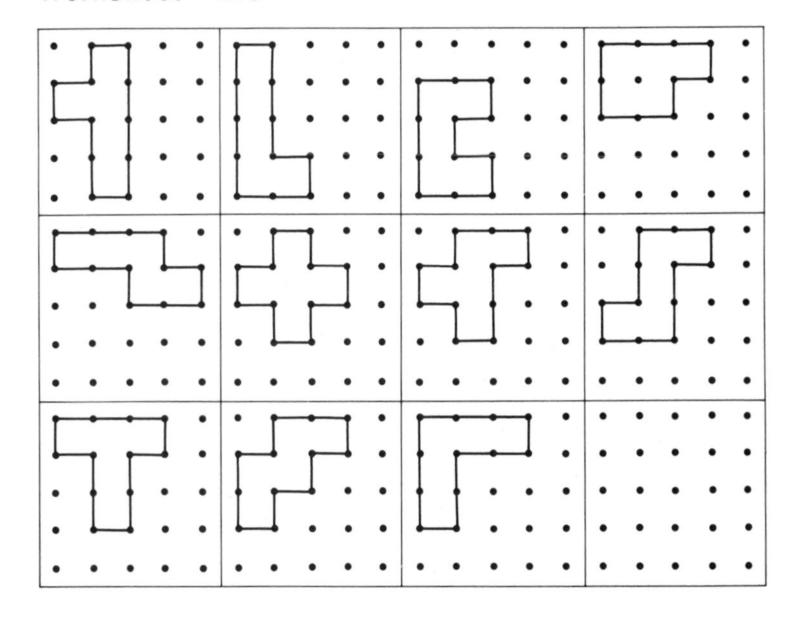

Worksheet 4.11

Answers will vary. Here are a few examples.

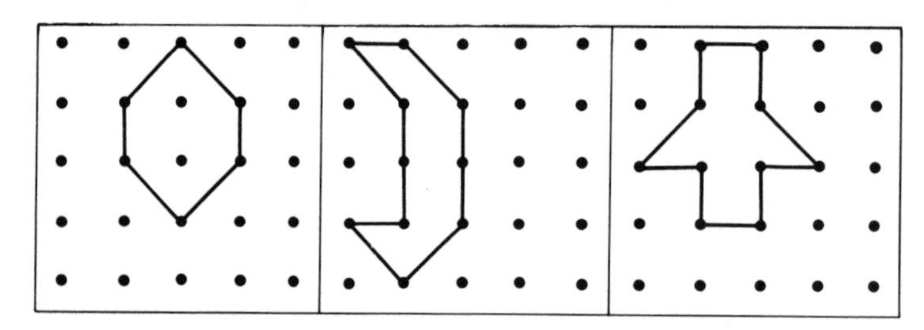

Worksheet 4.12

The areas of these shapes are measured in square units.
1. 5. **2.** 5. **3.** 4. **4.** $3\frac{1}{2}$. **5.** $5\frac{1}{2}$. **6.** 6. **7.** 10. **8.** 5. **9.** 7.

Worksheet 4.13

Answers will vary.

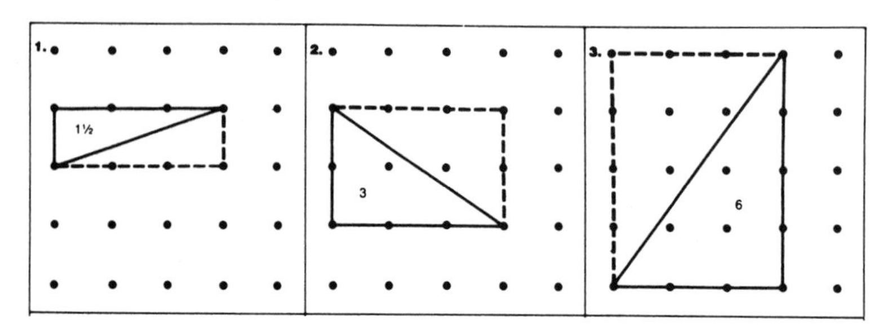

Worksheet 4.14

The areas of these shapes are measured in square units.
1. 2. **2.** 8. **3.** 7. **4.** 6. **5.** 10. **6.** 6. **7.** $7\frac{1}{2}$. **8.** $7\frac{1}{2}$. **9.** 8

Worksheet 4.15

The areas of these shapes are measured in square units.
1. 1. **2.** 1. **3.** 10. **4.** 8. **5.** $2\frac{1}{2}$. **6.** 5. **7.** 6. **8.** 8. **9.** $2\frac{1}{2}$.

Worksheet 4.16

2. 4 square units, 2 square units, $\frac{1}{2} \times 1 \times 4 = 2$.

3. 8 square units, 4 square units, $\frac{1}{2} \times 2 \times 4 = 4$.

4. 3 square units, $1\frac{1}{2}$ square units, $\frac{1}{2} \times 3 \times 1 = 1\frac{1}{2}$.

5. 12 square units, 6 square units, $\frac{1}{2} \times 3 \times 4 = 6$.

6. 8 square units, 4 square units, $\frac{1}{2} \times 4 \times 2 = 4$.

Worksheet 4.17

1. isosceles, 1 square unit.
2. isosceles, 8 square units.
3. scalene, 4 square units.
4. scalene, 3 square units.
5. isosceles, 4 square units.
6. scalene, $1\frac{1}{2}$ square units.
7. isosceles, $4\frac{1}{2}$ square units.
8. isosceles, 2 square units.
9. scalene, 3 square units.
10. isosceles, 3 square units.
11. scalene, 6 square units.
12. scalene, 3 square units.

Worksheet 4.18

1. 3, $\frac{1}{2}$; 4, 1; 5, $1\frac{1}{2}$ 6, 2; 7, $2\frac{1}{2}$; . . . 10, 4.
2. 3, $1\frac{1}{2}$; 4, 2; 5, $2\frac{1}{2}$; 6, 3; 7, $3\frac{1}{2}$; . . . 10, 5; T, $T \div 2$; rule: divide the number of nails touching by 2.

3a. $56 \div 2 - 1 = 27$.
3b. $100 \div 2 - 1 = 49$.
3c. $68 \div 2 = 34$.
3d. $100 \div 2 = 50$.

4. 3, $2\frac{1}{2}$; 4, 3; 5, $3\frac{1}{2}$; 6, 4; . . . 10, 6; T, $T \div 2 + 1$; rule: divide the number of nails touching by 2, then add 1.
5. 3, $3\frac{1}{2}$; 4, 4; 5, $4\frac{1}{2}$; 6, 5; . . . 10, 7; T, $T \div 2 + 2$; rule: divide the number of nails touching by 2, then add 2.

6a. $74 \div 2 + 1 = 38$.
6b. $100 \div 2 + 1 = 51$.
6c. $54 \div 2 + 2 = 29$.
6d. $100 \div 2 + 2 = 52$.

Worksheet 4.19

There are many patterns in the following chart, both horizontal and vertical. The general rule may be stated in the following way: Divide the number of nails touching (T) by 2, then add one less than the number of nails inside (I).

1. $93\frac{1}{2}$ square units. **2.** $127\frac{1}{2}$ square units. **3.** $T \div 2 + I - 1$.

Touching

Inside	3	4	5	6	7	8	9	10
0	½	1	1½	2	2½	3	3½	4
1	1½	2	2½	3	3½	4	4½	5
2	2½	3	3½	4	4½	5	5½	6
3	3½	4	4½	5	5½	6	6½	7
4	4½	5	5½	6	6½	7	7½	8
5	5½	6	6½	7	7½	8	8½	9
6	6½	7	7½	8	8½	9	9½	10
7	7½	8	8½	9	9½	10	10½	11

Worksheet 4.20

Answers will vary.

Worksheet 4.21

1. 42 cubic units, 82 square units.
2. 5 cubic units, 22 square units.
3. 36 cubic units, 72 square units.
4. 40 cubic units, 76 square units.

Worksheet 4.22

1. 24 cubic units, 52 square units.
2. 12 cubic units, 38 square units.
3. 30 cubic units, 62 square units.
4. 16 cubic units, 40 square units.
5. 27 cubic units, 54 square units.

Worksheet 4.23

1a. 6 rolls. **1b.** $35.70. **1c.** 4 rolls, $13.95 each, cost $55.80.

2a. Need 34 pails for a thick coat, costing $441.66.

2b. Need only 12 pails for a thin coat, costing $155.88, saving $285.78.

3a. 27 cubic feet. **3b.** 1,000,000 cubic centimeters.

3c. 1728 cubic inches. **3d.** 1680 cubic inches for each window box, which equals 5040 cubic inches, which is almost 3 cubic feet.

3e. If you buy 3, at a cost of $3.79 each, it will cost $11.37.

3f. If you buy 1 for $3.79 and 2 for $6.79, it will cost $10.58, which saves $.79.

Worksheet 4.24

1. $200,000 ÷ $6.50 = 30,769.23 square meters in all; 30,769.23 ÷ 300 = 102.56 meters long; $200,000 ÷ 102.56 = $1950.08 per meter. **2.** 13,000 square feet (a rectangle 50 feet x 200 feet = 10,000 square feet, plus a triangle, $\frac{1}{2}$ [30 feet x 200 feet] = 3,000 square feet). **3.** 43,560 x 3 = 130,680; 130,680 ÷ 5,280 = 24.75; *answer:* the road is about 25 feet wide. **4.** 1686 square feet. **5.** 36 feet x 24 feet x $\frac{1}{3}$ foot = 288 cubic feet; 3456 ÷ 27 = 10.67; 10.67 cubic yards of concrete for $13.00 per cubic yard equals $138.71. **6a.** 384 square feet x $.69 = $264.96. **6b.** 384 square feet x $1.09 = $418.56. **6c.** 384 square feet x $1.79 = $687.36; this would be $268.80 more than the brick tiles.

Using Pictures

Problem 2: Algebra; calculus; 50 miles; 90 miles.

Problem 3: no; round 3; round 5; George; can't tell because the results from rolling 1 die are random and only luck determines who goes off the board first.

Problem 4: *Figure 5.6,* 2 blocks north, 1 block east; *Figure 5.7,* 4 blocks north, 3 blocks east; *Figure 5.8,* 4 blocks north, 3 blocks west; *Figure 5.9,* 0 blocks north, 0 blocks east; (example: HHTTTTH will get you back to the starting point; many answers; HHH and TTT are the two shortest sequences that will get you back to a starting point; THT is one example to take you two blocks north and two blocks west; answers will vary).

Problem 5: 5 x $1.50 = $7.50.

Pictures for Fractions

Problem 7: $1.50; $7.50. ***Problem 8:*** $2.10. ***Problem 9:*** $40.00; $160.00.

Pictures for Algebra

Problem 10: $70.00; $280.00. ***Problem 11:*** literature; 3 boxes; 32 literature books; 96 math books. ***Problem 15:*** 21, 22, 23.

Guess Charts

Problem 16: 10 blouses, 7 skirts. ***Problem 17:*** Melissa, 28; Nancy, 23.
Problem 18: 7, 34. ***Problem 19:*** 30 nickels, 15 dimes, 45 pennies.
Problem 20: 72 pennies, 18 dimes, 88 nickels.

Worksheet 5.1

1b. 4. **1c.** 3. **2.** 7. **3a.** 6. **3b.** $20.00.
4a. 1217; 1234. **4b.** gain; 29. **4c.** Friday; Monday. **4d.** Tuesday; Friday.
5a. gain. **5b.** Monday; Tuesday. **5c.** 1154. **5d.** 986; 987.
6a. back at start. **6b.** back at start. **6c.** 1 block north, 1 block east.
6d. 0 blocks north; 1 block east. **6e.** 2 blocks south, 1 block west.
6f. Answers will vary. **6g.** Answers will vary.

Worksheet 5.2

1. 12 pounds. **2.** 72 walnuts. **3.** 69 pickles. **4.** $1.16. **5.** $120.00.

Worksheet 5.3

1. 8 feet, 13 feet. **2.** 18, 24. **3.** 6, 36. **4.** $.30, $1.80. **5.** 11, 12, 13, 14.
6. Elizabeth, 28; Kris, 56; Jane, 112. **7.** shirt, $20.00; shoes, $40.00; jacket, $120.00. **8.** milk, $.50; plain burrito, $1.50; burrito with extra cheese, $1.80.

Worksheet 5.4

1. 25, 30. **2.** 5, 50. **3.** First side is shortest; 20 feet; 50 feet; 60 feet; 70 feet.
4. 8. **5b.** 5. **6.** 11. **7.** classical, 10; rock, 60; jazz, 26. **8c.** 7. **9.** Answers will vary.

Worksheet 5.5

1. 12 – 8. **2.** 13 + 5. **3.** 3 x 5 or 3(5) or 3 · 5. **4.** 2(7 + 2) or 2 x (7 + 2) or 2 · (7 + 2). **5.** 4 x 3. **6.** 12 ÷ (5 + 3) or $\frac{12}{(5+3)}$. **7.** $\frac{1}{5}$ x 30 or 30 ÷ 5. **8.** (8 + 10) – 5. **9.** (5 x 4) + 5. **10.** 20 ÷ (4 – 5) or $\frac{20}{(4-5)}$. **11.** Twenty-three more than fourteen. **12.** The product of seven and five. **13.** Seven less than twenty. **14.** One-third of fifteen. **15.** Five more than the difference between ten and three. **16.** Seven less than the sum of eight and six. **17.** Eighteen divided by the product of two and three. **18.** Thirty-six divided by the sum of five and four.

Worksheet 5.6

1a. 40.	**1b.** 20.	**1c.** 47.	**1d.** 31.
2a. $10,500.	**2b.** $22,500.	**2c.** $16,000.	**2d.** $22,500.
3a. $19,000.	**3b.** $34,000.	**3c.** $11,000.	
4a. $24,000.	**4b.** $16,000.	**4c.** $18,000.	**4d.** $35,000.
5a. 51.	**5b.** 75.	**5c.** 8.	**5d.** 16.
6a. $1600.	**6b.** $2400.	**6c.** $7000.	**6d.** $10,000.

Worksheet 5.7

1. Jack, 11; Jill, 7. **2.** Sara, 21; Eric, 31. **3.** living room, 12 yards; bedroom, 4 yards. **4.** $289, $155. **5.** 17, 68. **6.** $4.50, $13.50. **7.** 12, 72. **8.** 5 inches.

Worksheet 5.8

1. Jennifer, 9; Stephen, 5; Alice, 10. **2.** $.34. **3.** $4.14. **4.** length, 15 feet; width, 6 feet. **5.** 7 quarters. **6.** 28 miles. **7.** 65, 70, 14. **8.** $.25.

Worksheet 5.9

The directions on this worksheet ask for an algebraic equation, not the solution. However, several solutions are included here for your information.

1. $b + (b + 23) = 87$ or $j + (j - 23) = 87$ (Jim, 55; Bill, 32).
2. $j + (j + 9) = 117$ or $s + (s - 9) = 117$ (Sara, 63 inches; Jennifer, 54 inches).
3. $o + (2o + 3) = 24$ (7 oranges; 17 apples).
4. $n + (8n + 7) = 295$ (first number, 263; second number, 32).
5. $d + (d - 5) = 75$ or $q + (q + 5) = 75$ (40 dimes, 35 quarters).
6. $d + (d + 1.50) = \$7.36$ or $h + (h - 1.50) = \$7.36$ (Holly, $4.43; Dolly, $2.93).
7. $s + (s + 53) = \$137.00$ or $b + (b - 53) = \$137.00$ (shoes, $42; boots, $95).
8. $a + (2a + 23) = 299$ (Alice, 92 pounds; Ted, 207 pounds).

Worksheet 5.10

The directions on this worksheet ask for an algebraic equation, not the solution. However, several solutions are included here for your information.

1. $q + 2q + 4q = 49$ or $d + \frac{d}{2} + 4(\frac{d}{2}) = 49$ or $n + \frac{n}{4} + 2(\frac{n}{4}) = 49$ (28 nickels, 14 dimes, 7 quarters).

2. $k + (k + 7) + (k - 7) = 63$ or $j + (j + 7) + [(j + 7) + 7] = 63$ or $l + (l - 7) + [(l - 7) - 7] = 63$ (Jane, 14; Kathy, 21; Linda, 28).

3. $2(w + 5w) = 96$ or $2(l + \frac{l}{5}) = 96$ (width, 8 inches; length, 40 inches).

4. $3a + 2(a + 8) = \$1.11$ or $3(p - 8) + 2p = \$1.11$ (apples, \$.19; pears, \$.27).

5. $(.10)d + (.01)2d + (.05)(3d - 5) = \$2.99$ or $(.01)p + (.10)(\frac{p}{2}) + (.05)[3(\frac{p}{2}) - 5] = \$2.99$ (24 pennies, 12 dimes, 31 nickels).

6. $n + (3n - 7) + [(3n - 7) + 4] = 88$ (Nancy, 14; Diane, 35; Liz, 39).

7. $n + (3n - 2) + [(3n - 2) + 8] = 67$ (first number, 25; second number, 9; third number, 33).

8. $3c + 4\ (2c) = \$19.25$ or $4a + 3\ (\frac{a}{2}) = \$19.25$ (children, \$1.75; adults, \$3.50).

CHAPTER 6: PROBABILITY AND STATISTICS

Probability Experiments

Blue Die

Red Die	1	2	3	4	5	6
1	2	3	4	5	6	7
2	3	4	5	6	7	8
3	4	5	6	7	8	9
4	5	6	7	8	9	10
5	6	7	8	9	10	11
6	7	8	9	10	11	12

Figure 6.3

Probabilities when rolling two dice and adding:
$Pr(2) = \frac{1}{36}$; $Pr(3) = \frac{2}{36} = \frac{1}{18}$; $Pr(4) = \frac{3}{36} = \frac{1}{12}$; $Pr(5) = \frac{4}{36} = \frac{1}{9}$; $Pr(6) = \frac{5}{36}$; $Pr(7) = \frac{6}{36} = \frac{1}{6}$; $Pr(8) = \frac{5}{36}$; $Pr(9) = \frac{4}{36} = \frac{1}{9}$; $Pr(10) = \frac{3}{36} = \frac{1}{12}$; $Pr(11) = \frac{2}{36} = \frac{1}{18}$; $Pr(12) = \frac{1}{36}$.

The Chi-Square Test

Table 6.2

Sum	Observed (O)	Expected (E)	$O-E$	$(O-E)^2$	$\frac{(O-E)^2}{E}$
2	0	5	-5	25	5.00
3	11	10	1	1	0.10
4	18	15	3	9	0.60
5	16	20	-4	16	0.80
6	25	25	0	0	0.00
7	36	30	6	36	1.20
8	31	25	6	36	1.44
9	21	20	1	1	0.05
10	10	15	-5	25	1.67
11	10	10	0	0	0.00
12	2	5	-3	9	1.80
				Total	12.66

Worksheet 6.1

1a. $\frac{4}{10} = \frac{2}{5}$. **1b.** $\frac{6}{10} = \frac{3}{5}$.

2a. 1, 2, 3, . . ., 24, 25. **2b.** 5, 10, 15, 20, 25. **2c.** $\frac{5}{25} = \frac{1}{5}$.

2d. 21, 22, 23, 24, 25. **2e.** $\frac{5}{25} = \frac{1}{5}$. **2f.** $\frac{20}{25} = \frac{4}{5}$. **2g.** 3, 6, 9, 12, 15, 18, 21, 24.
2h. 2, 4, 6, 8, 10, 12, 14, 16, 18, 20, 22, 24. **2i.** $\frac{4}{25}$.

Worksheet 6.2

1a. $\frac{1}{100}$. **1b.** $\frac{99}{100}$. **1c.** $\frac{1}{1000}$. **1d.** $\frac{999}{1000}$. **1e.** $\frac{1}{99}$. **1f.** $\frac{1}{999}$.
2a. $\frac{3}{11}$. **2b.** $\frac{8}{11}$.
3a. $B1W$, $B2W$, $B1R$, $B2R$, RW, $B1B2$. **3b.** $\frac{1}{6}$. **3c.** $\frac{2}{6} = \frac{1}{3}$.
3d. $\frac{2}{6} = \frac{1}{3}$. **3e.** $\frac{1}{6}$. **3f.** $\frac{1}{6} + \frac{1}{3} + \frac{1}{3} + \frac{1}{6} = 1$. **3g.** $\frac{5}{6}$.
4a. $\frac{6}{10} = \frac{3}{5}$. **4b.** $\frac{1}{10}$. **4c.** $\frac{9}{10}$.

Worksheet 6.3

1a. GR, GB, WR, WB; 4. **1b.** $\frac{1}{4}$. **1c.** $\frac{1}{4}$. **1d.** $\frac{2}{4} = \frac{1}{2}$.
2a. 2 x 4 x 6 x 3 = 144. **2b.** 2 x 4 x 6 = 48.
3a. 10 x 10 x 10 x 26 x 26 x 26 = 17,576,000.
3b. $\frac{1}{17{,}576{,}000}$ = 0.0000000569. **4a.** 175,760,000. **4b.** $\frac{1}{175{,}760{,}000}$.
5a. 3 x 4 x 5 x 4 = 240. **5b.** 3 x 2 x 5 x 4 = 120. **5c.** $\frac{120}{240} = \frac{1}{2}$. **5d.** $\frac{1}{2}$.
6a. 2 x 2 = 4. **6b.** GG, BB, GB, BG. **6c.** $\frac{1}{2}$.
7a. 2 x 2 x 2 x 2 = 16. **7b.** GGGG, GGGB, GGBG, GBGG, BGGG, GGBB, GBBG, GBGB, BBGG, BGGB, BGBG, GBBB, BGBB, BBGB, BBBG, BBBB. **7c.** $\frac{6}{16} = \frac{3}{8}$.

Worksheet 6.4

1a. $5 \times 4 \times 3 \times 2 \times 1 = 120$. **1b.** $3 \times 2 \times 1 = 6$.
1c. $4 \times 3 \times 2 = 24$. **1d.** $2 \times 1 = 2$.
2a. $6 \times 5 \times 4 \times 3 \times 2 \times 1 = 720$. **2b.** $\frac{1}{720}$.
3a. $26 \times 26 \times 26 \times 26 \times 26 = 11{,}881{,}376$.
3b. $26 \times 25 \times 24 \times 23 \times 22 = 7{,}893{,}600$; $\frac{7{,}893{,}600}{11{,}881{,}376} = 0.66$.
3c. $1 - 0.66 = 0.34$. **4a.** $10 \times 9 \times 8 = 720$. **4b.** $\frac{1}{720}$.

Worksheet 6.5

1. $Pr(0) = \frac{6}{36} = \frac{1}{6}$; $Pr(1) = \frac{10}{36} = \frac{5}{18}$; $Pr(2) = \frac{8}{36} = \frac{2}{9}$; $Pr(3) = \frac{6}{36} = \frac{1}{6}$;
$Pr(4) = \frac{4}{36} = \frac{1}{9}$; $Pr(5) = \frac{2}{36} = \frac{1}{18}$.

Blue Die

Red Die	1	2	3	4	5	6
1	0	1	2	3	4	5
2	1	0	1	2	3	4
3	2	1	0	1	2	3
4	3	2	1	0	1	2
5	4	3	2	1	0	1
6	5	4	3	2	1	0

2. Theoretical frequencies: for 0, 30; 1, 50; 2, 40; 3, 30; 4, 20; 5, 10.
3. Answers will vary. **4.** Answers will vary.

Worksheet 6.6

1. Answers will vary. **2.** 11. **3.** Answers will vary. **4.** Answers will vary.

Worksheet 6.7

1. Answers will vary. **2.** 5. **3.** 11.07. **4.** Answers will vary. **5.** 15.09.
6. Answers will vary.

Cooperative Logic

Problem 1:

Cinderella	Alice in Wonderland	Peter Pan
Hansel and Gretel	Wizard of Oz	Goldilocks

Problem 2:

Henrietta teaches geometry; Martha, trigonometry; Elena, calculus.

Problem 3:

Sue brought chicken casserole; Bill, salad; Donna, apple pie; George, spaghetti.

Some Well-Known Problems

Problem 4:

Betty, left; Becky, middle; Barbara, right.

Problem 5:

1 gallon: Fill up the 9, pour into the 4, empty the 4, pour into the 4 again, leaves one gallon in the 9.
2 gallons: Fill up the 9, pour into the 4 two times leaving 1 in the 9; empty the 4; pour 1 in the 4, fill the 9, pour into the 4; only 3 will go into the 4, leaving 6 in the 9; empty the 4; pour the 6 into the 4, leaving 2 in the 9.
3 gallons: Get 7 in the 9 (see below); pour into the 4, leaves 3 in the 9.
4 gallons: Fill up the 4.
5 gallons: Fill up the 9, pour into the 4, leaving 5 in the 9.
6 gallons: Fill up the 9, pour into the 4 two times leaving 1 in the 9; empty the 4; pour 1 in the 4; fill the 9, pour into the 4 (only 3 will fit), leaving 6 in the 9.
7 gallons: Get 2 in the 9 (see above); pour into the 4, fill up the 9, pour into the 4 (only 2 will fit), leaving 7 in the 9.
8 gallons: Fill up the 4, pour into the 9; repeat; there are 8 gallons in the 9.
9 gallons: Fill up the 9.
10 gallons: Fill up the 9, pour into the 4 two times, leaving 1 gallon in the 9; empty the 4; pour that 1 into the 4, then fill up the 9 once more, giving 9 in the 9 and 1 in the 4, a total of 10.
11 gallons: Get 2 in the 9 (see above); pour into the 4, fill up the 9, totaling 11.
12 gallons: Fill up the 4, pour into the 9; repeat; fill up the 4 for the third time, gives 8 gallons in the 9 and 4 in the 4, totaling 12.
13 gallons: Fill up the 4 gallon and fill up the 9 gallon containers.

Problem 6: Choose a sock from the box labeled BG. If the sock is BLUE, then that box should be labeled BB: the box on the left is then GG, and the box in the middle is BG. If the sock you choose is GREEN, then that box should be labeled GG, the box on the left BG, and the box in the middle BB.

Problem 7: 5 coins: Place 2 coins in each pan; if they balance, then the counterfeit coin is the one not in the pans; if they don't balance, weigh the two coins that are lighter.
6 coins: Weigh two coins in each pan; if they balance, weigh the two coins remaining; if they don't balance, weigh the two coins that are lighter.
7 coins: Weigh 3 coins in each pan; if they balance, then the counterfeit coin is the coin that remains; if not, then the problem becomes a 3-coin problem for the three coins that are lighter.
8 coins: Weigh 3 coins in each pan; if they balance, the remaining 2 coins must be weighed; if not, the problem becomes a 3-coin problem for the three lighter coins.

Spatial Puzzles

Tangram Puzzles

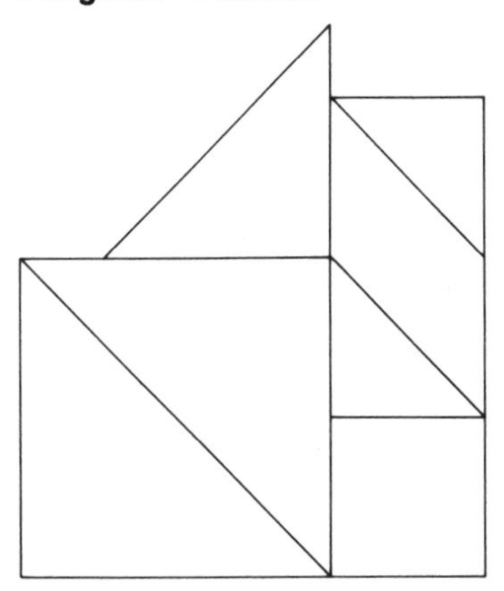

Figure 7.16

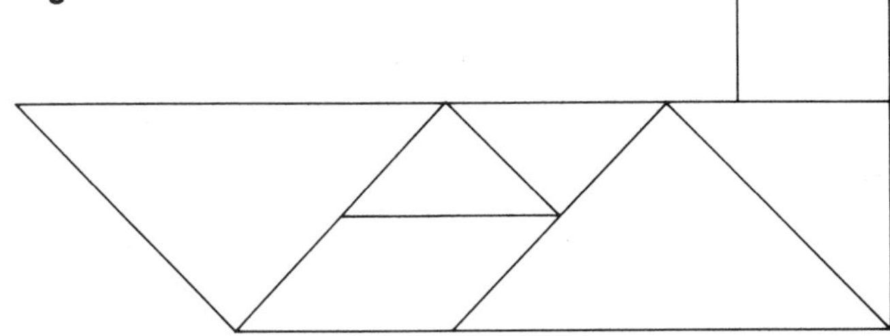

Figure 7.17

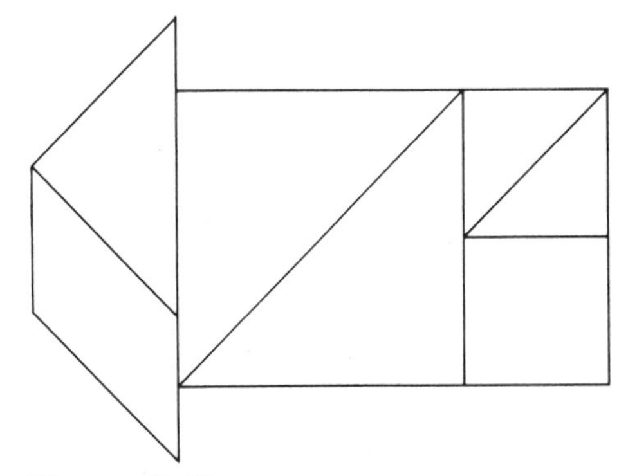

Figure 7.18

Toothpick Puzzles

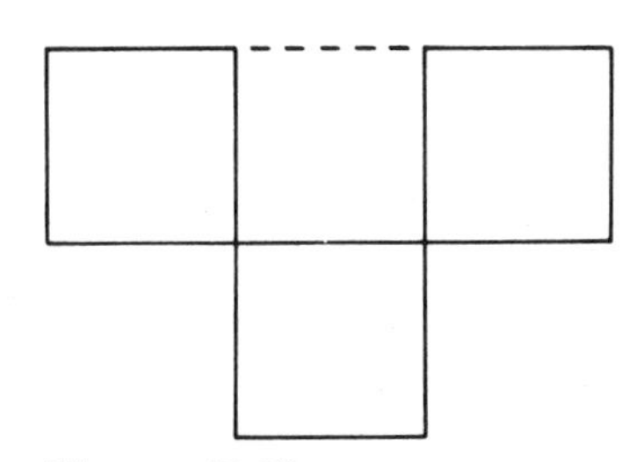

Figure 7.19

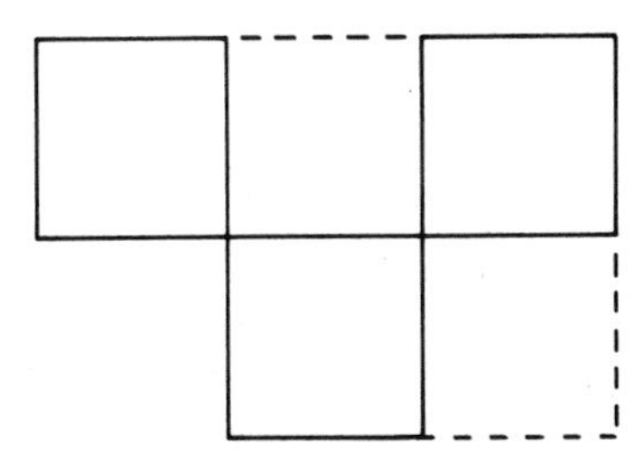

Figure 7.20

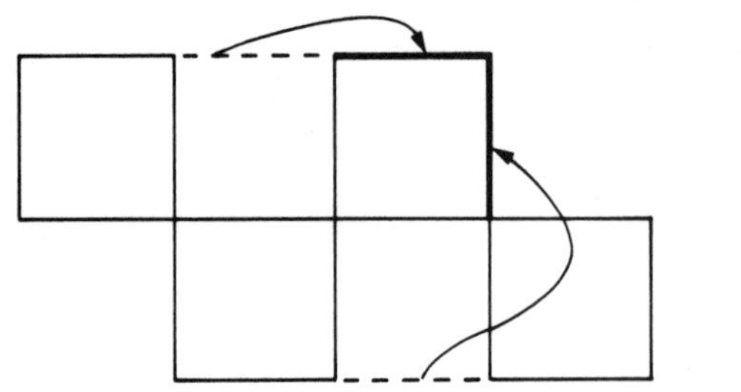

Figure 7.21

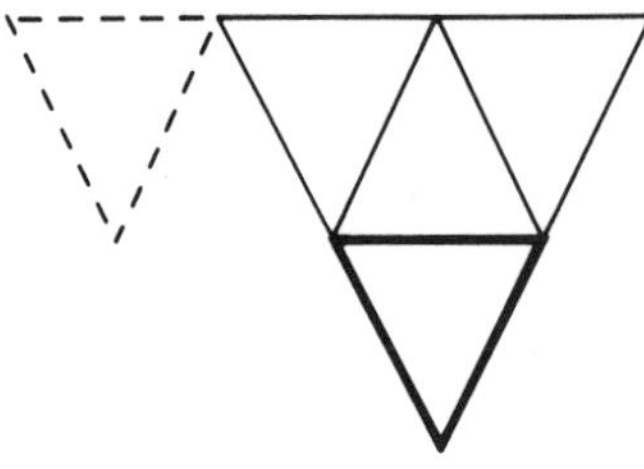

Figure 7.22

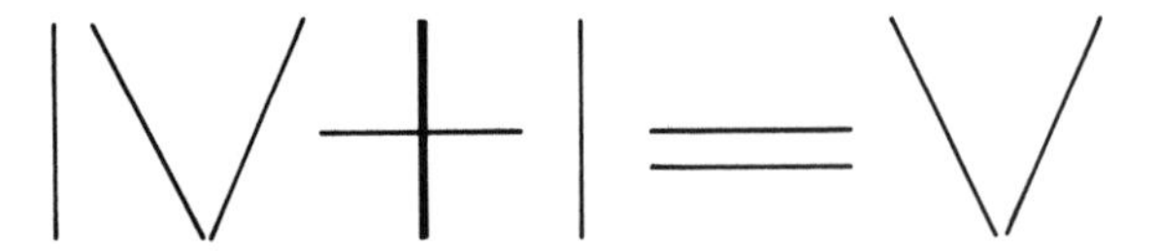

Figure 7.23

Perceptual Puzzle Blocks

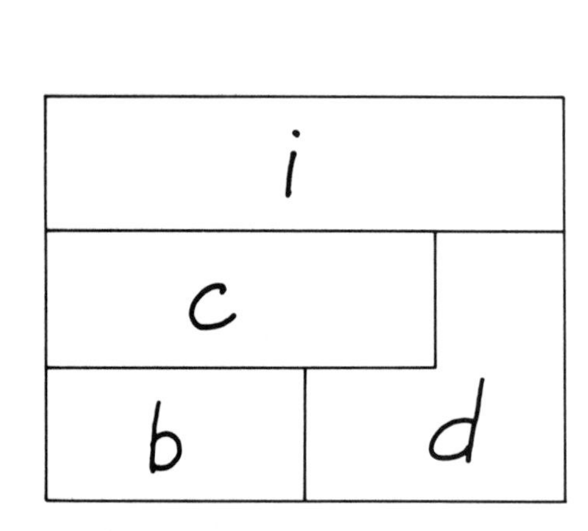

Figure 7.28

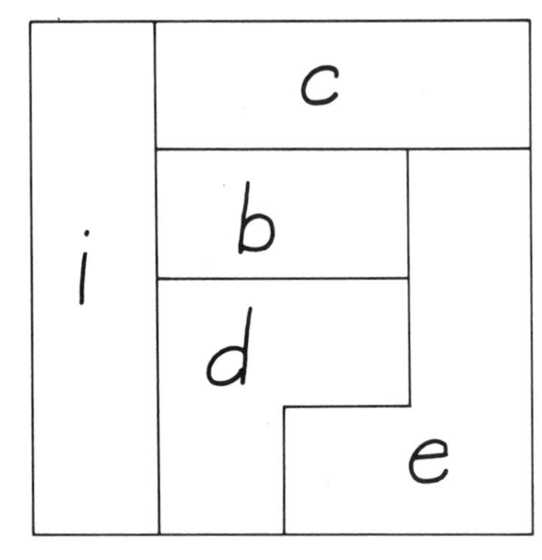

Figure 7.29

Worksheet 7.1

1. Mark, mousse; Nancy, cheesecake; Roger, pecan pie.
2. Luke, Colleen, Anna, Tom, Diana.
3. Monday, apricot; Tuesday, blueberry; Wednesday, boysenberry; Thursday, pineapple; Friday, strawberry.
4. Conrad, violin; Valerie, piano; Frances, cello; Penelope, flute.
5. Kilometer, hectometer, decameter, meter, decimeter, centimeter, millimeter.
6. Alice, Italy; Beverly, Spain; Charles, England; Donald, France.

Worksheet 7.2

1. 37. **2.** 18. **3.** 29. **4.** 12. **5.** 357.
6. 523. **7.** 189. **8.** 140. **9.** 4067.

Index